Abortion Bibliography

for 1980

Abortion Bibliography

for 1980

The Whitston Publishing Company
Troy, New York
1982

TABLE OF CONTENTS

PREFACE

Abortion Bibliography for 1980 is the eleventh annual list of books and articles surrounding the subject of abortion in the preceeding year. It appears serially each fall as a contribution toward documenting in one place as comprehensively as possible the literature of one of our central social issues. It is an attempt at a comprehensive world bibliography.

Searches in compiling this material have covered the following sources: *Abstracts on Criminology & Penology; Abstracts on Police Science; Access; Air University Library Index to Military Periodicals; Alternative Index; American Humanities Index; American Reference Books Annual; Applied Science & Technology Index; Art Index; Bibliographic Index; Biological Abstracts; Biological & Agricultural Index; British Humanities Index; Business Periodicals Index; Canadian Education Index; Canadian Periodicals Index; Catholic Periodical & Literature Index; Communication Abstracts; College Student Personnel Abstracts; Completed Research in Health, Physical Education, & Recreation; Criminal Justice Abstracts (form: Crime & Delinquency Literature); Criminal Justice Periodical Index; Cumulative Book Index; Cumulated Index to Nursing Literature; Current Index to Journals in Education; Dissertation Abstracts International: A. Social Sciences & Humanities; Dissertation Abstracts International: B. The Sciences & Engineering; Education Index; Environment Abstracts; Environment Index; Essay & General Literature Index; Government Reports Announcements and Index; Hospital Literature Index; Human Resources Abstracts; Humanities Index; Index Medicus; Index to Legal Periodicals; Index to Jewish Periodicals; International Bibliography of the Social Sciences; International Nursing Index; Journal of Human Services Abstracts; Library of Congress Catalog: Subject Catalog;*

Library of Congress Catalogs: Films & Other Materials for Projection; Media Review Digest; Monthly Periodical Index; PAIS; Philosophers Index; Popular Periodical Index; New Periodicals Index 1978; Nursing Literature (now—Nursing and Allied Health Literature); Masters Abstracts; Index to Periodical Articles Related to Law; Population Sciences: Index of Biomedical Research; Psychological Abstracts; Readers Guide to Periodical Literature; Religion Index One: Periodicals (form: Index to Religious Periodical Literature); Sage Urban Studies Abstracts, Social Sciences Index; Social Work Research & Abstracts (form: Abstracts for Social Workers); Sociological Abstracts; The Wall Street Journal Index; and Women's Studies Abstracts.

The bibliography is divided into two sections: a title section in alphabetical order; and a subject section. Thus, if the researcher does not wish to observe the subject heads of the compiler, he can use the title section exclusively. The subject heads have been allowed to issue from the nature of the material indexed rather than being imposed from Library of Congress subject heads or other standard lists.

The Book section includes Government Publications and Monographs.

The Subject Head Index includes page numbers.

LIST OF PERIODICALS CITED

AORN Journal: Association of Operating Room Nurses, Inc.
Acta Cytologica
Acta Dermato-Venereologica
Acta Obstetrica y Ginecologica Hispana-Lusitana
Acta Obstetricia et Gynecologica Scandinavica
Acta Paediatrica Scandinavica
Acta Psychiatrica Belgica
Acta Physiologica Polonica
Acta Vitaminologica et Enzymologica
Actual Odontostomatol
L'Actualite
Adolescence
Advances in Prostaglandin and Thromboxane Research
Advertising Age
Air Force Times
Akusherstvo i Ginekologiia
America
American Bar Association Journal
American Journal of Chinese Medicine
American Journal of Clinical Nutrition
American Journal of Community Psychology
American Journal of Diseases of Children
American Journal of Epidemiology
American Journal of Gastroenterology
American Journal of Hospital Pharmacy
American Journal of Human Genetics
American Journal of Jurisprudence
American Journal of Law and Medicine
American Journal of Medical Genetics
American Journal of Nursing
American Journal of Obstetrics and Gynecology

American Journal of Orthopsychiatry
American Journal of Public Health
American Journal of Surgical Pathology
American Journal of Trial Advocacy
American Medical News
American Nurse
Anaesthesia
Anesthesia and Analgesia
Andrologia
Annales Chirurgiae et Gynaecologiae
Annales d'Anatomie Pathologique
Annales de Cardiologie et d'Angeiologie
Annales de Chirurgie
Annales de Genetique
Annals of Clinical and Laboratory Science
Annals of Internal Medicine
Annali Sclavo
Annual Review of Medicine
Archives d'Anatomie et de Cytologie Pathologique
Archives Internationales de Pharmacodynamie et de Therapie
Archives of General Psychiatry
Archives of Gynecology
Archives of Obstetrics and Gynecology
Archives of Sexual Behavior
Archivio per le Scienze Mediche
Arizona Law Review
Arizona Medicine
Arizona Nurse
Arizona State Law Journal
Ars Aequi
Arzneimittel Forschung
Asian Journal of Psychology and Education
Asian Survey
Atlantic Monthly
Australian and New Zealand Journal of Obstetrics and Gynaecology
Australian Family Physician
Australian Nurses Journal

Bangladesh Development Studies
Bangladesh Medical Research Council Bulletin

Beitraege zur Gerichtlichen Medizin
Biological Reproduction
Biology of the Neonate
Biomedicine
Birth Defects
Boletin-Asociacion Medica de Puerto Rico
Boletin de la Oficina Sanitaria Panamericana
Bollettino dell Istituto Sieroterapico Milanese
Bolletino della Societa Italiana di Biologia Sperimentale
Boston
Branching Out
Bratislavske Lekarska Listy
Brigham Young University Law Review
British Journal of Clinical Pharmacology
British Journal of Clinical Practice
British Journal of Medical Psychology
British Journal of Obstetrics and Gynaecology
British Journal of Psychiatry
British Journal of Urology
British Medical Journal
Bulletin de L'Acadamie de Chirurgie Dentaire
Business Insurance
Business Week

California Nurse
Canadian Forum
Canadian Journal of Psychiatry
Canadian Journal of Public Health
Canadian Journal of Surgery
Canadian Labour
Canadian Medical Association Journal
Canadian Nurse
Canadian Psychiatric Association Journal
Cancer
Cancer Treatment Reports
Capital University Law Review
Catholic Charismatic
Catholic Digest
Catholic Lawyer
Central African Journal of Medicine
Ceskoslovenska Gynekologie
Ceskoslovenska Neurologie a Neurochirurgio

FDA Consumer
Family Community Health
Family Coordinator
Family Health
The Family Law Reporter: Court Opinions
Family Planning Perspectives
Family Relations
Far Eastern Economic Review
Federal Register
Federation Proceedings
Fel'dsher i Akusherka
Fertility and Sterility
Florida Bar Journal
Fordham Law Review
Forest Industries
Forgorvosi Szemle
Fortschritte der Medizin

GEN
Gallup Opinion Index
Gastroenterologie Clinique et Biologique
Geburtschilfe und Frauenheilkunde
Genetics
Georgetown Law Journal
Ginecologia y Obstetricia de Mexico
Ginekologia Polska
Ginornale Italiano di Psicologia
Glamour
Glustizia Penale
Godisen Zbornik na Medicinskiot Fakultet vo Skopje
Golden Gate University Law Review
Good Housekeeping
Guardian
Gynecologic and Obstetric Investigation

Harefuah
Harper's Bazaar
Harvard Theological Review
Hastings Center Report
Hautarzt
Health and Social Work

JAMA: Journal of the American Medical Association
JOGN Nursing: Journal of Obstetric, Gynecologic and Neonatal
    Nursing
JPMA: Journal of the Pakistan Medical Association
Japanese Circulation Journal
Jerusalem Quarterly
John Marshall Law Review
Journal de Chirurgie
Journal of the American College Health Association
Journal of the American Dental Association
Journal of the American Dietetic Association
Journal of Applied Social Psychology
Journal of the Association of Physicians of India
Journal of Biosocial Science
Journal of Clinical Endocrinology and Metabolism
Journal of Clinical Investigation
Journal of Clinical Psychiatry
Journal of Divorce
Journal of Drug Research
Journal of the Egyptian Medical Association
Journal of the Egyptian Public Health Association
Journal of Endocrinological Investigation
Journal of Family Law
Journal of Family Practice
Journal of Family Welfare
Journal of Gerontology
Journal de Gynecologie Obstetrique et Biologie de la Reproduc-
    tion
Journal of Health and Social Behavior
Journal of the Indian Medical Association
Journal of the Indiana State Medical Association
Journal of Interdisciplinary History
Journal of International Medical Research
Journal of Laboratory and Clinical Medicine
Journal of Marital and Family Therapy
Journal of Marriage and the FAmily
Journal of the Medical Association of Georgia
Journal of the Medical Association of Thailand
Journal of Medical Ethics

Journal of Medical Genetics
Journal of Medical Philosophy
Journal of the Medical Society of New Jersey
Journal of the National Medical Association
Journal of Nurse-Midwifery
Journal of Obstetrics and Gynecology of India
Journal of Occupational Medicine
Journal of Pediatrics
Journal of Personality and Social Psychology
Journal of Personality Assessment
Journal of Pharmacology
Journal of Philosophy
Journal of Politics
Journal of Population
Journal of Postgraduate Medicine
Journal of Religion and Health
Journal of Reproductive Medicine
Journal of the Royal College of General Practitioners
Journal of School Health
Journal of Sex Research
Journal of Social Psychology
Journal of Sociology and Social Welfare
Journal of Steroid Biochemistry
Judicature
Jugoslavenska Ginekologija i Opstetricija
Juvenile Law Digest

Katilolehti
Khirurgiia
Klinische Monatsblaetter fur Augenheilkunde
Kritische Justiz

Lakartidningen
Lancet
Law and Policy Quarterly
Law Quarterly Review
Legal Medical Quarterly
Liguorian
Lijecnicki Vjesnik
Lille Medical

Linacre Quarterly
Lipids
Listener

MMW: Muenchener Medizinishe Wochenschrift
Ms Magazine
Maclean's
Mademoiselle
Man and Medicine
Marriage
Maryland State Medical Journal
Materia Medica Polona
McCalls
Medecine et Chirurgie Digestives
Medical Hypotheses
Medical Journal of Australia
Medical Journal of Malaysia
Medical Times
Medical World News
Medicina Clinica
Medicinski Arhiv
Medizin und Gesellschaft
Medizinische Klinik
Medizinische Monatsschrift fur Pharmazeuten
Medizinische Welt
Metabolism
Michigan Law Review
Midwife, Health Visitor and Community Nurse
Midwives Chronicle
Minerva Ginecologia
Minerva Medica
Missouri Law Review
Modern Healthcare
Month
Morphologie et Embryologie
Mother Jones
Mt. Sinai Journal of Medicine
Mutation Research

Nation

National Catholic Reporter
National Review
Naturwissenschaften
Nebraska Medical Journal
Nederlands Tijdschrift voor Geneeskunde
Neurology
New Blackfriars
New Covenant
New England Journal of Medicine
New England Law Review
New Jersey Nurse
New Republic
New Scientist
New Society
New Statesman
New West
New York State Department of Health Report
New York State Law School Law Review
New York Times
New Zealand Medical Journal
Newsweek
Niger Medical Journal
Nigerian Medical Journal
Nordisk Medicin
North Dakota Law Review
Notre Dame Lawyer
Nouvelle Presse Medicale
Nouvelle Revue Theologique
Nurse Practitioner
Nursing
Nursing Administration Quarterly
Nursing Journal of India
Nursing Journal of Singapore
Nursing Mirror
Nursing Mirror and Midwive's Journal
Nutrition Reviews

Observer
Obstetrical and Gynecological Survey
Obstetrics and Gynecology
Oeffentliche Gesundheitswesen

Off Our Backs
Oklahoma Observer
Ophthalmologica
Orbit
Origins
Orvosi Hetilap
L'Osservatore Romano
Other Side
Oui
Our Sunday Visitor

Pacific Philosophical Quarterly
Pahlavi Medical Journal
Papau New Guinea Medical Journal
Parents
Pastoral Psychology
Pathology, Research and Practice
Paysans
Pediatric Annals
Pediatric Research
Pediatrics
Pediatriia Akusherstvo i Ginekologiia
Pennsylvania Medicine
People
Perceptual and Motor Skills
Personalist
Pharmacological Research Communications
Pharmazie
Philippine Sociological Review
Philosophical Studies
Physiology and Behavior
Policy Studies Journal
Political Studies
Polski Tygodnik Lekarski
Population
Population and Development Review
Population and Environment
Population and Environment: Behavioral and Social Issues
Population Bulletin
Population Council
Population Reports

Populi
Postgraduate Medical Journal
Practitioner
Praxis
Presse Medicale
Product Marketing
Progress in Clinical and Biological Research
Progressive
Prostaglandins
Prostaglandins and Medicine
Przeglad Lekarski
Psychiatric Annals
Psychiatry
Psychologica Belgica
Psychological Medicine
Psychological Reporter
Psychology
Psychology Today
Psychopharmacology
Public Health
Public Health Reports

Quaderni Sclavo di Diagnostica Clinica e di Laboratorio
Queen's Law Review
Quest

RN
Readers Digest
Redbook
Religion in Life
Reproduction
Review of Public Data Use
Revista Chilena de Obstetricia y Ginecologia
Revista de la Asociacion Argentina de Microbologia
Revista del Colegio Nacional de Enfermeras
Revista Espanola de Investigaciones Sociologicas
Revista Italiana di Stomatologia
Revista Lationoamericana de Psicologia
Revista Medica de Chile
Revue de Droit Universite de Sherbrooke

Revue d'Epidemiologie et de Sante Publique
Revue de l'Infirmiere et de l'Assistante Sociale
Revue Medicale de la Suisse Romande
Rivista di Neurobiologia
Rivista Italiana di Ginecologia

Saint Anthony Messenger
St. Vladimir's Theological Quarterly
Same-Day Surgery
Samsom Uitgeverij
Sangyo Igaku
Santa Clara Law Review
Sbornik Lekarsky
Sbornik Vedeckych Praci Lekarske Fakulty Karlovy Univerzity
    v Hradci Kralove
Schweizerische Medizinische Wochenschrift
Science
Science for the People
Science News
The Sciences
Scientific American
Scottish Medical Journal
Security Systems Digest
Semaines des Hopitaux de Paris
Seminars in Perinatology
Signs
Singapore Medical Journal
Social Biology
Social Casework
Social Forces
Social Indicators Research
Social Psychiatry
Social Psychology Quarterly
Social Science and Medicine
Social Service Review
Social Thought
Social Work
Society and Welfare
Sociological Review Monograph
Soins
Sojourners

Soldiers
South African Journal of Science
South African Medical Journal
South Dakota Law Review
Southern California Law Review
Southern Illinois University Law Journal
Southern Journal of Philosophy
Southern Medical Journal
Sovetskaia Meditsina
Srpski Arhiv za Celokupno Lekarstvo
Studies in Family Planning
Studies in Short Fiction
Suffolk University Law Review
Sunday Times
Sygeplejersken

Tablet
Teen
Temple Law Quarterly
Teratology
Texas International Law Journal
Texas Nursing
Theological Digest
Theological Studies
Therapie der Gegenwart
Therapie Hungarica
Thrombosis and Haemostasis
Thrombosis Research
Tidsskrift for den Norske Laegeforening
Time
Times (London)
Toxicon
Transactions of the American Neurological Association
Transactions of the Pacific Coast Obstetrical and Gynecological
    Society
Tropical Doctor
Tulane Law Review
Tunisie Medicale

US Catholic

US News and World Report
Ugeskrift for Laeger
Union Medicale du Canada
Union W.A.G.E.
United States Medicine
University of Detroit Journal of Urban Law
University of Michigan Journal of Law Reform
Urologic Clinics of North America
Urology

Valparaiso University Law Review
Vasa
Vasectomy
Vermont Law Review
The Village Voice
Virchows Archiv
Vogue
Voprosy Okhrany Materinstva i Detstva
Vox Sanguinis

WHO Chronicles
Wall Street Journal
Washburn Law Journal
Washington Monthly
Weekly
West Indian Medical Journal
Western Journal of Medicine
Wiadomosci Lekarskie
Wiener Klinische Wochenschrift
Wiener Medizinische Wochenschrift
William Mitchell Law Review
Women's Rights Law Reporter
Working Women
World Health
World Health Statistics Quarterly

Xenobiotica

Yao Hsueh Hsueh Pao; Acta Pharmaceutica Sinica

Youth and Society

ZFA: Zeitschrift fur Allgemeinmedizin
Zdravookhraneniye Belorussii
Zdravookhraneniye Rossiiskol Federatzii
Zeitschrift fur die Gesamte Innere Medizin und ihre Grenzgebiete
Zeitschrift fur Medizinische Laboratoriums-diagnostik
Zeitschrift fur Urologie und Nephrologie
Zentralblatt fur Gynaekologie

SUBJECT HEADING INDEX

BOOKS, GOVERNMENT PUBLICATIONS, AND MONOGRAPHS

Allen, J. E., et al. MANAGING TEENAGE PREGNANCY. New York: Holt, Rinehart & Winston, 1980.

Atkinson, G., et al. A MORAL EVALUATION OF CONTRACEPTION AND STERILIZATION. St. Louis: Pope John XXIII Medical-Moral Research and Education Center, 1979.

Banerjee, S. FAMILY PLANNING COMMUNICATION. Radiant Publications, 1979.

Boyle, B. HUMAN LIFE: CONTROVERSIES AND CONCERNS. New York: Wilson, 1979.

Canada. Statistics Canada Health Division. THERAPEUTIC ABORTIONS. Ottawa: The Division, 1980.

Chan, W. Y., et al. ADVANCES IN PROSTAGLANDIN AND THROMBOXANE RESEARCH, VOL. 8. 4TH INTERNATIONAL PROSTAGLANDIN CONFERENCE, WASHINGTON, D.C., USA, MAY 28-31, 1979. New York: Raven Press, 1980.

Chatterjee, P. K. ASPECTS OF HUMAN FERTILITY: A SOCIOECONOMIC STUDY. Kalyani, West Bengal, India: University of Kalyani, 1979.

LA CONTRACCEZIONE NELLA ADOLESCENTE. Milano: Longanesi, 1979.

CONTRACEPTION, SCIENCE, TECHNOLOGY, AND APPLICATION. National Academy of Sciences, 1979.

Djerassi, C. THE POLITICS OF CONTRACEPTION. New York: Norton, 1980.

Feldman, D. M. BIRTH CONTROL IN JEWISH LAW. Westport, Connecticut: Greenwood Press, 1980.

Fisher, W. Affective, additional, and normative determinants of contraceptive behavior among university men, Purdue University, 1978 (PhD dissertation).

Francescato, D., et al. LE CONDIZIONI DELLA SESSUALITA FEMMINILE: MATERNITA, ABORTO, CONSULTORIO. Bari, Italy: De Donato, 1979.

Garton, J. S. WHO BROKE THE BABY? Minneapolis: Bethany Fellowship, 1979.

Garvey, J., et al. ABORTION. Thomas More Association, 1979.

Grisez, G. LIFE AND DEATH WITH LIBERTY AND JUSTICE: A CONTRIBUTION TO THE EUTHANASIA DEBATE. Notre Dame: University of Notre Dame Press, 1979.

Hammerstein, J., et al. "Methods for evaluation of antifertility agents in the male," in WORKSHOP ON THE TESTIS, 5TH, GEILO, NORWAY, 1978. ENDOCRINE APPROACH TO MALE CONTRACEPTION. Copenhagen: Scriptor, 1978.

Hawkins, D. F., et al. HUMAN FERTILITY CONTROL. Woburn, Massachusetts: Butterworth & Co., 1979

Humber, J. M., et al. BIOMEDICAL ETHICS AND THE LAW. New York: Plenum Press, 1976.

THE IMPACT OF FAMILY PLANNING PROGRAMS ON FERTILITY RATES. Chicago: University of Chicago Community and Family Study Center, 1979.

INDUCED ABORTION: GUIDELINES FOR THE PROVISION OF CARE AND SERVICES. New York: WHO Offset Publications, 1979.

International Workshop on New Developments in Vaginal Contraception, 1979. VAGINAL CONTRACEPTION. New York: Harper & Row, 1979.

INVENTORY OF POPULATION PROJECTS IN DEVELOPING COUNTRIES AROUND THE WORLD, 1978/79: MULTILATERAL ASSISTANCE, BILATERAL ASSISTANCE, NON-GOVERNMENTAL, ORGANIZATION ASSISTANCE. New York: UN Fund for Population Activities, 1980.

Kern, E. DIE MENSCHLICHE UBERZAHL UND IHRE FOLGEN: GIBT IS EINEN AUSWEG? Germany: Braumuller, 1979.

Khan, M. E. FAMILY PLANNING AMONG MUSLIMS IN INDIA. Manohar Publications, 1979.

Leal, L. M., ed. EL PROBLEMA DEL ABORTO EN MEXICO. Mexico City: Porrua, 1980.

Leibowitz, B. A., et al. SELECTED INTERNATIONAL BIBLIOGRAPHY ON VOLUNTARY STERILIZATION. 2D ED. Association for Voluntary Sterilization, 1979.

Liskin, L. S. COMPLICATIONS OF ABORTION IN DEVELOPING COUNTRIES. Baltimore: Population Information Program, Johns Hopkins University, 1980.

Manier, E., et al. ABORTION: NEW DIRECTIONS FOR POLICY STUDIES. Notre Dame: Notre Dame University Press, 1977.

Mardfin, D. Economics of abortion demand by pregnant married women: the ultimate fertility choice. University of Hawaii, 1979 (PhD dissertation).

MEDICAL, NURSING AND OSTEOPATHIC SCHOOL ADMISSIONS POLICY RELATING TO ABORTIONS/STERILIZATION. Bethesda: Systems Sciences, 1978.

MISSION ON NEEDS ASSESSMENT FOR POPULATION ASSISTANCE. JORDAN; REPORT. New York: UN Fund for

Population Activities, 1979.

MISSION ON NEEDS ASSESSMENT FOR POPULATION AS-SISTANCE. MALAYSIA; REPORT. New York: UN Fund for Population Activities, 1979.

—. MAURITANIA; REPORT. New York: UN Fund for Population Activities, 1979.

—. NEPAL; REPORT. New York: UN Fund for Population Activities, 1979.

—. PAKISTAN; REPORT. New York: UN Fund for Population Activities, 1979.

—. REPUBLIC OF INDONESIA; REPORT. New York: UN Fund for Population Activities, 1979.

—. SOMALIA; REPORT. New York: UN Fund for Population Activities, 1979.

—. THE STATE OF BAHRAIN; REPORT. New York: UN Fund for Population Activities, 1979.

—. THAILAND; REPORT. New York: UN Fund for Population Activities, 1979.

—. UNITED REPUBLIC OF TANZANIA; REPORT. New York: UN Fund for Population Activities, 1979.

Nathanson, B. N., et al. ABORTING AMERICA. New York: Doubleday, 1979.

Nelson, J. L. VALUES, RIGHTS, AND THE NEW MORALITY: DO THEY CONFLICT? Englewood Cliffs: Prentice-Hall, 1977.

Neumann, F., et al. "Some comments on the use of steroid hormones for male contraception," in WORKSHOP ON THE TESTIS, 5TH, GEILO, NORWAY, 1978. ENDOCRINE APPROACH TO MALE CONTRACEPTION. Copenhagen: Scriptor, 1978.

4

New Zealand. Royal Commission on Contraception, Sterilization and Abortion. CONTRACEPTION, STERILIZATION AND ABORTION IN NEW ZEALAND. Wellington: The Commission, 1977.

Orleans, L. A., ed. CHINESE APPROACHES TO FAMILY PLANNING. White Plains, New York: Sharpe, 1979.

Pathak, S. SOCIAL WELFARE HEALTH, AND FAMILY NING IN INDIA. New Delhi: Marwah Publications, 1979.

Perera, L. SRI LANKA. New York: UN Fund for Population Activities, 1980.

Regan, T. MATTERS OF LIFE AND DEATH. New York: Random House, 1980.

Rice, C. E. BEYOND ABORTION. Chicago: Franciscan Herald Press, 1979.

Saksena, D. N. FAMILY PLANNING IN THE INDUSTRIAL SECTOR AND ASIAN RESPONSE; A BIBLIOGRAPHY REVIEWED. Lucknow University. Demographic Research Centre, 1976.

Schaeffer, F. A., et al. WHATEVER HAPPENED TO THE HUMAN RACE? Old Tappan, New Jersey: Revell, 1979.

Schearer, S. B., et al. "Hormonal contraception for men," in WORKSHOP OF THE TESTIS, 5TH, GEILO, NORWAY, 1978. ENDOCRINE APPROACH TO MALE CONTRACEPTION. Copenhagen: Scriptor, 1978.

Schenck, B., et al. "Some comments on the use of antiandrogens for male contraception," in WORKSHOP ON THE TESTIS, 5TH, GEILO, NORWAY, 1978. ENDOCRINE APPROACH TO MALE CONTRACEPTION. Copenhagen: Scriptor, 1978.

Schultz-Larsen, P., et al. "Carcinoembryonic proteins: Recent progress; Meeting, Copenhagen," in SCANDINAVIAN JOURNAL OF IMMUNOLOGY, SUPPL. NO. 8., VOL. 8. Oxford: Blackwell Scientific Publications, 1978.

Somphong, S., et al. FERTILITY AND FAMILY PLANNING IN RURAL NORTHERN THAILAND. Chicago: University of Chicago. Community and Family Study Center, 1979.

Srinivasan, K., et al, eds. DYNAMICS OF POPULATION AND FAMILY WELFARE IN INDIA. Bombay: Popular Prakashan, 1980.

Steinberger, E., et al. "Suppression and recovery of sperm production in men treated with testosterone enanthate for one year. A study of a possible reversible male contraceptive," in WORKSHOP ON THE TESTIS, 5TH, GEILO, NORWAY, 1978. ENDOCRINE APPROACH TO MALE CONTRACEPTION. Copenhagen: Scriptor, 1978.

Steinbock, B. KILLING AND LETTING DIE. Englewood Cliffs, New Jersey: Prentice-Hall, 1980.

SURVEY OF LAWS ON FERTILITY CONTROL. New York; UN Fund for Population Activities, 1979.

Swerdloff, R. S., et al. "Male contraception: clinical assessment of chronic administration of testosterone enanthate," in WORKSHOP ON THE TESTIS, 5TH, GEILO, NORWAY, 1978. ENDOCRINE APPROACH TO MALE CONTRACEPTION. Copenhagen: Scriptor, 1978.

Tennessee. Department of Public Health. INDUCED ABORTIONS REPORTED IN TENNESSEE, 1976-1977. Nashville: The Department, 1979.

United Nations. Department of International Economic and Social Affairs. FACTORS AFFECTING THE USE AND NONUSE OF CONTRACEPTION: FINDINGS FROM A COMPARATIVE ANALYSIS OF SELECTED KAP SURVEYS. New York: United Nations, 1979.

United States. Center for Disease Control. ABORTION SURVEILLANCE: ANNUAL SUMMARY 1977. Atlanta: The Center, 1977.

—. National Center for Health Statistics. Division of Vital Statistics. CONTRACEPTIVE UTILIZATION: UNITED STATES. Hyattsville, Maryland: HEW, 1979.

Weinberg, R. D. FAMILY PLANNING AND THE LAW. 2D ED. Dobbs Ferry, New York: Oceana Publications, 1979.

Westoff, C. F., et al. ILLUSTRATIVE ANALYSIS: CONTRA-CEPTIVE STERILIZATION AND BIRTHS AVERTED IN PANAMA. International Statistics Institute, 1979.

Wickings, E. J., et al. "Inhibition of testicular steroids by anti-bodies—a feasible approach to male contraception," in WORKSHOP ON THE TESTIS, 5TH, GEILO, NORWAY, 1978. ENDOCRINE APPROACH TO MALE CONTRACEP-TION. Copenhagen: Scriptor, 1978.

WORKSHOP AND POSTGRADUATE COURSE ON PREG-NANCY TERMINATION: PROCEDURES, SAFETY, AND NEW DEVELOPMENTS, 1978. PREGNANCY TERMINA-TION. New York: Harper & Row, 1978.

Yezzi, R. MEDICAL ETHICS: THINKING ABOUT UNAVOID-ABLE QUESTIONS. New York: Holt, Rinehart & Winston, 1980.

PERIODICAL LITERATURE

TITLE INDEX

APHA recommended program guide for abortion services. A-
MERICAN JOURNAL OF PUBLIC HEALTH 70:652-656,
June, 1980.

Abdominal hysterectomy for abortion—sterilization. A report of
500 consecutive cases, by P. G. Stumpf, et al. AMERICAN
JOURNAL OF OBSTETRICS AND GYNECOLOGY 136(6):
714-720, March 15, 1980.

Abortion. FAMILY LAW REPORTER: COURT OPINIONS 6
(30):2536, June 3, 1980.

—, by L. K. Crockett. CLINICAL OBSTETRICS AND GYNAE-
COLOGY 6(1):57-76, 1979.

—, by M. Gould. CHRYSALIS 9:55-57, Fall, 1979.

—, by B. Hayler. SIGNS 5(2):307-323, 1979.

Abortion [letter]. BRITISH MEDICAL JOURNAL 2(6188):495-
496, August 25, 1979.

—, by M. Churchill. BRITISH MEDICAL JOURNAL 2(6191):
667, September 15, 1979.

—, by A. K. Clarke. BRITISH MEDICAL JOURNAL 2(6191):
666, September 15, 1979.

—, by P. H. Gosling. BRITISH MEDICAL JOURNAL 2(6191):

666, September 15, 1979.

—, by B. Johnson. BRITISH MEDICAL JOURNAL 2(6191): 666, September 15, 1979.

—, by D. M. Potts. MEDICAL JOURNAL OF AUSTRALIA 1(5):236, March 8, 1980.

—, by C. P. Rice-Oxley. BRITISH MEDICAL JOURNAL 2 (6191):666-667, September 15, 1979.

—, by A. Savage. BRITISH MEDICAL JOURNAL 2(6191):667, September 15, 1979.

—, by M. Simms. BRITISH MEDICAL JOURNAL 2(6191):667, September 15, 1979.

—, by C. P. Wendell-Smith. MEDICAL JOURNAL OF AUS-TRALIA 2(6):313, September 22, 1979.

Abortion: an affirmative public good; USCC brief. ORIGINS 9: 534-535, January 31, 1980.

Abortion (Amendment) Bill [letter]. BRITISH MEDICAL JOURNAL 280(6212):477-479, February 16, 1980.

—, by J. Ashton. LANCET 1(8163):315-316, February 9, 1980.

—, by M. A. Church. LANCET 1(8165):430, February 23, 1980.

—, by A. K. Clarke. LANCET 1(8160):156, January 19, 1980.

—, by A. D. Clift. LANCET 1(8165):429-430, February 23, 1980.

—, by S. Dundon. LANCET 1(8165):429, February 23, 1980.

—, by E. Fottrell. LANCET 1(8163):315, February 9, 1980.

—, by R. Graham-Brown. LANCET 1(8162):260, February 2, 1980.

—, by M. Simms. LANCET 1(8162):260, February 2, 1980.

Abortion and child abuse, by S. M. Smith. CANADIAN JOUR-
NAL OF PSYCHIATRY 24(7):589-591, November, 1979.

Abortion and Christian morality, by J. Gaffney. CATHOLIC
CHARISMATIC 5:31-33, June-July, 1980.

Abortion and the constitution [Supreme Court decision holding
the Hyde amendment constitutional]. AMERICA 143:24,
July 19-26, 1980.

Abortion and dissenting parents: a dialogue, by S. R. Levy.
ETHICS 90:162-163, Spring, 1980.

Abortion and the elections: Cardinal Medefros, by H. Medefros.
ORIGINS 10:239, September 25, 1980.

Abortion and fertility, by H. M. Hagmann. REVUE MEDICALE
DE LA SUISSE ROMANDE 99(12):905-912, December,
1979.

Abortion and the handicapped: present practice in the light of
history, by G. Hogan. SOCIAL THOUGHT 6:37-46, Summer, 1980.

Abortion and the Law in Nigeria: a psychiatrist's view, by J.
Edeh. NIGERIAN MEDICAL JOURNAL 9(5-6):631-634,
May-June, 1979.

Abortion and the law in 1980 [effects of U.S. supreme court decisions since 1972], by E. W. Paul, et al. NEW YORK STATE
LAW SCHOOL LAW REVIEW 25(3):497-525, 1980.

Abortion—and moral qualms, by M. M. Malinovich. MADEMOI-
SELLE 86:82+, September, 1980.

Abortion and the 1978 Congressional elections, by M. W. Traugott, et al. FAMILY PLANNING PERSPECTIVES 12:238-
245, September-October, 1980.

Abortion and plain language [letter], by R. B. Parker. LANCET.
1(8162):260, February 2, 1980.

Abortion and the poor [ruling by Judge John F. Dooling Jr., on the unconstitutionality of the Hyde amendment]. AMERICA 142:73, February 2, 1980.

Abortion and the presidential election of 1976: a multivariate analysis of voting behavior, by M. A. Vinovskis. MICHIGAN LAW REVIEW 77(7):1750-1771, August, 1979.

Abortion and the right to life, by A. H. Goldman. PERSON-ALIST 60:402-406, October, 1979.

Abortion and the right to life; a statement by the archbishops of Great Britain. TABLET 234:91-92, January 26, 1980.

Abortion and the use of anaesthesia. Observations after two years' experience, by M. Palot, et al. ANESTHESIA AND ANALGESIA 36(3-4):151-154, March-April, 1979.

Abortion as a local option; views of J. T. Noonan. AMERICA 141:426-427, December 29, 1979.

Abortion as 'deviance'. Traditional female roles vs. the feminist perspective, by R. H. Rosen, et al. SOCIAL PSYCHIATRY 15(2):103-108, 1980.

Abortion as it is described to us, by M. Six-Quivy, et al. LILLE MEDICAL 25(6):307-310, June-July, 1980.

Abortion associated with intrauterine infection by candida albi-cans. Case report, by R. Buchanan, et al. BRITISH JOUR-NAL OF OBSTETRICS AND GYNAECOLOGY 86(9): 741-744, September, 1979.

Abortion attitudes, 1965-1980: trends and determinants, by D. Granberg, et al. FAMILY PLANNING PERSPECTIVES 12: 250-261, September-October, 1980.

Abortion availability in the United States: eight in ten U.S. counties had no doctor, clinic or hospital in 1977 that pro-vided any abortions, by S. Seims. FAMILY PLANNING PER-SPECTIVES 12:88+, March-April, 1980.

Abortion: beyond halfway solutions, by M. Papa. NATIONAL
CATHOLIC REPORTER 17:12, November 14, 1980.

Abortion by extraamnial and intravenous administration of a new
prostaglandin E2 derivative, by J. Kunz, et al. ARCHIVES
GYNECOLOGY 228(1-4):423-424, July 20, 1979.

Abortion by means of suction curettage compared to the conventional metal curettage, by K. W. Schweppe, et al. MEDI-
ZINISCHE WELT 31(13):479-483, March 28, 1980.

Abortion—a Christian feminist perspective, by L. Campbell. NEW
BLACKFRIARS 61:370-377, September, 1980.

Abortion clinic zoning: the right to procreative freedom and the
zoning power, by L. Robinson. WOMEN'S RIGHTS LAW
REPORTER 5:283-299, Summer, 1979.

Abortion clinics rush to diversify. BUSINESS WEEK p.68+, December 10, 1979.

Abortion compromises wearing thin [news], by J. F. Brazda.
HOSPITAL PROGRESS 60(11):20, November, 1979.

Abortion consulting in progress, by K. Sundström-Feigenberg.
LAKARTIDNINGEN 77(7):552, February 13, 1980.

Abortion, contraception, and motherhood in post-war Japan and
the United States, by M. Franz, et al. INTERNATIONAL
JOURNAL OF WOMEN'S STUDIES 3:66-75, January-February, 1980.

Abortion: a convergence of concern, by J. Wallis, ed. SOJOUR-
NERS 9(3-4):13-25, November, 1980.

Abortion counselling by nurse specialists, by J. R. Newton, et
al. CONTRACEPTION 20(5):429-439, November, 1979.

Abortion: courting severe judgment: while all sins are equal,
some sins are more equal than others, by J. W. Montgomery.
CHRISTIANITY TODAY 24:54+, January 25, 1980.

Abortion deaths in Singapore (1968-1976), by L. S. Lim, et al. SINGAPORE MEDICAL JOURNAL 20(3):391-394, September, 1979.

Abortion debate, by D. Butler, et al. NEWSWEEK 95:37, January 7, 1980.

Abortion debate continues: a look at laws, regulations, restrictions and funding, by J. A. Smith. CALIFORNIA NURSE 76(1):8, June, 1980.

The abortion debate: facing up to reality, by T. Ross. NURSING MIRROR AND MIDWIVE'S JOURNAL 150(8):40-41, February 21, 1980.

The abortion debate: life is a serious business, by T. Philpot. NURSING MIRROR AND MIDWIVE'S JOURNAL 150(7): 34-36, February 14, 1980.

Abortion, deformed fetus, and the Omega pill, by L. M. Fleck. PHILOSOPHICAL STUDIES 36:271-283, October, 1979.

Abortion [directory of organizations]. MS MAGAZINE 9:76, August, 1980.

Abortion discussed at Notre Dame [October 1979] , by T. P. Wojcik. ST. FLADIMIR'S THEOLOGICAL QUARTERLY 24(1):52-58, 1980.

Abortion, distant peoples, and future generations, by J. P. Sterba. JOURNAL OF PHILOSOPHY 77:424-440, July, 1980.

Abortion: the effects of contraception and motivations. An enquiry in Bordeaux, by M. Lamy, et al. POPULATION 35:545-580, May-June, 1980.

Abortion entitlement: absolute or qualified, by J. Crawford. LINACRE 47:77-87, February, 1980.

Abortion experiences among New Zealand women, by B. J. Kirkwood, et al. NEW ZEALAND MEDICAL JOURNAL 90(645):294-297, October 10, 1979.

Abortion: the false charges, by R. Butt. TIMES (LONDON) p.16, February 7, 1980.

Abortion for fetal abnormalities [letter] . NEW ZEALAND MEDICAL JOURNAL 90(639):31, July 11, 1979.

Abortion for fetal abnormality [letter] , by P. S. Brooke. NEW ZEALAND MEDICAL JOURNAL 90(640):75-76, July 25, 1979.

Abortions for the poor [ruling by U.S. Judge J. F. Dooling, Jr., declaring Hyde amendment unconstitutional, by A. Press, et al. NEWSWEEK 95:81, January 28, 1980.

The abortion-funding cases and population control: an imaginary lawsuit (and some reflections on the uncertain limits of reproductive privacy), by S. F. Appleton. MICHIGAN LAW REVIEW 77(7):1688-1723, August, 1979.

The abortion funding cases: a response to Professor Perry, by C. Fahy. GEORGETOWN LAW JOURNAL 67(5):1205-1208, 1979.

Abortion funding: out of the courtroom, into the legislature, by J. Duerr. OUR SUNDAY VISITOR 69:4-5, October 5, 1980.

Abortion: how men feel about one of the biggest issues in a woman's life, by J. L. Collier. GLAMOUR 78:164-165+, February, 1980.

Abortion in adolescence: the ethical dimension, by T. Silber. ADOLESCENCE 15(58):461-474, Summer, 1980.

Abortion in India, with particular reference to West Bengal, by R. Dutta. JOURNAL OF BIOSOCIAL SCIENCE 12(2): 191-200, April, 1980.

Abortion in Queesland [letter] , by R. J. Wilson. MEDICAL JOURNAL OF AUSTRALIA 1(5):236, March 8, 1980.

Abortion in the USA, by J. Deedy. TABLET 234:369-370, April 19, 1980.

Abortion in the United States, 1976-1977, by J. D. Forrest, et al. FAMILY PLANNING PERSPECTIVES 10(5):271-279, September-October, 1978.

—, 1977-1978, by J. D. Forrest, et al. FAMILY PLANNING PERSPECTIVES 11:329-335+, November-December, 1979.

—: Past, present, and future trends, by R. Krannich. FAMILY RELATIONS 29(3):365-374, July, 1980.

Abortion induction with the PGE2 derivative sulprostone, by N. Dennemark. ARCHIVES OF GYNECOLOGY 228(1-4):425-426, July 20, 1979.

Abortion induction with prostaglandin, by W. Lichtenegger. ARCHIVES OF GYNECOLOGY 228(1-4):405-406, July 20, 1979.

Abortion induction with 3 mg PF2alpha gel, by H. Knabe, et al. ARCHIVES OF GYNECOLOGY 228(1-4):415-416, July 20, 1979.

Abortion inequities [editorial]. BUSINESS INSURANCE 14:8, January 21, 1980.

Abortion insignificant in caucuses. NATIONAL CATHOLIC REPORTER 16:3+, February 1, 1980.

Abortion is no answer. TABLET 234:75, January 26, 1980.

The abortion issue: exercising religion freely on both sides, by J. Maust. CHRISTIANITY TODAY 24:72+, September 5, 1980.

Abortion issue sparks denials. OKLAHOMA OBSERVER 12:12, March 10, 1980.

Abortion: an issue that won't go away [views of C. Gerster and F. Wattleton], by H. Epstein. NEW YORK TIMES MAGAZINE p44-46+, March 30, 1980.

Abortion: issues of access, policy, rights continue to be tested, by A. H. Bernstein. HOSPITALS 54(3):28-30, February 1, 1980.

Abortion: a Jewish view, by T. J. Silber. JOURNAL OF RELIGION AND HEALTH 19:231-239, Fall, 1980.

Abortion: the last resort, by C. McCray. ESSENCE 10:51-52+, November, 1979.

Abortion law in the UK [editorial]. SOUTH AFRICAN MEDICAL JOURNAL 57(20):803-804, May 17, 1980.

Abortion law reform in Europe: the European commission on human rights upholds German restrictions on abortion. TEXAS INTERNATIONAL LAW JOURNAL 15:162-186, Winter, 1980.

Abortion law's husband-notification requirement held unconstitutional. CRIMINAL LAW REPORTER: COURT DECISIONS AND PROCEEDINGS 26(17):2373-2375, January 30, 1980.

Abortion laws in Commonwealth countries, by R. J. Cook, et al. INTERNATIONAL DIGEST OF HEALTH LEGISLATION 30(3):395-502, 1979.

Abortion laws, religious beliefs and the First Amendment, by S. L. Skahn. VALPARAISO UNIVERSITY LAW REVIEW 14: 487-526, Spring, 1980.

Abortion: the left has betrayed the sanctity of life, by M. Meehan. PROGRESSIVE 44:32-34, September, 1980.

Abortion. Legal basis, methods, complications, by D. Wagner. ZFA ZEITSCHRIFT FUR ALLGEMEINMEDIZIN 55(26): 1413-1418, September 20, 1979.

Abortion: legal medical and social perspectives, by J. Widdicombe, et al. FAMILY COMMUNITY HEALTH 2(3):17-28, November, 1979.

Abortion: the liberals have abandoned the poor, by D. Baldwin.

PROGRESSIVE 44:28-31, September, 1980.

Abortion: a matter of clinical judgment [editorial] . BRITISH MEDICAL JOURNAL 280(6210):269, February 2, 1980.

Abortion—medicaid funding—equal protection. FAMILY LAW REPORTER: COURT OPINIONS 6(14):2221, February 12, 1980.

Abortion: mercy or murder?, by J. Bellini. LISTENER 103:162-163, February 7, 1980.

Abortion—Missouri. JUVENILE LAW DIGEST 12(5):160, May, 1980.

The abortion movement: retreat from reality, by D. DeMarco. HOMILETIC AND PASTORAL REVIEW 80:10-20, January, 1980.

Abortion 1979: the concept of viability, by J. M. Healey. CONNECTICUT MEDICINE 43(9):599, September, 1979.

Abortion of fetuses with spina bifida? [letter] , by P. F. Hall. CANADIAN MEDICAL ASSOCIATION JOURNAL 121(7): 846, October 6, 1979.

Abortion: only nice girls need apply [study of college students] , by E. Aligeier, et al. PSYCHOLOGY TODAY 13:95, January, 1980.

Abortion or contraception, by A. Goldsmith, et al. REPRODUCTION 4(1):55-68, January-March, 1980.

Abortion—parental notification—constitutionality of a statute— U.S. District Court (D. Maine). JUVENILE LAW DIGEST 12 (4):113-114, April, 1980.

Abortion—parental notification—constitutionality of a statute— Utah. JUVENILE LAW DIGEST 12(4):109-112, April, 1980.

Abortion—parental notification—judicial consent—constitutionality of a statute—U.S. District Court (S.D. Fla.). JUVENILE

LAW DIGEST 12(1):17-19, January, 1980.

Abortion—parental notification—judicial consent—constitutionality of a statute—U.S. Supreme Court. JUVENILE LAW DI-
GEST 11(10):299-303, October, 1979.

Abortion party has ruled too long, professor charges. OUR SUN-
DAY VISITOR 69:7, June 22, 1980.

Abortion: perversion of 'help'. Legal claims to killing free of
charge? 'Final solutions' of perverse emancipation, by J. Bökmann. CONCEPTE 15(4):27-32, 1979.

Abortion policy in Britain and the United States, by C. Francome. SOCIAL WORK 25(1):5-9, January, 1980.

Abortion politics and policy: is there a middle ground?, by M.
C. Segers. CHRISTIANITY AND CRISIS 40:21-27, February 18, 1980.

Abortion politics in the United States, by C. Francome. POLITI-
CAL STUDIES 28:613-621, December, 1980.

Abortion: the poor have rights. ECONOMIST 274:38, January 26, 1980.

Abortion PRO: the abortion controversy: will it ever disappear?
CON: should we change our attitudes about abortion?, by M.
S., et al. JOURNAL OF THE MEDICAL SOCIETY OF NEW
JERSEY 77(6):450-453, June, 1980.

The abortion problem from the moral point of view (Hebrew),
by A. Azmon. SOCIETY AND WELFARE 2(3):302-310,
1979.

The abortion problem in the USA and in the Netherlands. ARS
AEQUI 28(6):290-297, 1979.

Abortion: problems of legal logic, by J. M. B. Crawford. MONTH
13:122-127, April, 1980.

Abortion referral and MD emigration: areas of concern and study

for CMA, by D. A. Geekie. CANADIAN MEDICAL ASSOCI-
ATION JOURNAL 118(2):175+, January 21, 1978.

Abortion referrals [letter], by L. Bruce. NEW ZEALAND MEDI-
CAL JOURNAL 90(646):353, October 24, 1979.

Abortion repeaters, by A. Lake. MCCALLS 107:58+, September,
1980.

Abortion reporting, by M. R. Stark. ARIZONA MEDICINE 36
(11):834, November, 1979.

Abortion restrictions will have little impact. AIR FORCE TIMES
41:15, December 8, 1980.

Abortion rights [with reply by E. Morgan], by C. Poster. HU-
MANIST 40:42-44, September-October, 1980.

Abortion rights: Hyde and seek? UNION W.A.G.E. 61:10-11,
September-October, 1980.

Abortion rights of minors, by M. Griffin. WOMEN'S RIGHTS
LAW REPORTER 6:13-14, Fall-Winter, 1979-1980.

Abortion rights: overruling neo-fascists, by E. Willis. VILLAGE
VOICE 25:1+, February 4, 1980.

Abortion ruling [unconstitutionality of Hyde amendment; ruling by Judge J. F. Dooling, Jr.]. TIME 115:30, January 28,
1980.

Abortion services lacking in local areas, study says. UNITED
STATES MEDICINE 16(5):3-4, March 1, 1980.

Abortion: subjective attitudes and feelings, by E. W. Freeman.
FAMILY PLANNING PERSPECTIVES 10(3):150-155, May-
June, 1978.

Abortion support waning in college, says young pro-lifer. OUR
SUNDAY VISITOR 69:6, July 6, 1980.

Abortion surveillance shows slower increase. AORN JOURNAL

30(6):1108, December 30, 1979.

Abortion technics, by S. Trotnow, et al. ZFA. ZEITSCHRIFT
FUR ALLGEMEINMEDIZIN 55(29):1628-1631, October 20,
1979.

Abortion today [letter], by H. Chambers. NEW ZEALAND
MEDICAL JOURNAL 90(640):74-75, July 25, 1979.

—, by J. Dobson. NEW ZEALAND MEDICAL JOURNAL 90
(640):75, July 25, 1979.

—, by J. V. Hay. NEW ZEALAND MEDICAL JOURNAL 90
(639):30, July 11, 1979.

—, by P. Willcox. NEW ZEALAND MEDICAL JOURNAL 90
(641):117, August 8, 1979.

Abortion: towards continuing the dialogue, by M. B. Mahowald.
CROSS CURRENTS 29:330-335, Fall, 1979.

Abortion: two steps back [Britain]. ECONOMIST 273:30-31,
October 27, 1979.

Abortion: U.S. case bodes ill for poor, by L. Duncan. BRANCH-
ING OUT 7(2):54, 1980

Abortion: an unhappy stand-off [Harris vs McCrae], by R. L.
Shinn. CHRISTIANITY AND CRISIS 40:219+, August 18,
1980.

Abortion: unhealthy reform [Britain]. ECONOMIST 274:24,
February 2, 1980.

Abortion—welfare. FAMILY LAW REPORTER: COURT OPIN-
IONS 6(11):2173, January 22, 1980.

Abortion: what the Commons will be deciding today, by M.
Phillips. GUARDIAN p8, February 8, 1980.

Abortion: what to expect if you decide to have one. GLAMOUR
77:302+, October, 1979.

Abortion: which poll do you read? [Britain]. ECONOMIST 274: 24, February 9, 1980.

Abortion: why the arguments fail, by S. Hauerwas. HOSPITAL PROGRESS 61(1):38-49, January, 1980.

Abortion—zoning. FAMILY LAW REPORTER: COURT OPINIONS 6(11):2173-2174, January 22, 1980.

Abortions—funding. FAMILY LAW REPORTER: COURT OPINIONS 6(17):2283, March 4, 1980.

Abortions—statistics and reality, by E. J. Hickl. DEUTSCHE MEDIZINISCHE WOCHENSCHRIFT 105(13):423-426, March 28, 1980.

Abortive T5 bacteriophage infections of *Escherichia coli* containing the colicinogenic factor, colib, by J. Glenn. DISSERTATION ABSTRACTS INTERNATIONAL 40(8):3587-B, 1979.

Aborto y planificacion familiar: aspectos sociologicos, by H. R. Gerardo. REVISTA ESPANOLA DE INVESTIGACIONES SOCIOLOGICAS 5:137-163, January-March, 1979.

Aborto y sociologia: en torno a un articulo del Senor Hernandez, by J. de Miguel. REVISTA ESPANOLA DE INVESTIGACIONES SOCIOLOGICAS 4:171-175, October-December, 1978.

Acceptability and use-effectiveness of contraception for teenagers, by R. Coles. JOURNAL OF BIOSOCIAL SCIENCE [Suppl] (5):159-170, 1978.

Acceptability of drugs for male fertility regulation: a prospectus and some preliminary data. World Health Organization Task Force on Psychosocial Research in Family Planning. CONTRACEPTION 21(2):121-134, February, 1980.

Accumulation of ethinylestradiol in blood and endometrium of women taking oral contraceptives: the sequential therapy, by V. Cortes-Gallegos, et al. FERTILITY AND STERILITY 32 (5):524-527, November, 1979.

Acrosin inhibitors as vaginal contraceptives in the primate and their acute toxicity, by L. J. Zaneveld, et al. BIOLOGICAL REPRODUCTION 20(5):1045-1054, June, 1979.

Actinomyces-like organisms in cervical smears from women using intrauterine contraceptive devices, by H. L. Duguid, et al. BRITISH MEDICAL JOURNAL 6239:534-537, August 23, 1980.

Action of oral contraceptives on the gingival mucosa and some components of mixed saliva, by P. D. Laforgia, et al. RIVISTA ITALIANA DI STOMATOLOGIA 48(5):13-18, May, 1979.

Active and inactive renin in pregnancy and in women on estrogen-containing oral contraceptives, by M. Hayashi, et al. GYNECOLOGIC AND OBSTETRIC INVESTIGATION 10 (5):246-253, 1979.

Active immunization of female rabbits with purified rabbit acrosin and effect on fertility, by F. N. Syner, et al. FERTILITY AND STERILITY 32(4):468-473, October, 1979.

Activists fight sterilization of women in hazardous jobs, by M. E. McKee. BUSINESS INSURANCE 13:2+, October 29, 1979.

Activities of abortion commissions, by D. Fukalova. CESKO-SLOVENSKA GYNEKOLOGIE 44(10):752-754, December, 1979.

Activity of various enzymes of venous blood serum in advanced normal pregnancy and in pregnancy complicated by threatened abortion and premature labor, by T. Laudanski, et al. WIADOMOSCI LEKARSKIE 32(12):833-836, J June 15, 1979.

Acute bacterial endocarditis following criminal abortion [letter], by R. L. Bhoola, et al. SOUTH AFRICAN MEDICAL JOURNAL 56(3):85, July 21, 1979.

Acute intermittent porphyria versus porphyria variegata: a

diagnostic uncertainty, by L. P. Betancor, et al. MEDICINA CLINICA 74(2):61-64, January 25, 1980.

Acute intermittent porphyria with pancreatitis and myocardial damage due to oral contraceptives, by O. H. Brinkmann, et al. ZFA. ZEITSCHRIFT FUR ALLGEMEINMEDIZIN 55 (22):1227-1233, August 10, 1979.

Acute renal failure with hemolytic crisis as a complication of septic abortion, by N. Rojansky, et al. HAREFUAH 96(5):241-243, March 1, 1979.

Acute renal insufficiency after criminal and septic abortion, by T. Szepietowski, et al. GINEKOLOGIA POLSKA 50(11):927-934, November, 1979.

Adenoma of the liver and focal nodular hyperplasia. Relationship with oral contraceptives, by G. Goldfarb, et al. ENTEROLOGIE CLINIQUE ET BIOLOGIQUE 3(5):465-472, May, 1979.

Adjustments of circulation including blood pressure to orthostatic reaction and physical exercise during application of a low estrogen dose steroid oral contraceptive, by B. Sandström, et al. ACTA OBSTETRICIA ET GYNECOLOGICA SCANDINAVICA [Suppl] 88:49-55, 1979.

Adjuvants in tubal surgery, by W. H. Pfeffer. FERTILITY AND STERILITY 33(3):245-256, March, 1980.

Adolescent contraceptive use: comparisons of male and female attitudes and information, by E. W. Freeman, et al. AMERICAN JOURNAL OF PUBLIC HEALTH 70:790-797, August, 1980.

Adolescent contraceptive use: experience in 1,762 teenagers, by L. E. Edwards, et al. AMERICAN JOURNAL OF OBSTETRICS AND GYNECOLOGY 137(5):583-587, July 1, 1980.

Adolescent perspectives on sexuality, contraception, and pregnancy, by V. McNamara, et al. JOURNAL OF THE MEDICAL ASSOCIATION OF GEORGIA 68(9):811-814,

Adolescent pregnancy decision-making: are parents important?, R. H. Rosen. ADOLESCENCE 15:43-54, Spring, 1980.

Adolescent pregnancy prevention services in high school clinics, by L. E. Edwards, et al. FAMILY PLANNING PERSPEC- TIVES 12(1):6-7+, January-February, 1980.

Adolescent pregnancy prevention: sexual learning and self- esteem, by C. H. Shapiro. HUMAN ECOLOGY FORUM 10: 21-24, Spring, 1980.

Adolescent sexual behavior. An indication of the need for com- prehensive family planning programs, by J. R. Faulkenberry, et al. THE HEALTH OF THE PEOPLE 10(3):5-7, May-June, 1979.

Advantages and disadvantages of low-dose oral contraceptives, by B. Law. JOURNAL OF GYNAECOLOGY AND OBSTE- TRICS 16(6):556-560, 1978-1979.

Advantages and limitations of steroid contraception: considera- tions on 14 cases of post-pill amenorrhea observed by the au- thor, by M. Faggiano, et al. ARCHIVES OF OBSTETRICS AND GYNECOLOGY 83(5-6):143-155, May-December, 1978.

Adverse effects after use of oral contraceptives. A comparison of 1966-1970 and 1974-1978, by G. Boman, et al. LAKARTID- NINGEN 77(24):2249-2252, June 11, 1980.

Adverse pregnancy outcomes in the Love Canal area, by N. Vi- anna, et al. NEW YORK STATE DEPARTMENT OF REPORT (34):April, 1980.

After Hyde. NATIONAL CATHOLIC REPORTER 16:14, July 18, 1980.

After the Hyde Amendment: public funding for abortion in Feb- ruary 1978, by R. B. Gold. FAMILY PLANNING PERSPEC- TIVES 12(3):131-134, May-June, 1980.

Again, a rift over birth control [Synod of Bishops]. U. S. NEWS

AND WORLD REPORT 89:69, October 13, 1980.

Age of discontinuity, by R. E. Miles, Jr. POPULATION BULLE-
TIN 34:42-48, December, 1979.

Agent Orange and spontaneous abortions [letter], by R. R.
Cook. JAMA 243(14):1423, April 11, 1980.

Aging and conservatism: cohort changes in attitudes about legalized abortion, by S. J. Cutler, et al. JOURNAL OF GERON-
TOLOGY 35:115-123, January, 1980.

Agonist (ovulation induction) and post-coital contraceptive properties of [D-Ala6] and [D-Trp6]-LHRH series, by A. Corbin,
et al. ENDOCRINE RESEARCH COMMUNICATIONS 6(1):
1-14, 1979.

The agony of abortion, by J. F. Alexander, et al. OTHER SIDE
(105):5-59, June, 1980.

Alcohol and spontaneous abortion [editorial]. LANCET 2(8187):
188, July 26, 1980.

Alcohol, smoking, and incidence of spontaneous abortions in the
first and second trimester, by S. Harlap, et al. LANCET 2
(8187):173-176, July 26, 1980.

Alpha fetoprotein and HbF cells in maternal blood in prostaglandin abortion, by D. H. Maas, et al. ARCHIVES OF GYNE-
COLOGY 228(1-4):398-399, July 20, 1979.

Alterations in rheology of cervical mucus—a new approach to
contraception, by V. P. Kamboj, et al. INDIAN JOURNAL
OF EXPERIMENTAL BIOLOGY 17(12):1379-1380, December, 1979.

Altered haemorpheology in oral contraceptive users, by P. C.
Buchan, et al. BRITISH MEDICAL JOURNAL 6219:978-
979, April 5, 1980.

Alternative pathways for abortion services [editorial]. LANCET
1(8178):1121, May 24, 1980.

American Academy of Pediatrics: Committee on Drugs. Medrox-yprogesterone acetate (Depo-Provera). PEDIATRICS 65(1): A74, January, 1980.

American Association of Gynecologic Laparoscopists' 1977 membership survey, by J. M. Phillips, et al. JOURNAL OF REPRODUCTIVE MEDICINE 23(2):61-64, August, 1979.

American nurse-tourist: lesson from the Phillipines, by M. Clymer. TEXAS NURSING 54(5):6-7, May, 1980.

The American press and birth control: preparing the ground for dissent. HOMILETIC AND PASTORAL REVIEW 80:10-26, July, 1980.

Amniocentesis and abortion for sex choice. PROGRESS IN CLINICAL AND BIOLOGICAL RESEARCH 38:75-78, 1980.

—. Case for discussion. PROGRESS IN CLINICAL AND BIOLOGICAL RESEARCH 38:79, 1980.

—. Summary of discussion results. PROGRESS IN CLINICAL AND BIOLOGICAL RESEARCH 38:103-104, 1980.

Amniotic-fluid embolism and abortion [letter], by R. J. Guidotti, et al. LANCET 2(8148):911-912, October 27, 1979.

Analysis of the geographical variations of twinning rate in An indirect approach to study spontaneous abortions, by D. Hemon, et al. REVUE D EPIDEMIOLOGIE ET DE SANTE PUBLIQUE 27(2):91-99, September 18, 1979.

Analysis of harmful factors in abortion and premature labor, by J. Kuczynski, et al. GINEKOLOGIA POLSKA Suppl:95-97, 1979.

An analysis of the influences of maternal age, gestational age, contraceptive method, and the mode of primary treatment of patients with hydatidiform moles on the incidence of subsequent chemotherapy, by M. Stone, et al. BRITISH OF OBSTETRICS AND GYNAECOLOGY 86(10):782-792, October, 1979.

Analysis of patients and indications for induced abortion, by A. von Trotha, et al. ARCHIVES OF GYNECOLOGY 228(1-4): 382, July 20, 1979.

Analysis of tubal sterilization in the Maternity Unit of the Hospital Salvador over a 12-month period, by P. Gayan, et al. REVISTA CHILENA DE OBSTETRICIA Y GINECOLOGIA 43(2):124-125, 1978.

Anamnestic criteria for evaluation of the 'risk' in hormonal contraception, by S. Gneo, et al. MINERVA GINECOLOGIA 31 (9):625-628, September, 1979.

Anatomical lesions of the liver and oral contraceptives, by P. Delavierre, et al. SEMAINES DES HOPITAUX DE PARIS 55 (23-26):1172-1176, June 18-25, 1979.

Androgens and sexual behaviour in women using oral contraceptives, by J. Bancroft, et al. CLINICAL ENDOCRINOLOGY 12(4):327-340, April, 1980.

Another five-year plan for family planning, by R. Wigg. TIMES (LONDON) pIII, June 16, 1980.

Anovulation after pregnancy termination: ovarian versus hypothalamic-pituitary factors, by G. S. DiZerega, et al. JOURNAL OF CLINICAL ENDOCRINOLOGY AND METABOLISM 49(4):594-599, October, 1979.

Anti-abortion group fights church bans on soliciting, by B. Kenkelen. NATIONAL CATHOLIC REPORTER 16:3, September 12, 1980.

Anti-abortion groups oppose Baker. (Sen. Baker's pro-abortion record). HUMAN EVENTS 40:3+, May, 1980.

Anti-D immunoglobulin and abortion [letter], by D. Tovey. BRITISH MEDICAL JOURNAL 2(6193):793, September 29, 1979.

Antiepileptic drugs and oral contraceptives. Preliminary note, by M. Meduri, et al. BOLLETTINO DELLA SOCIETA ITALI-

28

ANA DI BIOLOGIA SPERIMENTALE 54(23):2462-2467, December 15, 1978.

Antiethinyloestradiol antibody activities in oral contraceptive users, by J. L. Beaumong, et al. CLINICAL AND EXPERIMENTAL IMMUNOLOGY 38(3):445-452, December, 1979.

"Anti-family" charge and a popular foe endanger McGovern; abortion is emotional issue in race against Radnor [senatorial race in South Dakota], by J. M. Perry. WALL STREET JOURNAL 196:1+, September 23, 2980.

Antifertility activities of newly synthesized steroids in rats administered postcoitally before and after implantation and their interceptive effects in the baboon, by J. Strecke, et al. PHARMAZIE 35(1):45-47, January, 1980.

Antifertility activity of a medicinal plant of the genus Andrografi wall (family Acanthaceae). Part II, by M. Shamsuzzoha, et al. BANGLADESH MEDICAL RESEARCH COUNCIL BULLETIN 5(1):14-18, June, 1979.

Antifertility effects of 6-chloro-6-deoxy-glucose in the male rat, by F. Heitfeld, et al. CONTRACEPTION 19(6):543-555, June, 1979.

Antifertility efficacy of twice daily oral administration of 6-chloro-6-deoxy-D-glucose (6 CDG) in male rats, by L. A. Warren, et al. CONTRACEPTION 20(3):275-289, September, 1979.

Antithrombin and heparin-neutralizing activity in sera of women using and not using hormonal contraceptives, by M. Stepanauskas, et al. ZEITSCHRIFT FUR MEDIZINISCHE LABORATORIUMSDIAGNOSTIK 20(5):295-301, 1979.

Appel aux hommes de bonne volonte au sujet de la loi sur l'avortement, by L. Elchinger. LA DOCUMENTATION CATHOLIQUE 76:890-893, October 21, 1979.

Appropriate contraception for middle-aged women, by R. B. Greenblatt, et al. JOURNAL OF BIOSOCIAL SCIENCE

[Suppl] (6):119-141, 1979.

Are combined oral contraceptives appropriate therapy for primary dysmenorrhea?, by J. H. Goodwin. JOURNAL OF NURSE-MIDWIFERY 25(2):17-19, March-April, 1980.

Are the severe complications of induced abortion being abolished? Statistics from the emergency unit ofthe Claude Bernard Hospital 1970-1977, by F. Vachon, et al. NOUVELLE PRESSE MEDICALE 8(27):2247-2249, June 16, 1979.

Are there psychiatric grounds fro terminating a pregnancy?, by W. Murdoch. CENTRAL AFRICAN JOURNAL OF MEDICINE 25(7):158-160, July, 1979.

Are there still severe complications in induced abortion? [letter], by D. Kleinknecht, et al. NOUVELLE PRESSE MEDICALE 9(7):460, February 9, 1980.

Arkansas criminal abortion laws suffer constitutional flaws. CRIMINAL LAW REPORTER: COURT DECISIONS AND PROCEEDINGS 27(17):2365-2366, July 30, 1980.

Artificial birth control backers bemoan lack of funds. OUR SUNDAY VISITOR 69:7, August 24, 1980.

Artificial gestation: new meaning for the right to terminate pregnancy, by R. J. Favole. ARIZONA LAW REVIEW 21(3):755-776, 1979.

Artificial regulation of the generative functions of men by means of contraceptive agents, by D. Vasilev. AKUSHERSTVOI GINEKOLOGIIA 19(3):259-260, 1980.

Aspectos medicos del aborto, by S. Cobos. CHRISTUS 45:6-11, March, 1980.

Assay of estradiol receptors in a liver adenoma observed after taking an estrogen-progestogen combination [letter], by J. Gastard, et al. NOUVELLE PRESSE MEDICALE 9(1):43, January 5, 1980.

Assessment of family planning service delivery in Egypt, by M. T. Hassouna. STUDIES IN FAMILY PLANNING 11:159-166, May, 1980.

Association of induced abortion with subsequent pregnancy loss, by A. A. Levin, et al. JAMA 243(24):2495-2499, June 27, 1980.

Attempt to establish a relationship between ultraviolet irradiation and early spontaneous abortions, by V. Donchev. A-KUSHERSTVO I GINEKOLOGIIA 19(2):99-103, 1980.

Attitudes and choice of contraceptive, by A. E. Reading, et al. PSYCHOLOGICAL REPORTER 44(3 Pt 2):1243-1246, June, 1979.

Attitudes on abortion and firearms control. AMERICAN BAR ASSOCIATION JOURNAL 65:1634-1635, November, 1979.

Attitudes toward abortion: a comparative analysis of correlates for 1973 and 1975, by T. C. Wagenaar. JOURNAL OF SO-CIOLOGY AND SOCIAL WELFARE 4(6):927-944, July, 1977.

Attitudes toward abortion have changed little since mid-70s. GALLUP OPINION INDEX p6-7, June, 1980.

Attitudes toward abortion: a pilot cross-cultural comparison, by V. L. Zammuner. GIORNALE ITALIANO DI PSICOLO-GIA 3(1):75-116, April, 1976.

Attitudinal and nonattitudinal determinanats of contraception: a cross-cultural study, by S. B. Kar, et al. STUDIES IN FAM-ILY PLANNING 11(2):51-64, February, 1980.

Autoimmune disease and the theory of clonal abortion: is it still relevant?, by E. Bitteau. JOURNAL OF PHARMACOL-OGY 10(1):69-72, 1979.

Avant le debat parlementaire sur l'avortement: substituer a une loi de mort une loi de vie, by G. Duchene. LA DOCUMEN-TATION CATHOLIQUE 76:893-895, October 21, 1979.

Avoidance of late abortion [editorial] . LANCET 2(8152):1113-1114, November 24, 1979.

Avortement: quelle legislation pour demain?, by P. Verspieren. ETUDES 351:319-338, October, 1979.

Avortement volontaire, incitations et resistances a la contraception, by M. Bourgeois. L'EVOLUTION PSYCHIATRIQUE 42(2):397-417, April-June, 1977.

Baby budgeting. ECONOMIST 274:38, March 1, 1980.

Barrier contraceptive practice and male infertility as related factors to female breast cancer, by A. N. Gjorgov. GODISEN ZBORNIK NA MEDICINSKIOT FAKULTET VO SKOPJE 24:101-121, 1978.

Barrier contraceptive practice and male infertility as related factors to breast cancer in married women. Preliminary results, by A. N. Gjorgov. GODISEN ZBORNIK NA MEDICINSKIO FAKULTET VO SKOPJE 24:133-137, 1978.

Barrier methods, by L. B. Tyrer, et al. CLINICAL OBSTETRICS AND GYNAECOLOGY 6(1):39-55, April, 1979.

Barrier methods of contraception: a reappraisal, by E. B. Connell. INTERNATIONAL JOURNAL OF GYNAECOLOGY AND OBSTETRICS 16(6):479-481, 1978-1979.

Behavioral response to vasectomy, by R. L. Vaughn. ARCHIVES OF GENERAL PSYCHIATRY 36(7):815-821, July, 1979.

Beliefs about the permissibility of abortion and their relationship to decisions regarding abortion, by J. G. Smetana. JOURNAL OF POPULATION 2(4):294-305, 1979.

Benign heptomata while taking oral contraceptives, by W. Dusel, et al. MMW: MUENCHENER MEDIZINISCHE WOCHENSCHRIFT 122(19):693-696, May 9, 1980.

Benign tumours of the liver and oral contraceptives, by F. Lesbros, et al. ARCHIVES D'ANATOMIE ET DE CYTOLOGIE

PATHOLOGIQUE 28(1):24-31, 1980.

Benign tumors of the liver and oral contraceptives. Apropos of two cases, by M. Peffault de Latour, et al. ANNALES D'An-ATOMIE PATHOLOGIQUE 24(1):73-78, 1979.

Between abortion and infanticide, by P. Langham. SOUTHERN JOURNAL OF PHILOSOPHY 17:465-471, Winter, 1979.

Beyond personal piety. CHRISTIANITY TODAY 23:13, November 16, 1979.

Biochemical basis for evaluating oral contraceptives, by M. H. Briggs. AUSTRALIAN FAMILY PHYSICIAN Suppl:25-29, February, 1980.

Biochemical basis for the selection of oral contraceptives, by M. H. Briggs. INTERNATIONAL JOURNAL OF GYNAECOLOGY AND OBSTETRICS 16(6):509-517, 1978-1979.

Biodegradable systems for the sustained release of fertility-regulating agents, by G. Benagiano, et al. JOURNAL OF STEROID BIOCHEMISTRY 11(1B):449-455, July, 1979.

Bioethical issues in family planning, by D. Brieland. SOCIAL WORK 24:478-484, November, 1979.

Biological paternity, social maternity: on abortion and infanticide as unrecognized indicators of the cultural character of maternity, by N. C. Mathieu. SOCIOLOGICAL REVIEW MONOGRAPH 28:232-240, 1979.

Biological profile of 3-(2-benzofuranyl)-2,2-dimethyl-3-ethyl-propionic acid—a new oral antifertility agent, by K. V. Rao, et al. INDIAN JOURNAL OF EXPERIMENTAL BIOLOGY. 17(7):678-679, July, 1979.

Birth among strangers: pregnancy, delivery and perinatal care of poor women in an American city, by S. S. Hopper. DISSERTATION ABSTRACTS INTERNATIONAL 1979.

Birth Control, by G. G. Panter. PARENTS 55:72+, July, 1980.

Birth control and family planning in Hungary in the last two decades, by A. Klinger. WORLD HEALTH STATISTICS QUARTERLY 32(4):257-268, 1979.

Birth control: cases; Doe v. Irwin 615 F 2d 116Z. AMERICAN JOURNAL OF TRIAL ADVOCACY 4:470-473, Fall, 1980.

Birth-control chart: what works, what's safe now, by M. L. Schildkraut. GOOD HOUSEKEEPING 190:274-275, May, 1980.

Birth control: different conceptions, by R. V. Wells. JOURNAL OF INTERDESCIPLINARY HISTORY 10:511-516, Winter, 1980.

Birth-control etiquette, by B. Snider. OUI 9:92-95, September, 1980.

Birth control: facing the facts of life [teenagers], by J. Marks. TEEN 24:18+, March, 1980.

Birth control grabs headlines but issue distorts synod, by D. O'Grady. OUR SUNDAY VISITOR 69:8, October 19, 1980.

Birth control a hot issue at bishops' synod on families, by D. O'Grady. OUR SUNDAY VISITOR 69:3, October 12, 1980.

Birth control: the minor and the physician. QUEENS LAW REVIEW 5:269-287, 1980.

Birth control: the new breakthroughts, by M. Abrams. HARPERS BAZAAR 113:154-155+, April, 1980.

Birth control: not for women only?, by T. Schultz. FAMILY HEALTH 12:44, June, 1980.

Birth control pill: good news for some women, by E. R. Dobell. REDBOOK 155:27+, September, 1980.

Birth control practices and conservatism, by V. C. Joe, et al. JOURNAL OF PERSONALITY ASSESSMENT 43(5):536-540, October, 1979.

Birth-control shots: FDA moves slowly [Depo-Provera] . MEDI-
CAL WORLD NEWS 21:40, December 8, 1980.

Birth planning in China [nine articles] , by S. L. Camp, ed.
DRAPER FUND REPORT p1-28, March, 1980.

Birthrights at the barricades [bill designed to toughen abortion
law] , by C. Kennedy. MACLEANS 93:32-33, February 18,
1980.

Births following oral contraceptive failures, by S. Harlap, et al.
OBSTETRICS AND GYNECOLOGY 55(4):447-452, April,
1980.

Bishop hits 'teen crisis' booklet sent to public schools, by F.
Franzonia. OUR SUNDAY VISITOR 68:6, March 23, 1980.

Bishops appeal pregnancy discrimination act ruling. OUR SUN-
DAY VISITOR 69:7, June 29, 1980.

Bishops' Conference reaffirms Church's stand on contraceptive
sterilization. L'OSSERVATORE ROMANO (31):2+, August 4, 1980.

Bishops one-hundred percent behind Humanae Vitae but..., by
J. Delanv. OUR SUNDAY VISITOR 69:8, November 30,
1980.

Bishops reassert sterilization position, by S. Russell. NATIONAL
CATHOLIC REPORTER 16:4+, July 18, 1980.

Bishops soft on abortion, say critics, by J. Michaels, Jr. NATION-
AL CATHOLIC REPORTER 16:9, January 18, 1980.

Bishops' statement reaffirms Church's reverence for spousal love,
by D. McCarthy. HOSPITAL PROGRESS 61:41-42, September, 1980.

Bleeding and ovulation control with use of a small contraceptive
vaginal ring releasing levonorgestrel and estradiol, by J. Toivonen, et al. CONTRACEPTION 20(1):11-18, July, 1979.

Bleeding hepatic adenoma and its relation to oral contraceptives, by E. J. Eichelbaum, et al. GEN 32(4):355-361, April-June, 1978.

Blood coagulation and fibrinolysis in laparoscopic tubal sterilization, by K. Schander, et al. ARCHIVES OF GYNECOLOGY 228(1-4):627-628, July 20, 1979.

Blood pressure and oral progestational agents. A prospective study of 119 black women, by W. D. Hall, et al. AMERICAN JOURNAL OF OBSTETRICS AND GYNECOLOGY 136(3):344-348, February 1, 1980.

Body weight and cycle control of injectable contraceptives, by S. el-Mahgoub. JOURNAL OF REPRODUCTIVE MEDICINE 24(3):119-126, March, 1980.

Books on abortion, by N. Caynar. NEW COVENANT 10:31, November, 1980.

Both sides of the abortion argument, by A. Ferriman. TIMES (LONDON) p10, February 6, 1980.

Bowel injury in septic abortion: the need for more aggressive management, by U. Megafu. INTERNATIONAL JOURNAL OF GYNAECOLOGY AND OBSTETRICS 17(5):450-453, March-April, 1980.

Brazil: community-based distribution in Rio Grande do Norte [of oral contraceptives], by M. E. Gorosh, et al. INTERNATIONAL FAMILY PLANNING PERSPECTIVES 5:150-159, December, 1979.

Breast cancer and oral contraceptive therapy in premenopausal women, by R. D. Gambrell, Jr., et al. JOURNAL OF REPRODUCTIVE MEDICINE 23(6):265-271, December, 1979.

The British retrospective and prospective studies, by J. McEwan. INTERNATIONAL JOURNAL OF GYNAECOLOGY AND OBSTETRICS 16(6):525-528, 1978-1979.

British women sue pill manufacturer [Syntex], by J. Miller.

BUSINESS INSURANCE 13:84, October 29, 1979.

Brooklyn judge rules against Hyde Amendments: federal funding of abortion. ORIGINS 9:525+, January 31, 1980.

CLC statement on abortion. CANADIAN LABOUR 24:8,December 14, 1979.

Can libertarians support abortion. (1 libertarian argument against abortion), by E. A. Opitz. HUMAN EVENTS 40:10, March 22, 1980.

Carbohydrate metabolism prospectively studied in women using a low-estrogen oral contraceptive for six months, by W. N. Spellacy, et al. CONTRACEPTION 20(2):137-148, August, 1979.

Cardinal beards the political lion with abortion,by F. Franzonia. OUR SUNDAY VISITOR 69:3, September 28, 1980.

Cardiovascular side effects from oral contraceptives, by H. J. Engel, et al. THERAPEUTISCHE UMSCHAU 37(2):96-104, February, 1980.

The case against IUD: the story continues [letters]. NEW WEST 5:86-87, June 2, 1980.

The case against IUD'S, by J. Kasindorf. NEW WEST 5:21, May 5, 1980.

Case of coexistent intra- and extrauterine pregnancy, by M. Semczuk, et al. WIADOMOSCI LEKARSKIE 33(2):137-139, January 15, 1980.

Case of complicated septic abortion in the 16th week of pregnancy, by J. Lysakowski, et al. WIADOMOSCI LEKARSKIE 32 (17):1249-1251, September 1, 1979.

Castration of sex offenders: treatment or punishment? A review and critique of recent European literature, byN. Heim. ARCHIVES OF SEXUAL BEHAVIOR 8(3):281-304, May,1979.

A casual model of psychosomatic reactions to vacuum aspiration abortion, by M. B. Bracken. SOCIAL PSYCHIATRY 13(3): 135-145, 1978.

Catecholamine metabolic characterisitcs of women with habitual abortion, by I. P. Hryzhak. PEDIATRIIA AKUSHERSTVO I GINEKOLOGIIA (4):55-56, July-August, 1979.

The Catholit Church and reform of abortion legislation, by A. Lorenzer. KRITISCHE JUSTIZ 13(1):28-38, 1980.

Catholics agree with Protestants that abortion and contraception should be widely available [news]. FAMILY PLANNING PERSPECTIVES 12(1):51, January-February, 1980.

Causes of clinic drop-out among Iranian pill users, by C. Lee, et al. JOURNAL OF BIOSOCIAL SCIENCE 10(1):7-15, January, 1978.

Celioscopic sterilizations with Yoon rings. 300 cases. Immediate complications, effectiveness and reversibility, by J. M. Lambercy, et al. JOURNAL OF GYNECOLOGIE OBSTE-TRIQUE ET BIOLOGIE DE LA REPRODUCTION 8(2): 157-162, March, 1979.

Center for Life provedes accessible maternity care, by B. Myerson. HOSPITAL PROGRESS 60(10):30+, October, 1979.

Central action of prostaglandins in spawning behavior of female goldfish, by N. E. Stacey, et al. PHYSIOLOGY AND BE-HAVIOR 22(6):1157-1162, June, 1979.

Cerebral absess associated with an intrauterine contraceptive device, by N. Kum, et al. OBSTETRICS AND GYNECOLOGY 54(3):375-378, 1979.

Cerebral pseudotumor and oral contraceptives (cerebral case), by B. Jandolo, et al. RIVISTA DI NEUROBIOLOGIA 24 (1-2):106-108, January-June, 1978.

Cerebral vascular occlusion and nodular hyperplasia of the liver caused by contraceptives, by I. Babaryka, et al. MEDIZI-

NISCHE KLINIK 75(2):76-79, January 18, 1980.

Cerebrovascular accidents among users of oral contraceptives. An analysis of Japanese cases, by Y. Umeda, et al. GYNECO-LOGIC AND OBSTETRIC INVESTIGATION 10(2-3):88-94, 1979.

Cervical cap, by J. M. Kintzing. MADEMOISELLE 86:108+, August, 1980.

—, by K. Littman. BOSTON 72:179, June, 1980.

Cervical priming prior to first-trimester suction abortion with a single 15-methyl-prostaglandin F2 alpha vaginal suppository, by N. H. Lauersen, et al. AMERICAN JOURNAL OF OBSTETRICS AND GYNECOLOGY 135(8):1116-1118, December 15, 1979.

Cervix rupture after prostaglandin-induced late abortion, by A. Ingvardsen, et al. UGESKRIFT FOR LAEGER 141(51): 3531-3532, December 17, 1979.

Change in ovarian and adrenal gland function under the effect of artificial abortion, by V. I. Hryshchenko, et al. PEDIATRIIA AKUSHERSTVO I GINEKOLOGIIA (3):61-62, 1980.

Change of factor XIII activity in pregnancy termination using suction curettage, by E. Kidess, et al. ARCHIVES OF GYNECOLOGY 228(1-4):627, July 20, 1979.

The change of urinary steroid excretions in liver disease with special reference to an implication of hepatic dysfunction in pill users, by M. Kodama, et al. JOURNAL OF CLINICAL ENDOCRINOLOGY AND METABOLISM 49(5):748-752, November, 1979.

Changes in acceptors' and users' ages: a test of an explanatory mechanism, by J. A. Ross, et al. POPULATION STUDIES 34:367-380, July, 1980.

Changes in the fibrinogen level and the risk of debigrination after the intra-amniotic instillation of a saline solution used for abortion purposes, by A. Atanasov. AKUSHERSTVO I GI-NEKOLOGIIA 19(3):206-209, 1980.

Changing attitudes toward abortion, by M. Potts. WESTERN JOURNAL OF MEDICINE 131(5):455-459, November, 1979.

Characteristics of successful distributors in the community based distribution of contraceptives in Guatemala, by J. T. Bertrand, et al. STUDIES IN FAMILY PLANNING 11:274-285, September-October, 1980.

Characteristics of vasectomy patients at a family planning clinic, by R. J. Gandy. JOURNAL OF BIOSOCIAL SCIENCE 10 (2):125-132, April, 1978.

Chemical methods of abortion, by H. Schmidt-Matthiesen. ARCHIVES OF GYNECOLOGY 228(1-4):365-378, July 20, 1979.

Chemical sterilization of male dogs (Canis familiaris) after single intratesticular administration of methallibure (ICI-33828), dexamethasone, metopiron (SU-4885, Ciba), niridazole (33644-Ba, Ciba), alpha-chlorohydrin (U-5897) and danazol, by V. P. Dixit. INDIAN JOURNAL OF EXPERIMENTAL BIOLOGY 17(9):937-940, September, 1979.

Chest pain among oral contraceptive users, by K. Williams. JOURNAL OF THE ROYAL COLLEGE OF GENERAL PRACTITIONERS 30(210):33-34, January, 1980.

Childbirth and abortion 1975-1978, by L. B. Knudsen, et al. UGESKRIFT FOR LAEGAR 141(31):2134-2135, July 30, 1979.

Childfree marriage—a theological view, by D. Doherty. CHICAGO STUDIES 18:137-145, Summer, 1979.

Children: the blessed burden, by W. Williman. RELIGION IN LIFE 49:24-34, Spring, 1980.

China invents male birth control pill, by W. Wen. AMERICAN

JOURNAL OF CHINESE MEDICINE 8(1-2):195-197, Spring-Summer, 1980.

China meets its population problem [based on address] , by H. Y. Tien, et al. INTERNATIONAL FAMILY PLANNING PERSPECTIVES 6:65-73, June, 1980.

China sets ever more stringent targets for fertility reduction, by M. Chen. POPULATION AND DEVELOPMENT REVIEW 5: 723-730, December, 1979.

China's all-out push to slash its birth rate, by H. Ellithorpe. BUSINESS WEEK p67, November 19, 1979.

China's birth planning: organization since the cultural revolution, by K. C. Lyle. HUMAN ORGANIZATION 39:197-201, Summer, 1980.

China's new birth policy: one baby is enough, by B. J. Culliton. SCIENCE 206:429, October 26, 1979.

Chinese cotton on, by L. De Silva. GUARDIAN p15, March 3, 1980.

Choice of a contraceptive method, by J. C. Guillat. SOINS 25 (8):13-14, April 20, 1980.

Choice of method and complication prevention in induced abortion, by K. A. Walz, et al. ARCHIVES OF GYNECOLOGY 228(1-4):393-395, July 20, 1979.

Cholangiocarcinoma and oral contraceptives [letter] , by E. R. Littlewood, et al. LANCET 1(8163):310-311, February 9, 1980.

Cholesterol cholelithiasis in adolescent females: its connection with obesity, parity, and oral contraceptive use—a retrospective study of 31 cases, by L. H. Honore. ARCHIVES OF SURGERY 115(1):62-64, January, 1980.

Choosing to adopt on your own, by M. Hellwig. OUR SUNDAY VISITOR 69:6, August 10, 1980.

Choosing to be child free, by W. H. Harris, et al. JOURNAL OF SCHOOL HEALTH 49(7):379-382, September, 1979.

Chorea associated with oral contraceptive therapy, by D. J. Dove. AMERICAN JOURNAL OF OBSTETRICS AND GYNECOLOGY 137(6):740-742, July 15, 1980.

Chorea induced by oral contraceptives, by P. A. Nausieda, et al. NEUROLOGY 29(12):1605-1609, December, 1979.

Chromogenic and immunological determination of antithrombin III and of antiplasmin in subjects under treatment with oral hormonal contraceptives, by R. Savoldi, et al. QUADERNI SCLAVO DI DIAGNOSTICA CLINICA E DI LABORATORIO 15(1):152-163, March, 1979.

Chromosomal polymorphic variants in couples with recurrent spontaneous abortions, by I. Tejada, et al. CLINICAL GENETICS 17(1):90, 1980.

Chromosome studies and a 1-antitrypsin phenotypes in recurrent abortions, by J. P. M. Geraedts, et al. CLINICAL GENETICS 17(1):68, 1980.

Chromosome variants and abnormalities detected in 50 married couples with repeated spontaneous abortions, by P. Genest. CLINICAL GENETICS 16(6):387-389, December, 1979.

Chronic occlusion of the rabbit Fallopian tube with silicone polymer, by R. H. Davis, et al. GYNECOLOGIC AND OBSTETRIC INVESTIGATION 10(6):281-288, 1979.

Chrysalis reviews abortion as politics and experience, by E. Willis, et al. CHRYSALIS 9:51-54, Fall, 1979.

Church and state in Boston [pastoral letter], by H. Medeiros. AMERICA 143:180, October 4, 1980.

Cicloxilic acid and the bile lipids in oral contraceptive users, by M. Zuin, et al. ARZNEIMITTEL-FORSCHUNG 29(5):837-838, 1979.

Cigarette smoking, alcohol intake, and oral contraceptives: relationships to lipids and lipoproteins in adolescent schoolchildren, by J. A. Morrison, et al. METABOLISM 28(11): 1166-1170, November, 1979.

Circadian changes of rheobase in patients with imminent abortion and premature labor, by H. Fendel, et al. ARCHIVES OF GYNECOLOGY 228(1-4):175-176, July 20, 1979.

Circulatory disease in association with oral contraceptive use [letter], by C. Kay. LANCET 2(8141):521, September 8, 1979.

Citizens United for Life: status politics, symbolic reform and the anti-abortion movement, by S. L. Markson. DISSERTATION ABSTRACTS INTERNATIONAL 40(8):4770-A, 1979.

The claim for wrongful conception. Forcing physicians to raise their patients' children, by D. Savage. JOURNAL OF REPRODUCTIVE MEDICINE 24(2):51-60, February, 1980.

Classification and treatment of missed abortion, by S. Levin, et al. GEBURTSCHILFE UND FRAUENHEILKUNDE 39(8): 727-733, August, 1979.

Clearance of bacteriuria on discontinuing oral contraception, by D. A. Evans, et al. BRITISH MEDICAL JOURNAL 280 (6208):152, January 19, 1980.

Clinic staffing patterns and the pregnant adolescent, by M. J. Kieffer, et al. JOGN 8(6):333-335, November-December, 1979.

Clinical application of vas deferens puncture, by S. Li. CHINESE MEDICAL JOURNAL 93(1):69-70, 1980.

Clinical evaluation of two biphasic and one triphasic norgestrel/ ethinyl estradiol regimens, by A. Larrañaga, et al. INTERNATIONAL JOURNAL OF FERTILITY 23(3):193-199, 1978.

Clinical pharmacology of contraceptive steroids. Report on a workshop conference held in Igls, Austria May 4-7, 1978, by J. Hammerstein, et al. CONTRACEPTION 20(3):187-200, September 20, 1979.

Clinical study results with the vaginal contraceptive preparation, traceptin, by K. V. Chachava, et al. AKUSHERSTVO I GINEKOLOGIIA (3):46-47, March, 1980.

Clinical trial of a new oral contraceptive pill containing the natural oestrogen 17 beta-oestradiol, by B. Astedt, et al. BRITISH JOURNAL OF OBSTETRICS AND GYNAECOLOGY 86(9): 732-736, September, 1979.

Coercive and noncoercive abortion deterrence policies: a comparative state analysis, by C. A. Johnson, et al. LAW AND POLICY QUARTERLY 2:106-108, January, 1980.

Coital frequency of urban couples attending a family planning clinic at Bombay, by I. Kapoor, et al. JOURNAL OF FAMILY WELFARE 26:50-63, June, 1980.

Crohn's disease and oral contraceptive, by C. Conri, et al. SEMAINES DES HOPITAUX DE PARIS 55(37-38):1733-1735, November 8-15, 1979.

Combined epithelial and sarcomatous elements in a liver cancer associated with oral contraceptive use, by L. Ladaga, et al. AMERICAN JOURNAL OF SURGICAL PATHOLOGY 3 (2):185-190, April, 1979.

Combined pills may decrease endometrial cancer risk; sequentials may increase it [news]. FAMILY PLANNING PERSPECTIVES 12(3):162, May-June, 1980.

The combined use of oral medroxyprogesterone acetate and methyltestosterone in a male contraceptive trial programme, by J. Bain, et al. CONTRACEPTION 21(4):365-379, April, 1980.

Commentary from Westminster. Abortion (Amendment) Bill, by R. Deitch. LANCET 1(8165):433-434, February 23, 1980.

Comments and the diagnosis of vitality of early pregnancy in threatening abortion, by H. Jung, et al. GEBURTSHILFE UND FRAUENHEILKUNDE 39(6):437-446, June, 1979.

Comments on the sterilization of mental incompetents in Canadian civil and common law, by R. P. Kouri, et al. REVUE DE DROIT UNIVERSITE DE SHERBROKKE 10:599-628, 1980.

Committee to Defend Reporductive Rights v. Myers (156 Cal Rptr 73): medi-Cal funding of abortion. GOLDEN GATE UNIVERSITY LAW REVIEW 9:361-419, 1978-1979.

Communicating the message: family planning campaigns can only be truly successful if the communicators avoid the "hard sell"—or avoid ignoring the issue altogether, by O. J. Sikes. POPULI 7(1):6-11, 1980.

Communication about sex and birth control between mothers and their adolescent children, by P. B. Rothenberg. POPULATION AND ENVIRONMENT 3(1):35-50, Spring, 1980.

Community-based integrated family planning programs, by E. S. Trainer. STUDIES ON FAMILY PLANNING 10(5):177-182, May, 1979.

Comparable effects of 30 and 50 microgram estrogen-progestogen oral contraceptives on blood clotting and fibrinolysis, by A. M. A. Sabra, et al. THROMBOSIS AND HAEMOSTASIS 42(1):25, 1979.

Comparative popularity of vasectomy and tubectomy, by S. D. R. Devi. JOURNAL OF FAMILY WELFARE 26:79-93, June, 1980.

Comparative studies of abortions before and after the reform of Abortion Law 218, by S. Granitzka, et al. ARCHIVES OF GYNECOLOGY 228(1-4):384-385, July 20, 1979.

Comparative study of abdominal tubal ligation at minilaparotomy by standard Pomeroy and Yoon ring technique, by S. Dhaniram, et al. JOURNAL OF THE INDIAN MEDICAL ASSOCIATION 72(4):75-77, February 16, 1979.

Comparative study of the effect of oral contraceptives containing 50 microgram of estrogen and those containing 20 microgram of estrogen on adrenal cortical function, by E. S. Amin, et al. AMERICAN JOURNAL OF OBSTETRICS AND GYNECOLOGY 137(7):831-833, August 1, 1980.

A comparative study of spontaneous and self-induced abortion cases in married women, by C. Bose. JOURNAL OF THE INDIAN MEDICAL ASSOCIATION 73(3-4):56-59, August, 1979.

Comparison between intraamniotic PGF2 alpha and vaginal PGE2 for second-trimester abortion, by J. P. Lebed, et al. OBSTETRICS AND GYNECOLOGY 56(1):90-96, July, 1980.

A comparison of birth control pill user data from two national surveys, by W. D. Mosher. REVIEW OF PUBLIC DATA USE 8:1-12, June, 1980.

Comparison of the effectiveness of metal and flexible plastic cannulas in abortion by vacuum aspiration, by L. Randic, et al. JUGOSLAVENSKA GINEKOLOGIJA I OPSTETRICIJA 18(3-4):229-237, May-August, 1978.

A comparison of the effects of anxiety on self-concept between pregnant women seeking an abortion and pregnant women not seeking an abortion, by E. Proud. DISSERTATION ABSTRACTS INTERNATIONAL 40(12):5827-B, 1979.

Comparison of intra- and paracervical anesthesia in induced abortion, by F. D. Peters, et al. ARCHIVES OF GYNECOLOGY 228(1-4):381-382, July 20, 1979.

Comparison of metabolic and clinical effects of four oral contraceptive formulations and a contraceptive vaginal ring, by S. Roy, et al. AMERICAN JOURNAL OF OBSTETRICS AND GYNECOLOGY 136(7):920-931, April 1, 1980.

Comparison of a paper pill with a conventional oral contraceptive tablet, by H. K. Basu, et al. JOURNAL OF INTERNATIONAL MEDICAL RESEARCH 8(2):148-152, 1980.

Comparison of the results of interruption of advanced pregnancy using prostaglandin F2-alpha and a NaC1 solution, by D. Dragovic, et al. SRPSKI ARHIV ZA CELOKUPNO LE-KARSTVO 107(1):43-51, January, 1979.

A comparison of three approaches to providing contraceptive counseling, by Y. M. DeCuir. DISSERTATION ABSTRACTS INTERNATIONAL 40(12):5806-B, 1980.

Comparison of two percent and five percent lidocaine solution for local anesthesia of both fallopian tubes in laparoscopic sterilization, by E. Neeser, et al. ARCHIVES OF GYNECOL-OGY 228(1-4):279, July 20, 1979.

Competence to consent of minors in a termination of pregnancy, by K. Albrecht, et al. BEITRAEGE ZUR GERICHTLICHEN MEDIZIN 37:249-251, 1979.

Competing ethical claims in abortion, by A. J. Davis. AMERI-CAN JOURNAL OF NURSING 80:1359, July, 1980.

Competition for the pill shapes up in lab. CHEMICAL WEEKLY 125:51-52, October 17, 1979.

Compliance with contraception among adolescent females, by I. F. Litt, et al. PEDIATRIC RESEARCH 13(4 Part 2):327, 1979.

Complications and sequelae of induced abortion in the 2d tri-mester by hypertonic saline solution and PGF2alpha, by J. Vujic, et al. ARCHIVES OF GYNECOLOGY 228(1-4):410-411, July 20, 1979.

Complications in induced abortions. Two-years material from Aker hospital, by O. H. Jensen, et al. TIDSSKRIFT FOR DEN NORSKE LAEGEFORENING 100(8-9):484-486, March 10, 1980.

Complications of laparoscopic tubal sterilization, by R. G. Cunanan, Jr., et al. OBSTETRICS AND GYNECOLOGY 55 (4):501-506, April, 1980.

Components of delay amongst women obtaining termination of pregnancy, by J. R. Ashton. JOURNAL OF BIOSOCIAL SCIENCE 12:261-274, July, 1980.

Compulsory sterilization in the Opole district during 1934-1938, by S. Kasperek. PRZEGLAD LEKARSKI 37(1):33-39, 1980.

Condition of fetuses and newborn infants in pregnancies complicated by threatened abortion, by J. Kuczynski, et al. GINE-KOLOGIA POLSKA Suppl:75-76, 1979.

Condom effectiveness [letter], by E. C. Corderoy. FAMILY PLANNING PERSPECTIVES 11(5):271, October, 1979.

Condoms for sexually active adolescents, by A. B. Bergman. AMERICAN JOURNAL OF DISEASES OF CHILDREN 134 (3):247-249, March, 1980.

Conducting delivery in primipara women who interrupted their first pregnancy by artificial abortion, by T. N. Kolgushkina, et al. ZDRAVOOKHRANENIYE BELORUSSII 0(9):61-62, 1978.

Congress and the Hyde amendment: how the House moved to stop abortions, by P. O'Hara. CONGRESSIONAL QUAR-TERLY WEEKLY REPORT 38:1038-1039, April 19, 1980.

Congressman Hyde cautiously optimistic about court. OUR SUNDAY VISITOR 69:7, May 11, 1980.

Congressmen challenge abortion funding order. OUR SUNDAY VISITOR 68:2, April 6, 1980.

Conscience, infallibility and contraception, by J. Finnis. MONTH 11:410-417, December, 1978.

Consent, sterilization and mental incompetence: the case of "Eve", by C. L. Sklar. CANADIAN NURSE 76:14-16+, March, 1980.

Consequences of vasectomy: an immunological and histological study related to subsequent fertility, by I. L. Jenkins, et al.

BRITISH JOURNAL OF UROLOGY 51(5):406-410, 1979.

Constitutional law—abortion—statutory interpretation—void for vagueness. DUQUESNE LAW REVIEW 18:161-172, Fall, 1979.

Constitutional law—due process—a state abortion statute that imposes a blanket parental consultation requirement on minors, and fails to distinguish between mature and immature minors constitutes a denial of due process. UNIVERSITY OF DETROIT JOURNAL OF URBAN LAW 57:337-363, Winter, 1980.

Constitutional law—minor's right of privacy-state may require third-party consent for a minor's abortion. TULANE LAW REVIEW 54:233-243, December, 1979.

Constitutional law—parental and judicial consent restrictions on a minor's decision to have an abortion. SUFFOLK UNIVERSITY LAW REVIEW 14:48-59, Winter, 1980.

Constitutional law: permissible requirements of parental consent for abortion. WASHBURN LAW JOURNAL 19:601-608, Spring, 1980.

Constitutional law—Supreme Court is undecided on parental notification requirement for minor's abortion. SANTA CLARA LAW REVIEW 31:604-616, February, 1980.

Constitutional law—United States Supreme Court abortion decision clarifies concept of fetal biability and scope of physician's discretion in determining when viability is reached. TEMPLE LAW QUARTERLY 52:1240-1259, 1979.

Contact with the hospital service caused helplessness, shame and guilt, by B. Rennerstedt. LAKARTIDNINGEN 77(7):533-536, February 13, 1980.

Containing the discussion: how to argue about abortion: II, by B. Harrison. CHRISTIANITY AND CRISIS 37(21):311-313, December 26, 1977..

Continuation of contraception on Java-Bali: preliminary results from the quarterly acceptor survey, by J. D. Teachman, et al. STUDIES ON FAMILY PLANNING 11(4):134-144, April, 1980.

Contraception, by J. C. Guillat. SOINS 25(8):3-7, April 20,1980.

Contraception, abortion and self concept, by R. H. Rosen, et al. JOURNAL OF POPULATION 2(2):118-139, Summer, 1979.

Contraception and diabetes [letter], by J. M. Steel, et al. DIABETES CARE 2(1):60, January-February, 1979.

Contraception and psychiatry, by M. Bourgeois. CONFRONTATION PSYCHIATRIQUES (16):237-284, 1978.

Contraception and responsibility, by E. Vacek. CATHOLIC CHARISMATIC 5:14-17, June-July, 1980.

Contraception and sexual behavior, by C. Thonet. REVISTA CHILENA DE OBSTETRICIA Y GINECOLOGIA 43(2):104-108, 1978.

Contraception and the synod, by B. Cooke. COMMUNITIES 107: 648-650, November 21, 1980.

Contraception by female sterilization [editorial]. BRITISH MEDICAL JOURNAL 280(6224):1154-1155, May 10, 1980.

Contraception: the cervical cap, by K. J. Littman. MS MAGAZINE 9:91-92, October, 1980.

Contraception for the male: problems with progress, by H. Jackson, et al. CLINICAL OBSTETRICS AND GYNAECOLOGY 6(1):129-155, April, 1979.

Contraception for teenage girls. Combination pill or IUD?, by E. Weiner, et al. ACTA OBSTETRICIA ET GYNECOLOGICA SCANDINAVICA [Suppl] 88:65-69, 1979.

Contraception in adolescence: an overview for the pediatrician, by D. E. Greydanus. PEDIATRIC ANNALS 9(3):111-118,

March, 1980.

Contraception in adolescence—a review of the literature, by E. Ryde-Blomqvist. JOURNAL OF BIOSOCIAL SCIENCE [Suppl] (5):129-158, 1978.

Contraception in the adolescent: current concepts for the pediatrician, by D. E. Greydanus, et al. PEDIATRICS 65(1):1-12, 1980.

Contraception in adrogenised women with a low-dose cyproterone-acetate containing one-phase preparation, by L. Moltz, et al. DEUTSCHE MEDIZINISCHE WOCHENSCHRIFT 104 (39):1376-1382, September 28, 1979.

Contraception in female risk patients, by A. S. Wolf. MEDIZINISCHE WELT 31(18):654-656, May 2, 1980.

Contraception in 1980, by G. Grillet. INFIRMIERE FRANCAISE (213):23-26, March, 1980.

Contraception in preclimacteric women with special regard to oral contraceptives, by H. Salzer, et al. WIENER MEDIZINISCHE WOCHENSCHRIFT 130(6):218-221, March 31, 1980.

Contraception in the teenager. A comparison of four methods of contraception in adolescent girls, by J. A. Goldman, et al. ISRAEL JOURNAL OF MEDICAL SCIENCES 16(7):510-513, July, 1980.

Contraception via topical application?-A review, by H. Schaefer, et al. CONTRACEPTION 20(3):225-236, September, 1979.

Contraception: which way for you?, by E. Blume. VOGUE 170: 254+, April, 1980.

Contraception with implanted gestagens, by N. C. Nielsen, et al. UGESKRIFT FOR LAEGER 141(45):3100-3103, November 5, 1979.

Contraceptive ads could be coming to radio and tv. OUR SUNDAY VISITOR 68:6, March 2, 1980.

Contraceptive attitude behavior consistency in adolescence, by S. Jorgensen. POPULATION AND ENVIRONMENT: BEHAVIORAL AND SOCIAL ISSUES 3(2):174-194, Summer, 1980.

Contraceptive choice of limiters ages 35-44 in the United States: an examination of selection of method from among a number of possible choices, by R. T. Gillaspy. SOCIAL BIOLOGY 26 (1):72-79, Spring, 1979.

Contraceptive counselor's dilemma: safety or effectiveness?, by C. Cooperman. JOURNAL OF SEX RESEARCH 14(3):145-150, August, 1978.

Contraceptive delivery systems: an evaluation of clinic vs. village in Indonesia, by J. D. Teachman, et al. EVALUATION REVIEW 4:75-92, Fall, 1980.

Contraceptive education favored by teenagers [news]. FAMILY PLANNING PERSPECTIVES 11(4):255, July-August, 1979.

Contraceptive efficacy: the significance of method and motivation [based on data from the 1970 and 1975 National fertility studies], by E. F. Jones, et al. STUDIES IN FAMILY PLANNING 11:39-50, February, 1980.

Contraceptive failure: a blessed event?. FLORIDA BAR JOURNAL 54:587-592, October, 1980.

Contraceptive-induced unilateral retinopathy, by A. Giovannini, et al. OPHTHALMOLOGICA 179(5):302-305, 1979.

Contraceptive market on a seesaw; OTC's fare better than oral Rx's, by A. W. Weil. PRODUCT MARKETING 9:1+, February, 1980.

Contraceptive patterns and premarital pregnancy among women aged 15-19 in 1976, by M. Zelnik, et al. FAMILY PLANNING PERSPECTIVES 10(3):135-142, May-June, 1978.

Contraceptive practice among New Zealand women, by B. J. Kirkwood, et al. NEW ZEALAND MEDICAL JOURNAL 90

(641):108-111, August 8, 1979.

Contraceptive practice and repeat induced abortion: an epidemiological investigation, by M. J. Shepard, et al. JOURNAL OF BIOSOCIAL SCIENCE 11(3):289-302, July, 1979.

Contraceptive practice and trends in coital frequency, by J. Trussell, et al. FAMILY PLANNING PERSPECTIVES 12:246-249, September-October, 1980.

The contraceptive practice of abortion patients, by M. J. Sparrow NEW ZEALAND MEDICAL JOURNAL 91(653):104-106, February 13, 1980.

Contraceptive properties of Lithospermum officinale L. grown under different agrotechnical conditions, by S. Stanosz. POLSKI TYGODNIK LEKARSKI 34(50):1971-1972, December 10, 1979.

Contraceptive properties of luteinising hormone releasing hormone [letter], by R. F. Lambe, et al. LANCET 2(8146):801, October 13, 1979.

Contraceptive research and development, by R. J. Aitken. BRITISH MEDICAL BULLETIN 35(2):199-204, May, 1979.

Contraceptive responsibility among male university students, by J. B. Cole. JOURNAL OF THE AMERICAN COLLEGE HEALTH ASSOCIATION 8(3):168-172, December, 1979.

Contraceptive sterilization: no panacea for human problems, by W. May. HOSPITAL PROGRESS 61:38-39+, September, 1980.

Contraceptive use and fertility levels in Sao Paulo state, Brazil, by M. S. Nakamura, et al. STUDIES IN FAMILY PLANNING 11:236-246, July-August, 1980.

Contraceptive use in Australia, by C. M. Young, et al. AUSTRALIAN AND NEW ZEALAND JOURNAL OF OBSTETRICS AND GYNAECOLOGY 19(1):1-6, February, 1979.

Contraceptive use rises in Netherlands: fertity falls among all groups. FAMILY PLANNING PERSPECTIVES 12:165-166, May-June, 1980.

Contraceptives, by C. Channing. THE SCIENCES 19:14+, December, 1979.

—, by C. Lacoste. REVUE DE L'INFIRMIERE ET DE L'ASSISTANTE SOCIALE 30(6):51-56, June, 1980.

Contraceptives and acute salpingitis, by L. Weström. LAKARTIDNINGEN 77(14):1290-1291, April 2, 1980.

Contraceptives—what you need to know to choose the best one for you, by A. Comer. MADEMOISELLE p7210-7211, August, 1980.

Contretemps over contraception [views of Archbishop P. R. Quinn]. TIME 116:74, October 13, 1980.

A contribution about serious ophthalmic complications with oral contraceptives, by H. Mayer. KLINISCHE MONATSBLAETTER FUR AUGENHEILKUNDE 175(5):677-680, November, 1979.

Contribution of chromosome abnormalities to stillbirths, neonatal deaths and abortions over 20 weeks of gestation, by R. Evans, et al. CLINICAL GENETICS 17(1):64, 1980.

Contribution to the etiology and prevention of missed abortion, by P. Drac. BRATISLAVSKE LEKARSKE LISTY 73(2): 217-223, February, 1980.

Controversy over abortion funding increases. HOSPITAL PROGRESS 61(3):32, March, 1980.

Co-occurring liver cell adenoma and focal nodular hyperplasia due to contraceptives. Case report, by B. Reichlin, et al. SCHWEIZERISCHE MEDIZINISCHE WOCHENSCHRIFT 110(22):873-874, May 31, 1980.

Corpus luteum dysfunction: serum progesterone levels in diagnonosis and assessment of therapy for recurrent and threatened abortion, by P. A. Hensleigh, et al. FERTILITY AND STERILITY 32(4):396-400, October, 1979.

The correlation of blood pressure, cholesterol and triglyceride concentration with the administration of hormonal contraceptives in women from 2 Erfurt large-scale plants, by J. Heinrich, et al. ZEITSCHRIFT FUR DIE GESAMTE INNERE MEDIZIN UND IHRE GRENZGEBIETE 34(18):540-544, September 15, 1979.

The cost of the termination of pregnancy. Delayed medical complications. A Lausanne study, by H. E. Stamm, et al. REVUE MEDICALE DE LA SUISSE ROMANDE 99(12):885-888, December, 1979.

—. Medical aspects, by C. Revaz, et al. REVUE MEDICALE DE LA SUISSE ROMANDE 99(12):873-883, December, 1979.

—. Psycho-social aspects, by M. Hurni. REVUE MEDICALE DE LA SUISSE ROMANDE 99(12):889-899, December, 1979.

Cottoning on to a pill for men, by D. Baird. MACLEAN'S 93:44-45, August 11, 1980.

Could right-wing alliance backfire for pro-lifers?, by L. Pumphrey. NATIONAL CATHOLIC REPORTER 16:9+, January 18, 1980.

Council of the Italian Episcopal Conference. L'OSSERVATORE ROMANO 11(572):6-9, March 11, 1979.

Counseling the abortion patient: a pastoral perspective, by J. R. Rzepka. PASTORAL PSYCHOLOGY 28:168-180, Spring, 1980.

Counseling women for tubal sterilization, by E. Barron, et al. HEALTH AND SOCIAL WORK 3(1):48-58, February, 1978.

The couple as a unit: sexual, social and behavioral considerations to reporductive barriers, by E. Mudd. JOURNAL OF MARITAL AND FAMILY THERAPY 6(1):23-28, January, 1980.

The court continues its bamboozlement. ECONOMIST 276:21-22, July 5, 1980.

Court dismisses NCCB abortion provisions tuit. NATIONAL CATHOLIC REPORTER 16:6, February 1, 1980.

Court frees tax dollars for abortions, for now at least. OUR SUNDAY VISITOR 68:7, March 2, 1980.

Court hears Hyde views. NATIONAL CATHOLIC REPORTER 16:3, May 2, 1980.

Court takes unique position in wrongful birth case, by F. Speaker. PENNSYLVANIA MEDICINE 82(12):15-16, December, 1979.

Court to rule on "Hyde Amendment." CONGRESSIONAL QUARTERLY WEEKLY REPORT 38:683, March 8, 1980.

Court upholds right to privacy in abortion matters, by F. Speaker. PENNSYLVANIA MEDICINE 83(6):38, June, 1980.

Court's abortion decision likely to affect all Medicaid patients. AMERICAN MEDICAL NEWS 23(27):1+, July 11, 1980.

The courts and elective abortions under Medicaid, by J. E. Menselson, et al. SOCIAL SERVICE REVIEW 54(1):124-134, 1980.

Court's opinion in Hyde amendment case [partial text of the Supreme court's majority opinion in Harris v. McRae, which upheld, 5-4, congressional restrictions on federal funding of abortions]. CONGRESSIONAL QUARTERLY WEEKLY REPORT 38:1864-1866, July 5, 1980.

Cultures from thymus and liver cells and blood lumphocytes for chromosome analysis in human abortions, by F. Bricarelli, et al. BOLLETTINO DELL ISTITUTO SIEROTERAPICO MILANESE 57(5):650-653, November 30, 1978.

Current concepts in prevention, by P. Holma. KATILOLEHTI 84(12):482, December, 1979.

Current contraceptive research, by J. M. Benditt. FAMILY
PLANNING PERSPECTIVES 12(3):149-155, May-June,
1980.

Cutaneous eruptions and intrauterine copper device, by G.
Frentz, et al. ACTA DERMATO-VENEREOLOGICA 60(1):
71, 1980.

Cyclical variations in mood in normal women taking oral contraceptives, by A. R. Forrest. BRITISH MEDICAL JOURNAL 2
(6202):1403, December 1, 1979.

Cytogenetic results in 96 couples with repeated abortions, by W.
Schmid. CLINICAL GENETICS 17(1):85, 1980.

Cytogenetic studies in 100 couples with recurrent spontaneous
abortions, by B. E. Ward, et al. AMERICAN JOURNAL OF
HUMAN GENETICS 32(4):549-554, July, 1980.

Cytogenetic studies in patients with a history of multiple abortions, by M. J. W. Faed, et al. CLINICAL GENETICS 17(1):
64, 1980.

DES daughters: new studies, same results. SCIENCE NEWS 117:
182, March 22, 1980.

Dalkon, or the case of the suspect shield, by N. Sheppard, Jr.
NEW YORK TIMES pE-22, March 28, 1980.

Day-care abortion [letter], by M. Simms. LANCET 1(8180):
1253, June 7, 1980.

Dealing with the unfit to breed, by E. S. Royce. INQUIRY 3:
9-11, May 26, 1980.

Deaths from legal and illegal abortion drop after 1973 decisions
[news]. FAMILY PLANNING PERSPECTIVES 11(5):318,
October, 1979.

Decision for induced abortion. A study on possible influences, by
R. Rauskolb, et al. ARCHIVES OF GYNECOLOGY 228(1-
4):392-393, July 20, 1979.

Decision-making regarding abortion: a value X expectancy analysis, by J. G. Smetana, et al. JOURNAL OF POPULATION 2 (4):338-357, Winter, 1979.

Decisions concerning applications for termination of pregnancy during the period from 1 April 1970 to 31 March 1979, by V. Sele. UGESKRIFT FOR LAEGER 142(12):788-791, March 17, 1980.

Declines in the age and family size of family planning program acceptors: international trends, by J. A. Ross. STUDIES IN FAMILY PLANNING 10(10):290-299, October, 1979.

Decoding the election games plan of the new right, by L. C. Wohl. MS MAGAZINE 8:57-59+, August, 1979.

Decreased risk of endometrial cancer among oral contraceptive users, by D. W. Kaufman, et al. NEW ENGLAND JOURNAL OF MEDICINE 303:1045-1047, October 30, 1980.

Defeated sexuality in the plays and novels of Samuel Beckett, by K. Morrison. COMPARATIVE DRAMA 14:18-34, Spring, 1980.

Delayed abortion in an area of easy accessibility, by W. A. Burr, et al. JAMA 244(1):44-48, July 4, 1980.

Delayed reproductive complications after induced abortion, by K. Dalaker, et al. ACTA OBSTETRICIA ET GYNECOLOGICA SCANDINAVICA 58(5):491-494, 1979.

Deliveries and abortions 1976-1979, by L. B. Knudsen, et al. UGESKRIFT FOR LAEGER 142(31):2003-2004, July 28, 1980.

Demographic and socio-economic characteristics of men choosing vasectomy, by M. A. Parsons, et al. JOURNAL OF BIOSOCIAL SCIENCE 10(2):133-139, April, 1978.

Demographic characteristics of acceptors of abortion in selected states of India, by S. B. V. Upadhyay. JOURNAL OF FAMILY WELFARE 25:63-67, June, 1979.

Demographic techniques in describing contraceptive use applied on the situation in Sweden, by O. Meirik, et al. ACTA OBSTETRICIA ET GYNECOLOGICA SCANDINAVICA [Suppl] 88:61-64, 1979.

Demographic trends of tubal sterilization in the United States, 1970-1975, by P. M. Layde, et al. AMERICAN JOURNAL OF PUBLIC HEALTH 70:808-812, August, 1980.

La denatalite en France et en Occident: ses causes, ses consequences, by P. Chaunu. PAYSANS 23:12-33, February-March, 1979.

Denial of medi-Cal funds for abortion: an establishment of religion. GOLDEN GATE UNIVERSITY LAW REVIEW 9:421-449, 1978-1979.

Department of Health, Education, and Welfare—abortions: final regulation. FEDERAL REGISTER 44(209):61597-61598, October 26, 1979.

Depo-provera: contraceptive risk? [letter], by A. Rosenfield. HASTINGS CENTER REPORT 10(2):4, April, 1980.

Depot gestagens as contraceptives, by S. Holbek, et al. UGESKRIFT FOR LAEGER 142(15):973-974, April 7, 1980.

Desired family size and contraceptive use in Pakistan, by N. M. Shah, et al. INTERNATIONAL FAMILY PLANNING PERSPECTIVES 5:143-149, December, 1979.

Destroying myths about birth control, by B. Branley. SOLDIERS 35:44-46, November, 1980.

Detection and composition of circulating immune complexes in oral contraceptive users, by V. Beaumont, et al. BIOMEDICINE 30(5):256-260, November, 1979.

The determinants of mothers' knowledge of the Down syndrome before genetic counseling: part II, by M. J. Seidenfeld, et al. AMERICAN JOURNAL OF MEDICAL GENETICS 6(1): 9-23, 1980.

Determination of HCG activity in the urine of women: possibilities of prognosis in abortion cases, by J. Peterek, et al. WIADOMOSCI LEKARSKIE 32(23):1681-1683, December 1, 1979.

The development and evaluation of an ovulation inhibitor (DIAne) containing an antiandrogen, by U. Lachnit-Fixson. ACTA OBSTETRICIA ET GYNECOLOGICA SCANDINAVICA [Suppl] 88:33-42, 1979.

Development of Commonwealth abortion laws, by B. M. Dickens, et al. INTERNATIONAL AND COMPARATIVE LAW QUARTERLY (4th series) 28:424-457, July, 1979.

Development of a scale to measure attitudes toward using birth control pills, by E. S. Herold, et al. JOURNAL OF SOCIAL PSYCHOLOGY 110(First Half):115-122, February, 1980.

Development without family planning will not speed, and may hinder, fertility decline [news]. FAMILY PLANNING PERSPECTIVES 12(1):60-61, January-February, 1980.

Diagnostic miniculdoscopy preceding laparoscopy when bowel adhesions are suspected, by D. A. van Lith, et al. JOURNAL OF REPORDUCTIVE MEDICINE 23(2):87-90, August, 1979.

Diagnostic value of serum HCG determination in disturbed early pregnancies (imminent abortion and extrauterine pregnancy), by V. G. Pahnke, et al. ARCHIVES OF GYNECOLOGY 228 (1-4):224-226, July 20, 1979.

The diaphragm: an appealing and effective contraceptive for many teenagers, by A. Marks, et al. PEDIATRIC RESEARCH 13(4 Part 2):328, 1979.

The diaphragn: its effective use among college women, by I. M. Hagen, et al. JOURNAL OF THE AMERICAN COLLEGATE HEALTH ASSOCIATION 28(5):263-266, April, 1980.

Dietary influence on the serum lipid profile of oral contraceptive users, by A. K. Kant, et al. FEDERAL PROCEEDINGS 39

(3):Abstract 2028, 1980.

Differences in contraceptive knowledge, attitudes, and practice by rural-urban residence history: currently married women aged 15-44, Phillippines, 1973. PHILIPPINE SOCIOLOGICAL REVIEW 23(1-4):101-118, January-October, 1975.

Differences in hormonal patterns during the first postabortion menstrual cycle after two techniques of termination of pregnancy, by A. S. Blazer, et al. FERTILITY AND STERILITY 33(5):493-500, May, 1980.

La diffusion des methodes contraceptives modernes en France de 1971 a 1978 (results of recent French legislation permitting the distribution of various types of contraceptives), by P. Collomb. POPULATION 34;(6):1045-1065, 1979.

Dilatation and evacuation for induced abortion in developing countries: advantages and disadvantages, by W. Cates, Jr., et al. STUDIES IN FAMILY PLANNING 11(4):128-133, April, 1980.

Dilemma of getting involved or playing safe, by M. Murphy, Sr. NATIONAL CATHOLIC REPORTER 16:18, March 28, 1980.

Disappearance of human chorionic gonadotropic and resumption of ovulation following abortion, by R. P. Marrs, et al. AMERICAN JOURNAL OF OBSTETRICS AND GYNECOLOGY 135(6):731-736, November 15, 1979.

Discussion on sterilization and abortion in middle age. JOURNAL OF BIOSOCIAL SCIENCE [Suppl] (6):157-162, 1979.

Diseases affecting contraceptive practice in middle age, by R. J. Beard. JOURNAL OF BIOSOCIAL SCIENCE [Suppl] (6): 143-156, 1979.

Dispute about abortion ad policy erupts. NATIONAL CATHOLIC REPORTER 16:43, February 15, 1980.

Dissent of four just men [Hyde Amendment] . MS MAGAZINE

61

9:24, September, 1980.

Do anticonvulsants reduce the efficacy of oral contraceptives?, by C. B. Coulam, et al. EPILEPSIA 20(5):519-525, October, 1979.

Do contraceptives influence the incidence of acute pelvic inflammatory disease in women with gonorrhoea?, by G. Ryden, et al. CONTRACEPTION 20(2):149-157, August, 1979.

Do oral contraceptives inhibit Trichomonas vaginalis?, by M. Bramley, et al. SEXUALLY TRANSMITTED DISEASES 6 (4):261-263, October-December, 1979.

Do severe complications still occur in induced abortion? (letter), by D. Hleinknecht, et al. NOUVELLE PRESSE MEDICALE 9(3):187, January 12, 1980.

Doctors and torture [letter], by R. C. Short. MEDICAL JOURNAL OF AUSTRALIA 2(2):89-90, July 28, 1979.

Does contraception discourage sex? [L. Tiger's study of stumptail macaque monkeys], by S. Begley. NEWSWEEK 96:77, July 21, 1980.

Does the Hyde amendment biolate religious freedom? Harris v. McRae (100 S Ct 2671) and the first amendment, by J. A. Gold. AMERICAN JOURNAL OF LAW AND MEDICINE 6:361-372, Fall, 1980.

Does laparoscopic tubal sterilization cause menstruation disorders?, by A. Weil, et al. ARCHIVES OF GYNECOLOGY 228(1-4):278-279, July 20, 1979.

Does life begin before birth: we cannot fix criteria of humanness and then conclude that, lacking these, the fetus is not human, by J. R. W. Stott. CHRISTIANITY TODAY 24:50-51, September 5, 1980.

Does pyridoxal phosphate have a non-coenzymatic role in steroid hormone action? NUTRITION REVIEWS 38:93-95, February, 1980.

Does use or oral contraceptives enhance the toxicity of carbon disulfide through interactions with pyridoxine and tryptophan metabolism?, by E. J. Calabrese. MEDICAL HYPOTHESES 6(1):21-33, January, 1980.

Does your mother know...?, by A. Torres. FAMILY PLANNING PERSPECTIVES 10(5):280-282, September-October, 1978.

Double conjoining vas deferens, by R. G. Gravesen. UROLOGY 15(3):283-284, 1980.

Drinking during pregnancy and spontaneous abortion, by J. Kline, et al. LANCET 2(8187):176-180, July 26, 1980.

Drug interaction with oral contraceptive steroids. BRITISH MEDICAL JOURNAL 6233:93-94, July 12, 1980.

Drugs: the CU-7—a new IUD risk, by J. Zackey. TRIAL 16:68-70, May, 1980.

Dyadic and social network influences on adolescent exposure to pregnancy risk, by S. R. Jorgensen, et al. JOURNAL OF MARRIAGE AND FAMILY 42:141-155, February, 1980.

ERA supporters deny pro-abortion link. OUR SUNDAY VISITOR 68:2, April 27, 1980.

Early and late complications after tubal ligations with the tuplaclip, by J. Babenerd, et al. GEBURTSHILFE UND FRAUENHEILKUNDE 39(10):888-891, October, 1979.

Early and late complications following surgical abortion, by F. K. Beller. ARCHIVES OF GYNECOLOGY 228(1-4):349-364, July 20, 1979.

Early fetal deaths due to the oral contraceptive lyndiol given to the male mouse, by B. N. Hemsworth. IRCS: MEDICAL SCIENCE: LIBRARY COMPENDIUM 7(3):140, 1979.

Early human pregnancy with the intrauterine contraceptive device in situ: incidence of heteroploidy, by L. H. Honore. TERATOLOGY 20(1):3-6, August, 1979.

Ecological values, the state, and the individual's right to liberty, by H. J. McCloskey. PACIFIC PHILOSOPHICAL QUARTERLY 61:212-232, July, 1980.

Ecology and conservation of the human species [letter], by D. Vann. MEDICAL JOURNAL OF AUSTRALIA 2(4):203, August 25, 1979.

Economic benefits of day care abortion, by J. C. Catford, et al. COMMUNITY MEDICINE 1(2):115-122, May, 1979.

Ectopic pregnancy after sterilization, by G. J. Hughes. MEDICAL JOURNAL OF AUSTRALIA 1(6):275, March 22, 1980.

Ectopic trophoblast as a complication of first-trimester induced abortion, by D. A. Dessouky. AMERICAN JOURNAL OF OBSTETRICS AND GYNECOLOGY 136(3):407-408, February 1, 1980.

Ecumenical war over abortion. TIME 113:62-63, January 29, 1979.

Edges of life. 1. COMMUNITIES 107:410-421, August 1, 1980.

—. 2. COMMUNITIES 107:421, August 1, 1980.

—. [supreme court's ruling on the Hyde Amendment]. COMMONWEAL 107:421, August 1, 1980.

Education in family planning in schools of nursing in various European countries. SOINS 25(8):33-37, April 20, 1980.

Education in family planning: What route to take? What difference does it make?, by O. J. Sikes. INTERNATIONAL JOURNAL OF HEALTH EDUCATION 22(4):206-210, 1979.

Effect of althesin anesthesia on blood loss during therapeutic abortion. A comparison with local and thiopental anesthesia, by B. R. Moller, et al. ACTA OBSTETRICIA ET GYNECOLOGICA SCANDINAVICA 58(5):481-483, 1979.

The effect of ampicillin on oral contraceptive effectiveness, by C.

I. Friedman, et al. OBSTETRICS AND GYNECOLOGY 55 (1):33-37, January, 1980.

The effect of contraceptive steroids on sister chromatid exchange and nuclear morphology, by R. T. Dutkowski, et al. HUMAN GENETICS 31(6):46A, 1979.

Effect of dietary carbohydrate and use of oral contraceptives by women on serum glucose lipid and hormone levels, by K. M. Behall, et al. FEDERAL PROCEEDINGS 39(3):Abstract 3763, 1980.

Effect of different contraception on microbial vaginal flora and immunoglobulin levels, by E. El Ghazzawi, et al. JOURNAL OF THE EGYPTIAN MEDICAL ASSOCIATION 54(3):138-153, 1979.

The effect of environment on tryptophan metabolism 'via kynurenine' in oral contraceptives users, by El-Zoghby, et al. ACTA VITAMINOLOGICA ET ENZYMOLOGICA 32(5-6): 167-175, 1978.

The effect of hormonal contraceptives on the EEG, by K. Dvorak, et al. CESKOSLOVENSKA NEUROLOGIE A NEUROCHIRURGIO 43(1):71-77, January, 1980.

The effect of induced abortion on the incidence of Downs Syndrome in Hawaii, by R. G. Smith, et al. FAMILY PLANNING PERSPECTIVES 12:201-205, July-August, 1980.

Effect of interrupting the 1st pregnancy on the course of the next pregnancy, labor, puerperium and the newborn infant's condition, by S. Lembrych, et al. WIADOMOSCI LEKARSKIE 33(5):345-350, March 1, 1980.

The effect of the intrauterine contraceptive device on the prevalence of morphologic abnormalities in human spontaneous abortions, by L. H. Honore. CONTRACEPTION 21(1):47-52, January, 1980.

Effect of kind of carbohydrate in the diet and use of oral contraceptives on metabolism of young women; serum glucose, insulin, and glucagon, by K. M. Behall, et al. AMERICAN JOURNAL OF CLINICAL NUTRITION 33:1041-1048, May, 1980.

—. II. Serum lipid levels, by K. M. Bahall, et al. AMERICAN JOURNAL OF CLINICAL NUTRITION 33(4):825-831, April, 1980.

—. III. Serum glucose, insulin, and glucagon, by K. M. Behall, et al. AMERICAN JOURNAL OF CLINICAL NUTRITION 33 (5):1041-1048, May, 1980.

The effect of laparoscopic sterilization by diathermy or silastic bands on post-operative pain, menstrual symptoms and sexuality, by S. Lawson, et al. BRITISH JOURNAL OF OBSTETRICS AND GYNAECOLOGY 86(8):659-663, August, 1979.

The effect of missed abortion and spontaneous abortion on the fate of subsequent pregnancies, by S. Levin, et al. ACTA OBSTETRICIA ET GYNECOLOGICA SCANDINAVICA 58 (4):371-373, 1979.

Effect of oral contraceptive agents on thiamin, riboflavin and pantothenic acid status in young women, by C. M. Lewis, et al. JOURNAL OF CLINICAL NUTRITION 33:832-838, April, 1980.

Effect of oral contraceptive agents on thiamin status, by S. C. Vir, et al. INTERNATIONAL JOURNAL FOR VITAMIN AND NUTRITION RESEARCH 49(3):291-295, 1979.

Effect of oral contraceptive agents on vitamin and mineral requirements, by V. J. Thorp. JOURNAL OF THE AMERICAN DIETETIC ASSOCIATION 76(6):581-584, June, 1980.

Effect of oral contraceptive on hematocrit level, by A. Fuertes-de la Haba, et al. BOLETIN-ASOCIACION MEDICA DE PUERTO RICO 71(11):425-433, November, 1979.

The effect of oral contraceptive steroids and enzyme inducing drugs on sex hormone binding globulin capacity in women [proceedings], by D. J. Back, et al. BRITISH JOURNAL OF CLINICAL PHARMACOLOGY 9(1):115P, January, 1980.

Effect of oral contraceptive usage on zinc and copper in serum and hair, by S. C. Vir, et al. INTERNATIONAL JOURNAL FOR VITAMIN AND NUTRITION RESEARCH 49(3):330-335, 1979.

Effect of oral contraceptive use on platelet prothrombin converting (platelet factor 3) activity, by B. Leff, et al. THROMBOSIS RESEARCH 15(5-6):631-638, 1979.

The effect of oral contraceptives on blood vitamin A levels and the role of sex hormones. NUTRITION REVIEWS 37(11): 346-348, November, 1979.

Effect of oral contraceptives on composition and volume of breast milk, by B. Lönnerdal, et al. AMERICAN JOURNAL OF CLINICAL NUTRITION 33(4):816-824, April, 1980.

The effect of oral contraceptives on mononuclear cell cholesteryl ester hydrolase activity, by F. C. Hagemenas, et al. LIPIDS 15(1):39-44, January, 1980.

The effect of oral contraceptives on mononuclear cell cholesterol ester hydrolase activity in premenopausal women taking oral contraceptives: relevance to atherosclerosis, by F. M. Yatsu, et al. TRANSACTIONS OF THE AMERICAN NEUROLOGICAL ASSOCIATION 103:53-55, 1978.

Effect of oral contraceptives on platelet noradrenaline and 5-hydroxytryptamine receptors and aggregation, by J. R. Peters, et al. LANCET 2(8149):933-936, November 3, 1979.

Effect of oral contraceptives on sex chromatin count during menstrual cycle, by F. Roohi, et al. JOURNAL OF THE ASSOCIATION OF PHYSICIANS OF INDIA 27(12):1071-1074, December, 1979.

The effect of oral contraceptives on sister chromatid exchange and micronuclei formation, by R. Dutkowski. GENETICS 91(4 Part 2 Suppl):s28-s29, 1979.

67

The effect of oral contraceptives on venous thrombosis and co-agulation parameters after gynecological operation in Chinese, by S. C. Tso, et al. THROMBOSIS AND HAEMOSTA-SIS 42(1):26, 1979.

Effect of oral contraceptives on vitamin B6 nutriture of young women, by S. C. Vir, et al. INTERNATIONAL JOURNAL FOR VITAMIN AND NUTRITION RESEARCH 50(1):29-34, 1980.

Effect of prior pregnancy and combined oral contraceptives on baseline menstrual blood loss and bleeding response to intra-uterine devices, by A. T. Andrade, et al. CONTRACEPTION 20(1):19-26, July, 1979.

Effect of prostaglandins on the steroidogenic function of the feto-placental system in second trimester pregnancy, by V. G. Kolod'ko. AKUSHERSTVO I GINEKOLOGIIA (8):11-14, August, 1979.

The effect of reproductive intentions on subsequent fertility among low-parity Korean women, 1971-1976, by K. G. Foreit, et al. STUDIES IN FAMILY PLANNING 11(3):91-104, March, 1980.

The effect of sequential oral contraceptive pill (Fysioquens) ad-ministration on carbohydrate and lipid metabolism, by J. Vähäpassi, et al. ANNALES CHIRURGIAE ET GYNAECOL-OGIAE 68(2):75-81, 1979.

The effect of smoking and oral contraceptives on the urinary ex-cretion of epinephrine and norepinephrine, by F. P. Zuspan. AMERICAN JOURNAL OF OBSTETRICS AND GYNE-COLOGY 135(8):1012-1015, December 15, 1979.

Effect of threatened abortion on the development of speech and motor functions in children, by N. I. Sokolova. VOPROSY OKHRANY MATERINSTVA I DETSTVA 24(11):69, No-vember, 1979.

Effect of three long-acting steroid contraceptives on urinary pregnanediol excretions in rats, by E. E. Galal, et al. JOUR-

NAL OF DRUG RESEARCH 10(1-2):59-72, 1978.

Effect of tocolysis on the clinical state of the fetus and newborn infant from pregnancy complicated by threatened abortion, by J. Bajorek, et al. GINEKOLOGIA POLSKA Suppl:91-93, 1979.

Effect of varying amounts of ethinyl oestradiol in the combined oral contraceptive on plasma sex hormone binding globulin capacity in normal women, by J. R. Pogmore, et al. BRITISH JOURNAL OF OBSTETRICS AND GYNAECOLOGY 86 (7):563-567, July, 1979.

The effect of vasectomy on serum uric acid levels, by G. Singh. IRCS (INTERNATIONAL RESEARCH COMMUNICATIONS SYSTEM) MEDIAL SCIENCE: LIBRARY COMPENDIUM 7(8):406, 1979.

Effectiveness and risks of contraception, by W. Droegemueller, et al. ANNUAL REVIEW OF MEDICINE 31:329-343, 1980.

Effectiveness of contraception counseling and decision before legal abortion, by S. Kunz, et al. ARCHIVES OF GYNECOLOGY 228(1-4):391-392, July 20, 1979.

Effectiveness of partusysten in the therapy of interrupted pregnancy, by H. G. Stepankivs'ka, et al. PEDIATRIYA, A-KUSHERSTVO I GINEKOLOHIYA (4):38-40, July-August, 1979.

Effects of an angiotensin II antagonist; [sarcosine 1, isoleucine 8] angiotensin II, on blood pressure, plasma renin activity and plasma aldosterone concentration in hypertensive and normotensive subjects taking oral contraceptives, by T. Ogihara, et al. ENDOCRINOLOGIA JAPONICA 26(5):591-597, October, 1979.

Effects of antenatal diagnosis and selective abortion on frequencies of genetic disorders, by A. G. Motulsky, et al. CLINICAL OBSTETRICS AND GYNAECOLOGY 7(1):121-133, April, 1980.

Effects of changed contraception patterns on fertility in Taiwan: applications of a non-Markovian stochastic model, by G. Pickens, et al. INTERNATIONAL JOURNAL OF BIOMEDICAL COMPUTING 11(1):1-19, January, 1980.

Effects of contraceptive steroids on serum lipoproteins and cardiovascular disease scrutinized at workshop in Bethesda, by B. Baggett, et al. CONTRACEPTION 21(2):115-120, February, 1980.

The effects of group counseling on locus of control with pregnant teenagers, by M. C. Golant. DISSERTATION ABSTRACTS INTERNATIONAL 40(10):5321-A, 1979.

Effects of hormonal contraception on hemostatic and lipidic profiles, by R. Masure, et al. THROMBOSIS AND HAEMOSTASIS 42(1):483, 1979.

The effects of oral contraceptive manufacture on blood clotting, by L. Poller, et al. THROMBOSIS AND HAEMOSTOSIS 42 (1):25, 1979.

The effects of oral contraceptives on carbohydrate, lipid, and protein metabolism in subjects with altered nutritional status and in association with lactation, by U. M. Joshi. JOURNAL OF STEROID BIOCHEMISTRY 11(1B):483-485, July, 1979.

The effects of oral contraceptives on the cytology of the inferior segment of the female urethra, by D. Rondelaud, et al. JOURNAL OF GYNECOLOGIE OBSTETRIQUE ET BIOLOGIE DE LA REPRODUCTION 8(2):107-110, March, 1979.

Effects of oral contraceptives on the vascular wall, by A. Basdevant, et al. NOUVELLE PRESSE MEDICALE 9(8):519-522, February 16, 1980.

Effects of pregnancy and contraceptive steroids on gallbladder function, by D. Z. Braverman, et al. NEW ENGLAND JOURNAL OF MEDICINE 302(7):362-364, February 14, 1980.

Effects of tubal sterilization on morbidity rates analyzed [news].

HOSPITAL PRACTICE 15(5):153+, May, 1980.

The effects of vasectomy on viscosity, pH and volume of semen in man, by V. Nikkanen. ANDROLOGIA 11(2):123-125, 1979.

Effects on sex hormone binding globulin of different oral contraceptives containing norethisterone and lynestrenol, by V. Odlind, et al. BRITISH JOURNAL OF OBSTETRICS AND GYNAECOLOGY 87(5):416-421, May, 1980.

Egypt's population explosion, by O. Yinon. JERUSALEM QUARTERLY (15):106-120, Spring, 1980.

Eighteen months contraception following subdermal insertion of silastic capsules containing norgestrienone, by A. R. Da Silva, et al. INTERNATIONAL JOURNAL OF FERTILITY 23 (3):185-192, 1978.

Eighty percent of Americans believe abortion should be legal, 70 percent approve Medicaid Funding [news] . FAMILY PLANNING PERSPECTIVES 11(3):189-190, May-June, 1979.

Electrocardiography and outpatient termination of pregnancy [letter] , by E. Major. ANAESTHESIA 34(9):919, October, 1979.

Emotional distress patterns among women having first or repeat abortions, by E. W. Freeman, et al. OBSTETRICS AND GYNECOLOGY 55(5):630-636, May, 1980.

Empirical contraindications to the sterilization of women, by H. J. Rönnau, et al. BEITRAEGE ZUR GERICHTLICHEN MEDIZIN 37:245-247, 1979.

Employee benefits: no abortion benefits, no contracts, by J. Geisel. MODERN HEALTHCARE 10(2):30, February, 1980.

Employee must complain to EEOC before feds force abortion payment, by J. Geisel. MODERN HEALTHCARE 10(3):34, 1980.

Endocrine effects of oral contraception, by S. C. MacLeod. INTERNATIONAL JOURNAL OF GYNAECOLOGY AND OBSTETRICS 16(6):518-524, 1978-1979.

Enhanced prostacyclin formation in veins of women under chronical treatment with oral contraceptive drugs, by H. Sinzinger, et al. PHARMACOLOGICAL RESEARCH COMMUNICATIONS 12(6):515-521, June, 1980.

Enzymatic activity in the blood of pregnant women undergoing acupuncture treatment in threatened abortion, by G. M. Vorontsova, et al. AKUSHERSTVO I GINEKOLOGIIA (4): 38-40, April, 1980.

Enzymatic activity in the erythrocytes in threatened abortion and in acupuncture treatment, by S. A. Brilliantova, et al. AKUSHERSTVO I GINEKOLOGIIA (4):40-42, April, 1980.

An epidemiologic study of risk factors associated with pregnancy following female sterilization, by I. C. Chi, et al. AMERICAN JOURNAL OF OBSTETRICS AND GYNECOLOGY 136(6): 768-773, March 15, 1980.

Epididymal and testicular enzymes as monitors for assessment of male antifertility drugs, by S. Nag, et al. JOURNAL OF STEROID BIOCHEMISTRY 11(1B):681-688, July, 1979.

Epithelial melanosis of the gingiva possibly resulting from the use of oral contraceptives, by R. S. Hertz, et al. JOURNAL OF THE AMERICAN DENTAL ASSOCIATION 100(5):713-714, May, 1980.

Equal Rights Amendment and abortion: separate and distinct, by E. Alexander, et al. AMERICA 142:314-318, April 12, 1980.

Estimates of the rate of illegal abortion and the effects of eliminating therapeutic abortion, Alberta 1973-1974, by S. A. McDaniel, et al. CANADIAN JOURNAL OF PUBLIC HEALTH 70(6):393-398, November-December, 1979.

Estradiol, estriol and human placental lactogen in serum in threatened abortion, by J. B. Hertz, et al. ACTA OBSTE-

TRICIA ET GYNECOLOGICA SCANDINAVICA 58(4):365-370, 1979.

Estrogen therapy for the climateric and thromboembolic risk, by C. Campagnoli, et al. MINERVA GINECOLOGIA 32(5):429-435, May, 1980.

Ethical aspects of abortion—some European views (Hebrew), by J. Tsafrir. SOCIETY AND WELFARE 2(3):341-347, 1979.

Ethics and nature, by A. Edwards. NEW BLACKFRIARS 60: 117-125, March, 1979.

The ethics of abortion, by R. F. Gardner. PRACTITIONER 223 (1334):244-248, August, 1979.

Ethics: what would you do? Abortion—moral or legal question. Part II, by C. Gilbert. NEW JERSEY NURSE 10(1):6, January-February, 1980.

—. Part III, by C. Gilbert. NEW JERSEY NURSE 10(2):9, March-April, 1980.

Ethnic differences in family planning acceptance in rural Guatemala, by J. T. Bertrand, et al. STUDIES IN FAMILY PLANNING 10(8-9):238-245, August-September, 1979.

Ethynyl-estradiol content in blood and endometrium caused by oral contraceptives, by V. Cortes-Gallegos, et al. JOURNAL OF STEROID BIOCHEMISTRY 12(0):487-490, 1980.

Etiologies and subsequent reproductive performance of 100 couples with recurrent abortion, by P. Thi Tho, et al. FERTILITY AND STERILITY 32(4):389-395, October, 1979.

Eugenic sterilization: medico-legal and sociological aspects, by F. C. Robinson, et al. JOURNAL OF THE NATIONAL MEDICAL ASSOCIATION 71(6):593-598, June, 1979.

Europe's fertility transition: new evidence and lessons for today's developing world, by E. van de Walle, et al. POPULATION BULLETIN 34:3-43, February, 1980.

Evaluation of abortion deaths, by S. Basak. JOURNAL OF OB-
STETRICS AND GYNECOLOGY OF INDIA 29(4):790-794,
1979.

An evaluation of the counseling given to patients having a thera-
peutic abortion, by R. B. Hunton, et al. AUSTRALIAN AND
NEW ZEALAND JOURNAL OF OBSTETRICS AND GY-
NAECOLOGY 19(3):169-173, August, 1979.

Evaluation of modern contraception, by M. Mall-Haefeli. MEDI-
ZINISCHE MONATSSCHRIFT FUR PHARMAZEUTEN
1(5):139-146, May, 1978.

The evaluation of prognosis in threatened early pregnancy, by
P. Jouppila. JOURNAL OF PERINATAL MEDICINE 8(1):3-
12, 1980.

Evaluation of some blood clotting parameters in relation to the
administration of estroprogestins, by F. Orlandi, et al. AR-
CHIVO PER LE SCIENCE MEDICHE 135(4):609-617,
October-December, 1978.

Evaluation of threatened abortion by ultrasound, by M. J. Ben-
net, et al. INTERNATIONAL JOURNAL OF GYNAECOL-
OGY AND OBSTETRICS 17(4):38-44, January-February,
1980.

Even abortionists having second thoughts. (interviews with 4
abortionists), by T. G. Gulick. HUMAN EVENTS 40:p15+,
April 12, 1980.

Even an atheist can have a change of heart on abortion, by L.
Phymphre. OUR SUNDAY VISITOR 69:8, October 5, 1980.

Evolution demographique et conscience morale, by C. Mertens.
NOUVELLE REVUE THEOLOGIQUE 102:519-538, July-
August, 1980.

Evolution of plasma levels of apolipoprotein B, cholesterol and
triglycerides in women during long-term oral contraception,
by A. Verine, et al. CLINICA CHIMICA ACTA 100(2):143-
148, January 15, 1980.

Experience from direct injection of low prostaglandin F2alpha doses into portio for low-complication dilatation of cervix for abruptio, by R. Voigt, et al. ZENTRALBLATT FUR GYNAEKOLOGIE 101(24):1592-1594, 1979.

Experience of a model counseling center after amendment 218 to the abortion law, by D. Hobich, et al. ARCHIVES OF GYNECOLOGY 228(1-4):383-384, July 20, 1979.

The experience of visitors of family planning clinics in Shiraz, Iran: contraceptive practice, side effects and rumors, by S. Tolnay. PAHLAVI MEDICAL JOURNAL 9(4):367-387, 1978.

Experience with the copper 7 intrauterine device in an adolescent population, by J. W. Kulig, et al. JOURNAL OF PEDIATRICS 96(4):746-750, April, 1980.

Experience with the induction of second-trimester abortion by extra-amniotic physiological saline infusion. Report of 127 cases, by M. Blum. EUROPEAN JOURNAL OF OBSTETRICS, GYNECOLOGY AND REPRODUCTIVE BIOLOGY 10(3):183-185, March, 1980.

Experiences of women refused National Health Service abortion, by J. R. Ashton. JOURNAL OF BIOSOCIAL SCIENCE 12 (2):201-210, April, 1980.

Experiences with the new oral contraceptive, by J. A. Ovysmen, et al. JOURNAL OF INTERNATIONAL MEDICAL RESEARCH 8(1):86-89, 1980.

Experiences with vacuum aspiration and uterotomy for induced abortion, by J. Kunz, et al. ARCHIVES OF GYNECOLOGY 228(1-4):388, July 20, 1979.

Experimental findings with spermantibodies: condom therapy (a case report), by D. R. Franken, et al. ANDROLOGIA 11(6): 413-416, 1979.

Experimental models in the search for antigestagenic compounds with menses-inducing activity, by L. Schenkel-Hulliger, et al.

JOURNAL OF STEROID BIOCHEMISTRY 11(1C):757-769, July, 1979.

Experimental pharmacologic studies on the male antifertility agent alpha-chlorohydrin and its analogues, by R. F. Lu, et al. YAO HSUEH HSUEH PAO; ACTA PHARMACEUTICA SINICA 14(7):402-407, July, 1979.

Experimental study of the permeability of the fallopian tubes in the rabbit after division of the isthmus and microsurgical anastomosis, by J. Barbot, et al. JOURNAL DE CHIRURGIE (PARIS) 116(4):307-310, April, 1979.

An extra week in case of the smallest doubt. SYGEPLEJERSKEN 80(12):20, March 19, 1980.

Extraamnial and intraamnial abortion induction using PGF2-alpha, by G. Göretzlehner, et al. ARCHIVES OF GYNECOLOGY 228(1-4):408-409, July 20, 1979.

Extraamniotic intermittent administration of prostaglandin F2 alpha during the first and second trimesters of pregnancy, by G. Goeretzlehner, et al. ANNALES CHIRURGIAE ET GYNAECOLOGIAE 68(3):100-103, 1979.

Facilitation of suction termination using extra-amniotic prostaglandins in gel, by I. L. Craft, et al. PROSTAGLANDINS 18 (1):143-152, July, 1979.

Factor analysis of the decision process for acceptance of medical termination of pregnancy, by S. A. R. Chaurasia, et al. JOURNAL OF FAMILY WELFARE 26:48-52, March, 1980.

Factors affecting adolescent contraception practices: implications for sex education, by M. H. Dembo, et al. ADOLESCENCE 14(56):657-664, Winter, 1979.

Factors affecting the incidence of miscarriage among the female employees, by H. Kashiwazaki, et al. SANGYO IGAKU 21 (3):250-256, May, 1979.

Factors associated with oral contraceptive use, by S. C. Hartz, et al. AMERICAN JOURNAL OF PUBLIC HEALTH 70:1105-1107, October, 1980.

Factors in the use of oral contraceptives by young women, by P. D. Wener, et al. JOURNAL OF APPLIED SOCIAL PSYCHOLOGY 9:537-547, November-December, 1979.

Factors influencing the dicision to seek abortion, by G. Geijerstam. LAKARTIDNINGEN 77(7):560-564, February 13, 1980.

Factors influencing the time of introduction of steroidal contraception in the breast-feeding mother, by J. W. Cox. AUSTRALIAN AND NEW ZEALAND JOURNAL OF OBSTETRICS AND GYNAECOLOGY 19(1):7-9, February, 1979.

Facts about abortion, by E. Fein. HARPER'S BAZAAR 113:75-76, May, 1980.

Failed laparoscopic clip sterilization, by A. Kenney, et al. BRITISH MEDICAL JOURNAL 2(6189):526, September 1, 1979.

Failure of gonadotropins in reversing the copper intrauterine device induced acyclicity in rats, by S. K. Nayyar. IRCS MEDICAL SCIENCE LIBRARY COMPENDIUM 7(4):174, 1979.

Family life education for the handicapped, by S. Gordon, et al. JOURNAL OF SCHOOL HEALTH 50(5):272-274, May, 1980.

Family planning, by J. Peel. PRACTITIONER 223(1337):611-612, November, 1979.

Family planning and the diabetic mother, by W. N. Spellacy. SEMINARS IN PERINATOLOGY 2(4):395-399, October, 1978.

Family planning and questionnaire, by S. Pobric, et al. MEDICINSKI ARHIV 33(2):145-150, March-April, 1979.

Family planning imperative. NATIONAL CATHOLIC REPORTER 16:14, August 15, 1980.

Family planning: Implications for marital stability, by F. Johnson. JOURNAL OF DIVORCE 3(3):273-281, Spring, 1980.

Family planning in Chile, by H. Romero. REVISTA MEDICA DE CHILE 105(10):724-730, October, 1977.

Family planning in urban Aboriginal and Islander communities. Part II, by M. T. Samisoni, et al. AUSTRALIAN NURSES JOURNAL 9(9):45-47+, April, 1980.

Family planning—is it working in the NHS?, by M. Jones. MIDWIFE, HEALTH VISITOR AND COMMUNITY NURSE 16(2): 58+, February, 1980.

Family Planning/MCH Training of foreign nurse-midwives and related personnel in the United States: A comparative assessment of curricula in use by the six leading training institutions, by G. Vansintejan. DISSERTATION ABSTRACTS INTERNATIONAL 40(09):4910-A, 1979.

Family planning: a new challenge. PEOPLE 7(2):18, 1980.

Family planning of Portuguese immigrants and integration in Belgium, by J. S. FerroBucher. PSYCHOLOGICA BELGICA 18(1):12-26,1978.

Family planning policy and community based innovations in Thailand, by C. R. Krannich, et al. ASIAN SURVEY 20: 1023-1037, October, 1980.

Family-Planning Program effects and attitudes of adolescent females toward authority, by V. D. Gill. DISSERTATION ABSTRACTS INTERNATIONAL 40(08):4423-A, 1979.

Fatal myocardial infarction and the role of oral contraceptives, by D. E. Krueger, et al. AMERICAN JOURNAL OF EPIDEMIOLOGY 111(6):655-674, June, 1980.

Fatal myocarditis associated with abortion in early pregnancy, by D. A. Grimes, et al. SOUTHERN MEDICAL JOURNAL 73 (2):236-238, February, 1980.

Fear barrier to teenage birth control [high school and college women's attitudes: study by Lucy Olson] , by L. Asher. PSYCHOLOGY TODAY 13:109, September, 1979.

Federal dollars for obstetrical care in Nebraska, by B. Cooper, et al. NEBRASKA MEDICAL JOURNAL 64(8):251-253, August, 1979.

Federal judge strikes down abortion funding restriction. OUR SUNDAY VISITOR 68:8, January 27, 1980.

Federal statutes—constitutional law— medicaid act requires states to fund all medically necessary abortions subject to Hyde amendment. NOTRE DAME LAWYER 55:412-423, February, 1980.

Feds may force contractors to pay abortion benefits, by J.Geisel. BUSINESS INSURANCE 14:9, January 14, 1980.

Female breast cancer: distribution, risk factors, and effect of steroid contraception, by K. C. Lyle. OBSTETRICAL AND GYNECOLOGICAL SURVEY 35(7):413-427, July, 1980.

Female sterilization, by H. G. Hillemanns, et al. ZFA. ZEITSCHRIFT FUR ALLGEMEINMEDIZIN 55(26):1419-1427, September 20, 1979.

Female sterilization, by R. M. Soderstrom, et al. CLINICAL OBSTETRICS AND GYNAECOLOGY 6(1):77-95, April, 1979.

Female sterilization and subsequent ectopic pregnancy, by G. C. Wolf, et al. OBSTETRICS AND GYNECOLOGY 55(1):17-19, January, 1980.

Female sterilization: a five-year follow-up in Auckland, by P. Jackson,et al. NEW ZEALAND MEDICAL JOURNAL 91 (654):140-143, February 27, 1980.

Female sterilization—no more tubal coagulation [letter] , by K. M. Huntington. BRITISH MEDICAL JOURNAL 280(6228): 1377, June 7, 1980.

Female tubal sterilization [editorial] , by G. P. Dutta. JOURNAL OF THE INDIAN MEDICAL ASSOCIATION 72(8):193-194, April 16, 1979.

Fertility and family planning in Fiji, by T. U. Bavadra, et al. STUDIES IN FAMILY PLANNING 11(1):17-23, January, 1980.

Fertility and family planning in Mexico, by R.Rodriguez-Barocio, et al. INTERNATIONAL FAMILY PLANNING PERSPECTIVES 6:2-9, March, 1980.

Fertility control, by I. M. Gardner. PUBLIC HEALTH 94(2): 103-104, March, 1980.

Fertility control in the United States before the contraceptive revolution, by D. A. Dawson, et al. FAMILY PLANNING PERSPECTIVES 12(2):76-86, March-April, 1980.

Fertility control programs in Asia: another look at the data, by K. A. Laidlaw, et al. ASIAN SURVEY 20:803-811, August, 1980.

Fertility control without modernization: evidence from a rural Indian community, by C. Vlassoff. JOURNAL OF BIOSOCIAL SCIENCE 11(3):325-339, July, 1979.

Fertility following legally induced abortion, by E. B. Obel. ACTA OBSTETRICIA ET GYNECOLOGICA SCANDINAVICA 58(6):539-542, 1979.

Fertility in adolescence: proceedings of the 7th International Planned Parenthood Federation Biomedical Workshop, London, November 17-18, 1977. JOURNAL OF BIOSOCIAL SCIENCE [Suppl] (5):1-259, 1978.

Fertility intentions and behavior: some findings from Taiwan, by N. K. Nair, et al. STUDIES IN FAMILY PLANNING 11(7-8):255-263, July-August, 1980.

Fertility, mortality, migration and family planning in Haiti, by J. Allman, et al. POPULATION STUDIES 33:505-521,

November, 1979.

Fertility planning status of Chicano couples in Los Angeles, by G. Sabagh. AMERICAN JOURNAL OF PUBLIC HEALTH 70(1):56-61, January, 1980.

Fertility regulation using 'triphasic' administration of ethinyl estradiol and levonorgestrel in comparison with the 30 plus 150 micrograms fixed dose regime, by G. Zador. ACTA OBSTETRICIA ET GYNECOLOGICA SCANDINAVICA [Suppl] 88:43-48, 1979.

Fetal adoption: a technological solution to the problem of abortion ethics, by R. A. Freitas, Jr. HUMANIST 40:22-23, May-June, 1980.

Fetal damage caused by contraceptive tablets, by E. Czeizel. ORVOSI HETILAP 121(1):3-9, January 6, 1980.

Fetal-maternal transfusion following early abortion, by M. Leong, et al. OBSTETRICS AND GYNECOLOGY 54(4):424-426, October, 1979.

Fetal-politics, by J. E. Lalonde. WEEKLY 3(3):14, April 12, 1978.

Fewer adverse effects of oral contraceptives, by E. Johansson. LAKARTIDNINGEN 77(24):2241, June 11, 1980.

Fibrinolysis, renin activity, and prorenin in normal women: effects of exercise and oral contraceptive medication, by A. M. Hedlin, et al. JOURNAL OF CLINICAL ENDOCRINOLOGY AND METABOLISM 49(5):663-671, November, 1979.

Fibroadenoma in oral contraceptive users: a histopathologic evaluation of epithelial atypia, by V. A. LiVolsi, et al. CANCER 44(5):1778-1781, November, 1979.

A field study of the choice and continuity of use of three contraceptive methods in a rural area of Thailand, by A. Somboonsuk, et al. JOURNAL OF BIOSOCIAL SCIENCE 10(2):209-216, April, 1978.

Field tests with an oral contraceptive. Results with an estrogen-reduced contraceptive for the symptom of 'tight breast', by R. Heithecker, et al. ZFA. ZEITSCHRIFT FUR ALLEGE-MEINMEDIZIN 55(29):1665-1666, October 20, 1979.

Fifty years of natural family planning, by W. Fijalkowski. GINE-KOLOGIA POLSKA 50(11):909-916, November, 1979.

First clinical experiences with prostaglandin E derivative sul-prostone in extraamnial abortion induction, by R. C. Briel, et al. ARCHIVES OF GYNECOLOGY 228(1-4):425, July 20, 1979.

First experiences with abortion induction using subprostone, a prostaglandin E2 derivative, by U. Gethmann, et al. AR-CHIVES OF GYNECOLOGY 228(1-4):400-401, July 20, 1979.

The first three-stage preparation for hormonal contraception. Clinical results, by U. Lachnit-Fixson. MMW 121(43):1421-1426, October 26, 1979.

First year clinical experience with six levonorgestrel rods as sub-dermal contraception, by A. Faundes, et al. CONTRACEP-TION 20(2):167-175, August, 1979.

Florida law governing abortions held unconstitutional. FAMILY LAW REPORTER: COURT OPINIONS 6(10):2154-2156, January 15, 1980.

Focal nodular hyperplasia and hepatocytic adenoma in the liver of women taking contraceptive tablets, by I. Bartok, et al. ORVOSI HETILAP 120(42):2541-2544, October 21, 1979.

Folate for oral contraceptive users may reduce cervical cancer risk [news], by W. A. Check. JAMA 244(7):633-634, August 15, 1980.

Folate-induced regression of cervical intraepithelial neoplasia (CIN) in users of oral contraceptive agents (OCA) [from abstract of paper presented at the 10th annual meeting of the American Society for Clinical Nutrition, Washington, D. C.,

May 9-11, 1980], by C. E. Butterworth, Jr., et al. AMERI-CAN JOURNAL OF CLINICAL NUTRITION 33:926, April, 1980.

Follow-up during oral contraception [letter], by P. G. Crosignani. JOURNAL OF ENDOCRINOLOGICAL INVESTIGATION 1(1):97-98, January, 1978.

A follow-up of tubectomy clients in Bangladesh, by I. Swenson, et al. INTERNATIONAL JOURNAL OF GYNAECOLOGY AND OBSTETRICS 17(1):47-50, July-August, 1978-1979.

Follow-up study of school-age unwed pregnancy girls in Escambia County, Florida, by J. Dewitt. DISSERTATION ABSTRACTS INTERNATIONAL 40(09):4809-A, 1979.

A follow-up study of tubectomy acceptors in Bikaner, by C. K. Joshi, et al. JOURNAL OF THE INDIAN MEDICAL ASSOCIATION 73(1):1-4, July 1, 1979.

A follow-up study of two hundred cases of vasectomy, by V. K. Gandotra, et al. ACTA PHYSIOLOGICA SCANDINAVICA 107:19-32, September, 1979.

For a graduated scale of fees for legal abortion; against a graduated scale, by W. Cates, et al. FAMILY PLANNING PERSPECTIVES 12:219-221, July-August, 1980.

Forced sterilization inhuman, Virginia bishop asserts. OUR SUNDAY VISITOR 68:3, March 16, 1980.

Foreign aid for abortion, by D. P. Warwick. HASTINGS CENTER REPORT 10(2):30-37, April, 1980.

Four case histories of severe genital infections following insertion of intrauterine contraceptive devices, by F. Ebert, et al. ZENTRALBLATT FUR GYNAEKOLOGIE 107(6):362-367, 1980.

Four cases of benign hepatic tumors associated with oral contraception, by J. M. Jankowski, et al. SEMAINES DES HOPITAUX DE PARIS 55(21-22):1085-1090, June 8-15, 1979.

France fears falling birth rate, by J. Jessel. NEW STATESMAN 98:836, November 30, 1979.

A fraudulent means to circumvent the abortion law [letter], by E. D. Seegers. SOUTH AFRICAN MEDICAL JOURNAL 56 (14):545, September 29, 1979.

Free abortion and voluntary parenthood, by K. Sundström-Feigenberg. LAKARTIDNINGEN 77(7):522-525, February 13, 1980.

From arthritis pain to dysmenorrhea: a new indication for prostagladin inhibitors, by L. N. Gever. NURSING 10(4):81, April, 1980. From criminal offense to social service. An analysis of the social significance of induced abortion in The Netherlands, by E. Ketting. SAMSOM UITGEVERIJ 1978.

From natural fertility to family limitation: the onset of fertility transition in a sample of German villages, by J. Knodel. DEMOGRAPHY 16:493-521, November, 1979.

From the right to live to the right to choose—birth and legal abortion in Sweden, by H. Sjövall. LAKARTIDNINGEN 76(48): 4380-4386, November 28, 1979.

Frontlines: victory over Dalkon. (C. Palmer awarded $6.8 million for injuries suffered by using Dalkon IUD), by C. O'Conner. MOTHER JONES 5:12, January, 1980.

Full-term pregnancies following habitual abortions, by R. Berendes, et al. ARCHIVES OF GYNECOLOGY 228(1-4):553-554, July 20, 1979.

Functional state of the sumpathetic-adrenal system in interrupted pregnancy, by I. P. Gryzhak, et al. VOPROSY OKHRANY MATERINSTVA I DETSTVA 25(4):48-51, April, 1980.

Funded adoption: a "viable" alternative to abortion. BRIGHAM YOUNG UNIVERSITY LAW REVIEW 1979:363-393, 1979.

A further case of hepatocytic adenoma following oestrogenprogestogen treatment. Review of the literature, by J. P.

Grandjean, et al. SEMAINES DES HOPITAUX DE PARIS 56 (7-8):383-392, February 18-25, 1980.

——, also in: ANNALES DE CHIRURGIE 33(5):361-370, May, 1979.

Further studies on the trichosanthin-induced termination of pregnancy, by I. F. Lau, et al. CONTRACEPTION 21(1):77-86, January, 1980.

Further study on the effect of norethisterone enanthate, an injectable contraceptive on body functions, by M. N. Ali, et al. BANGLADESH MEDICAL RESEARCH COUNCIL BULLETIN 4(2):63-70, December, 1978.

Further methods of fertility regulation, by E. B. Connell. CLINICAL OBSTETRICS AND GYNAECOLOGY 6(1):171-184, April, 1979.

The future of family planning [editorial]. MIDWIFE, HEALTH VISITOR AND COMMUNITY NURSE 16(2):43, February, 1980.

Gall-bladder troubles and oral contraceptives, by J. P. Bourdais, et al. SEMAINES DES HOPITAUX DE PARIS 55(27-30): 1297-1304, September 8-15, 1979.

Gas-liquid chromatographic analysis of lynestrenol in contraceptive tablets, by M. Rizk, et al. PHARMAZIE 33(8):521-522, 1978.

Genes, chromosomes, and reproductive failure, by J. L. Simpson. FERTILITY AND STERILITY 33(2):107-116, February, 1980.

Genetic and epidemiologic investigation of spontaneous abortion: relevance to clinical practice, by D. Warburton, et al. BIRTH DEFECTS 15(5A):127-136, 1979.

Genetic indications for sterilization (letter), by E. Czeizel. ORVOSI HETILAP 121(2):117, January 13, 1980.

Genetic screening and genetic counseling: Knowledge, attitudes, and practices in two groups of family planning professionals, by E. W. Naylor. SOCIAL BIOLOGY 22(4):304-314, Winter, 1975.

Genetic studies in habitual abortion, by N. A. Karetnikova, et al. AKUSHERSTVO I GINEKOLOGIIA (4):42-46, April, 1980.

Genital infections in prenatal and family planning attendants in Swaziland, by A. Meheus, et al. EAST AFRICAN MEDICAL JOURNAL 57(3):212-217, March, 1980.

Genodermatoses as an indication for the interruption of pregnancy: hereditary epidermolysis, by U. W. Schnyder. HAUTARZT 31 Suppl 4:23-24, 1980.

Gestational trophoblastic disease within an elective abortion population, by B. A. Cohen, et al. AMERICAN JOURNAL OF OBSTETRICS AND GYNECOLOGY 135(4):452-454, October 15, 1979.

Gossypol as an oral contraceptive for men. JOURNAL OF THE MEDICAL SOCIETY OF NEW JERSEY 77(1):50, January, 1980.

Gossypol—a new antifertility agent for males. GYNECOLOGIC AND OBSTETRIC INVESTIGATION 10(4):163-176, 1979.

Gossypol, a new contraceptive agent for men, by F. Havranek. CESKOSLOVENSKA GYNEKOLOGIE 44(9):701, November, 1979.

Gossypol related hypokalemia. Clinicopharmacologic studies, by S. Z. Qian, et al. CHINESE MEDICAL JOURNAL 93(7): 477-482, July, 1980.

Government efforts to influence fertility: the ethical issues, by B. Berelson, et al. POPULATION AND DEVELOPMENT REVIEW 5:581-613, December, 1979.

Governor signs parental consultation bill. OUR SUNDAY VISITOR 69:2, June 22, 1980.

Great Britain: birthrights at the barricades, by M. McDonald. MACLEAN'S 93:40+, March 17, 1980.

Gregory Pinvus and steroidal contraception: a new departure in the history of mankind, by E. Diczfalusy. JOURNAL OF STEROID BIOCHEMISTRY 11(1A):3-11, July, 1979.

A guide to contraceptive advice, by J. Abrams. MEDICAL TIMES 108(3):1s-3s+, March, 1980.

Gynecologist used different suture material for tubal ligation; patient's complaint that she was not informed of this declared unfounded. NEDERLANDS TIJDSCHRIFT VOOR GENEESKUNDE 124(24):987-988, June 14, 1980.

The gynecologist's role in the natural family planning program, by A. Barba, Jr. LINACRE 47:274-278, August, 1980.

Haemoglobin levels in contraceptive users, by K. Prema. INDIAN JOURNAL OF MEDICAL RESEARCH 69:756-760, May, 1979.

Haemoperitoneum due to cornual endometriosis after laparoscopic sterilization, by F. I. Uri, et al. BRITISH JOURNAL OF OBSTETRICS AND GYNAECOLOGY 86(8):664-665, August, 1979.

Haemophilus influenzae septicemia and midtrimester abortion, by E. Ogden, et al. JOURNAL OF REPRODUCTIVE MEDICINE 22(2):106-108, 1979.

Hageman factor deficiency and oral contraceptives [letter], by A. K. Mangal, et al. LANCET 1(8171):774, April 5, 1980.

Has legal abortion replaced other methods of birth control?, by O. Meirik. LAKARTIDNINGEN 77(7):531+, February 13, 1980.

Have the abortions been dedramatized?, by M. Callersten. LAKARTIDNINGEN 77(7):553-554, February 13, 1980.

Health professionals' perception of the psychological conse-

quences of abortion, by U. Baluk, et al. AMERICAN JOUR-
NAL OF COMMUNITY PSYCHOLOGY 8(1):67-75, February, 1980.

Heat induction in copper-bearing intrauterine devices during
shortwave diathermy, by N. C. Nielson, et al. ACTA OBSTE-
TRICIA ET GYNECOLOGICA SCANDINAVICA 58(5):495,
1979.

Helping men cope with abortions, by J. Bosveld. MS MAGAZINE
8:21, May, 1980.

Helping people with cancer consider parenthood, by K. M. Ac-
cola, et al. AMERICAN JOURNAL OF NURSING 79(9):
1580-1583, September, 1979.

Hemingway hills: symbolism in Hills like white elephants, by L.
E. Weeks, Jr. STUDIES IN SHORT FICTION 17:75-77, Winter, 1980.

Hemolytic syndrome and recurrent uremia. Irreversible cortical
necrosis due to estro-progestational hormones (proceedings),
by G. Rifle, et al. JOURNAL OF UROLOGY 85(4-5):331,
April-May, 1979.

Hemosorption in hepatic insufficiency after septic abortion, by
A. D. Kozhanov, et al. AKUSHERSTVO I GINEKOLOGIIA
(7):42-43, July, 1979.

Hemostatic changes associated with hormonal contraceptive
treatment, by A. G. Dettori. THROMBOSIS AND HAEMO-
STASIS 42(1):24, 1979.

Hepatic adenomas and oral contraceptives. Report of two cases
and review of the literature, by L. M. Sabria, et al. MEDI-
CINA CLINICA 73(6):234-238, October 10, 1979.

Hepatic sinusoidal dilatation related to oral contraceptives. A
study of two patients showing ultrastructural changes, by M.
A. Spellberg, et al. AMERICAN JOURNAL OF GASTROEN-
TEROLOGY 72(3):248-252, September, 1979.

Heterochromatic polymorphism in spontaneous abortions, by L. Hemming, et al. JOURNAL OF MEDICAL GENETICS 16 (5):358-362, October, 1979.

Heteroploidy in JUD-associated pregnancy [editorial], by D. Warburton. TERATOLOGY 20(1):2, August, 1979.

Heterosexual interactions in laboratory-housed stumptail macaques (Macaca arctoides): Observations during the menstrual cycle and after ovariectomy, by A. K. Slob, et al. HORMONES AND BEHAVIOR 10(2):193-211, April, 1978.

High court may resolve Hyde Amendment controversy. OUR SUNDAY VISITOR 68:6, December 9, 1979.

High Court overturns Dooling decision ruling Hyde constitutional; HHS discontinues Medicaid financing for abortions, by K. Kaunitz. HEALTH LAW VIGIL 3(15):3-5, July 25, 1980.

High Court reinstates full abortion funding: suspends Hyde Amendment. HUMAN EVENTS 40:3+, March 1, 1980.

A high incidence of unbalanced translocations and triploidy in an unselected sample of human spontaneous abortion, by C. C. Lin, et al. GENETICS 91(4 part 2 suppl.):s68-s69, 1979.

High infant mortality may signal readiness for family planning [news]. FAMILY PLANNING PERSPECTIVES 12(1):58-59, January-February, 1980.

High rate of ectopic pregnancy following laparoscopic tubal coagulation failures. Incidence and etiology, by A. McCausland. AMERICAN JOURNAL OF OBSTETRICS AND GYNECOLOGY 136(1):97-101, January 1, 1980.

Hippocratic Oath as anachronistic [letter], by R. R. Winton. MEDICAL JOURNAL OF AUSTRALIA 2(7):365-366, October 6, 1979.

Histological appearances of the human placenta observed by electron microscopy after hypertonic saline abortion, by J. H. Stegeman, et al. ACTA OBSTETRICIA ET GYNECOLO-

GICA SCANDINAVICA 59(1):45-53, 1980.

Histological examination of abortion tissue, by B. Sikjaer. UGES-KRIFT FOR LAEGER 141(30):2049-2051, July 23, 1979.

The histology of liver tumors in oral contraceptive users observed during a national survey by the American College of Surgeons Commission on Cancer, by F. Nime, et al. CANCER 44(4):1481-1489, October, 1979.

Histomorphology of the breast under the influence of hormonal contraceptives, by K. Prechtel, et al. ARCHIVES OF GYNE-COLOGY 228(1-4):459-460, July 20, 1979.

The history of pregnancies that occur following female sterilization, by I. C. Chi, et al. INTERNATIONAL JOURNAL OF GYNAECOLOGY AND OBSTETRICS 17(3):265-267, November-December, 1979.

Home teaching in the North-West: a pilot survey, by I. Petrie, et al. CHILD: CARE, HEALTH AND DEVELOPMENT 6(1): 57-64, January-February, 1980.

Hormonal contraception, by G. Göretzlehner, et al. ZENTRAL-BLATT FUR GYNAEKOLOGIE 101(21):1361-1380, 1979.

Hormonal contraception and lipid metabolism. Prospective and retrospective studies of lipid metabolic parameters during the use of contraceptives, by P. Brockerhoff, et al. FORT-SCHRITTE DER MEDIZIN 97(41):1858-1861, November 1, 1979.

Hormonal contraceptives and high blood pressure, by J. M. Coderch Gimeno, et al. MEDICINA CLINICA 73(2):77-82, June 25, 1979.

Hormonal factors in the regulation of myometrial activity. An in vivo study, by T. Laudanski. ACTA OBSTETRICIA ET GY-NECOLOGICA SCANDINAVICA [Suppl] 91:1-32, 1979.

Hormone cytologic examination of the oral mucosa in women taking contraceptives pills, by M. Korondy, et al. FORGOR-

VOSI SZEMLE 73(4):103-105, April, 1980.

Hormone therapy of spontaneous abortion. Our experience with treatment with Graviginan, by A. Drazancic, et al. JUGO-SLAVENSKA GINEKOLOGIJA I OPSTETRICIJA 18(3-4): 325-333, May-August, 1978.

Hormone therapy: three perspectives. Fibrocystic breast disease: contraindication for oral contraceptive therapy, by D. Cook. JOURNAL OF NURSE-MEDWIFERY 25(2):15-16, March-April, 1980.

Hospital response to the legislation of abortion in New York state: an analysis of program innovation, by J. Miller. JOURNAL OF HEALTH AND SOCIAL BEHAVIOR 10:363-375, December, 1979.

Hospital support of legal abortion can overcome MD's negative attitudes. FAMILY PLANNING PERSPECTIVES 12:264-265, September-October, 1980.

House protects funding for child health program, adds anti-abortion rider, by E. Wehr. CONGRESSIONAL QUARTERLY WEEKLY REPORT 37:2764, December 8, 1979.

House takes hard line on abortion funding. AIR FORCE TIMES 41:4, October 6, 1980.

Household distribution of contraceptives in rural Egypt, by S. Gadella, et al. STUDIES IN FAMILY PLANNING 11(3):105-113, March, 1980.

How attitudes toward abortion are changing, by E. F. Jones. JOURNAL OF POPULATION 1(1):5-21, Spring, 1978.

How do you manage the teenage patient who comes to you for contraception?. INTERNATIONAL JOURNAL OF FERTILITY 24(2):78-85, 1979.

How many girls do parents drive to abortion, by M. Finley. OUR SUNDAY VISITOR 68:5, November 4, 1979.

How men who accompany women to an abortion service perceive the impact of abortion upon their relationship and themselves, by M. R. Smith. DISSERTATION ABSTRACTS INTERNATIONAL 40(07):3792-A, 1979.

Husbands' attidues towards abortion and Canadian abortion law, by R. W. Osborn, et al. JOURNAL OF BIOSOCIAL SCIENCE 12(1):21-30, January, 1980.

A husband's consent to his wife's abortion, by L. E. Rozovsky. DIMENSIONS IN HEALTH SERVICE 57(1):34-36, January, 1980.

The Hyde amendment. AMERICA 142:181, March 8, 1980.

—. SCIENCE NEWS 118:20-21, July 12, 1980.

The Hyde Amendment and the future, by J. I. Rosoff. FAMILY PLANNING PERSPECTIVES 12:172-173, July-August, 1980.

Hyde amendment ban on Medicaid abortions ruled unconstitutional. NATIONAL CATHOLIC REPORTER 16:20, January 25, 1980.

Hyde Amendment declared unconstitutional by U.S. District Court. FAMILY LAW REPORTER: COURT OPINIONS 6 (12):2181-2182, January 29, 1980.

Hyde amendment goes before U. S. Supreme Court. OUR SUNDAY VISITOR 69:7, May 4, 1980.

Hyde Amendment [Supreme Court's refusal to suspend Judge John Dooling's order for Federal funding of abortions]. AMERICA 142:181, March 8, 1980.

Hyde and hysteria: the liberal banner has been planted on the wrong side of the abortion debate, by R. J. Neuhaus. CHRISTIAN CENTURY 97:849-852, September 10-17, 1980.

Hyde ruling: abortion forces intensify fight: pro-choice 'will win in long run', by S. Russell. NATIONAL CATHOLIC RE-

PORTER 16:1+, July 18, 1980.

Hyde ruling opinions: from an opponent and a supporter, by E. McCormack. NATIONAL CATHOLIC REPORTER 16:22, July 13, 1980.

Hypertension, not pill use, found major factor in increased risk of subarachnoid hemorrhage [news]. FAMILY PLANNING PERSPECTIVES 12(1):53, January-February, 1980.

Hysterectomy following sterilization, by C. O'Herlihy, et al. INTERNATIONAL JOURNAL OF GYNAECOLOGY AND OBSTETRICS 17(3):263-264, November-December, 1979.

Hysterectomy for sterilisation? [letter], by J. Swinnen. NEW ZEALAND MEDICAL JOURNAL 90(649):477, December 12, 1979.

Hysterectomy-induced facilitation of lordosis behavior in the rat, by H. I. Siegel. HORMONES AND BEHAVIOR 11(3):273-278, December, 1978.

Hysterographic and hysterectomy findings after pregnancies in spite of a remaining intrauterine device, by T. Katzorke, et al. MEDIZINISCHE WELT 30(38):1393-1395, September 21, 1979.

Hysterographic studies of uterine contractile activity during partusysten treatment of threatened late abortion and premature labor, by O. I. Vinnyts'kyi. PEDIATRIIA AKUSHERSTVO I GINEKOLOGIIA (4):40-41, July-August, 1979.

Hysterosalpingographic control of patients sterilized by laparoscopy, by S. Davidsen, et al. UGESKRIFT FOR LAEGER 142(7):434-435, February 11, 1980.

Hysteroscopic oviductal blocking with formed-in-place silicone rubber plugs. I. Method and apparatus, by R. A. Erb, et al. JOURNAL OF REPRODUCTIVE MEDICINE 23(2):65-68, August, 1979.

—. II. Clinical studies, by T. P. Reed, et al. JOURNAL OF RE-

PRODUCTIVE MEDICINE 23(2):69-72, August, 1979.

IFRP supports search for safer methods in 30 developing lands [news] . FAMILY PLANNING PERSPECTIVES 11(5):315-316, October, 1979.

IUD compared with oral contraception in nulliparae, by A. Bergqvist, et al. CONTRACEPTION 20(4):407-415, October, 1979.

I.U.D. debate [risk of pelvic infections] . TIME 115:60, May 26, 1980.

IUD users may have higher risk of contracting PID, studies find: pill may have protective effect. FAMILY PLANNING PER-SPECTIVES 12:206-207, July-August, 1980.

Icterus induced by oral contraceptives, by F. Darnis, et al. MED-ECINE ET CHIRURGIE DIGESTIVES 8(5):423-425, 1979.

Identifying adolescents at risk for noncompliance with contra-ceptive therapy, by I. F. Litt, et al. JOURNAL OF PEDIA-TRICS 96(4):742-745, April, 1980.

If a ship is a person. What is a pre-born child, by D. Mothersill. OUR SUNDAY VISITOR 69:5, June 29, 1980.

If young women have the family size they say they want, U.S. population will not replace itself [news] . FAMILY PLAN-NING PERSPECTIVES 12(1):57-58, January-February, 1980.

Illegal abortion in Israel, by P. E. Slater. ISRAEL LAW REVIEW 13(3):411-416, July, 1978.

Immediate and late complications of laparoscopic sterilization, by B. L. Hejl, et al. UGESKRIFT FOR LAEGER 142(7): 436-438, February 11, 1980.

Immune studies in oral contraceptive users, by B. A. Ramalak-shmi. CONTRACEPTION 20(4):417-425, October, 1979.

Immunobiological examination of women with spontaneous a-bortions, by B. Mejsnarova, et al. SBORNIK LEKARSKY 81 (11-12):337-340, November-December, 1979.

Immunological observations following vasectomy, by C. Young. EXPERIENTIA 35(9):1243-1244, 1979.

Immunological tolerance of women during imminent abortion and during EPH-gestosis, by V. Knobloch, et al. CESKOSLO-VENSKA GYNEKOLOGIE 44(9):639-643, November, 1979.

The impact of abortion, by T. Cooke. ORIGINS 10:283-285, October 16, 1980.

Impact of the national family planning program on fertility in rutal Korea: a multivariate areal analysis, by K. G. Foreit, et al. STUDIES IN FAMILY PLANNING 11(3):79-90, March, 1980.

The impact of restricting Medicaid financing for abortion [based on conference paper], by J. Trussell, et al. FAMILY PLAN-NING PERSPECTIVES 12:120-123+, May-June, 1980.

Impaired elimination of caffeine by oral contraceptive steroids, by R. V. Patwardhan, et al. JOURNAL OF LABORATORY AND CLINICAL MEDICINE 95(4):603-608, April, 1980.

Implementation of a successful outpatient laparoscopic steriliza-tion program in Calcutta, by D. Lilaram, et al. INTERNA-TIONAL JOURNAL OF GYNAECOLOGY AND OBSTE-TRICS 17(1):15-18, July-August, 1978-1979.

Implementing the user perspective, by J. Bruce. STUDIES IN FAMILY PLANNING 11(1):29-34, January, 1980.

Importance of HDL-cholesterol as a negative risk factor and the relationship between HDL and oral contraceptives, by A. C. Arntzenius. NEDERLANDS TIJDSCHRIFT VOOR GE-NEESKUNDE 123(44):1910-1913, November 3, 1979.

Improved long-acting fertility regulating agents: what are the pro-blems?, by E. Diczfalusy. JOURNAL OF STEROID BIO-

CHEMISTRY 11(1B):443-438, July, 1979.

Improvement in artificial second-trimester abortion with a new tissue-selective prostaglandin E2 derivative, by R. Schmidt-Gollwitzer, et al. AMERICAN JOURNAL OF OBSTETRICS AND GYNECOLOGY 137(7):867-868, August 1, 1980.

In China, three's a crowd. NEWSWEEK 94:97, November 16, 1979.

In defense of life, by C. Anthony, et al. OUR SUNDAY VISITOR 68:4+, January 20, 1980.

In search of the perfect contraceptive, by C. Channing. THE SCIENCES 19:14+, December, 1979.

The incidence of abdominal surgical procedures in a population undergoing abortion, by T. M. King, et al. AMERICAN JOURNAL OF OBSTETRICS AND GYNECOLOGY 137(5): 530-533, July 1, 1980.

Incidence of chromosomal rearrangements in couples with reproductive loss, by N. B. Kardon, et al. HUMAN GENETICS 53(2):161-164, February, 1980.

Incidence of endometrial cancer in relation to the use of oral contraceptives, by N. S. Weiss, et al. NEW ENGLAND JOURNAL OF MEDICINE 302(10):551-554, March 6, 1980.

The incidence of gynecologic examination in pill monitoring, by F. P. Wibaut. NEDERLANDS TIJDSCHRIFT VOOR GENEESKUNDE 123(52):2230-2231, December 29, 1979.

Incidence of hyperprolactinemia during oral contraceptive therapy, by J. V. Reyniak, et al. OBSTETRICS AND GYNECOLOGY 55(1):8-11, January, 1980.

Incidence of pain among women undergoing laparoscopic sterilization by electrocoagulation, the spring-loaded clip, and the tubal ring, by I. C. Chi, et al. AMERICAN JOURNAL OF OBSTETRICS AND GYNECOLOGY 135(3):397-401, October 1, 1979.

'Inconvenient' babies [letter], by L. Hemingway. AUSTRALIAN FAMILY PHYSICIAN 8(7):800, July, 1979.

Increase in diaphragm use in a university population, by L. E. Berlin, et al. JOGN NURSING 8(5):280-282, September-October, 1979.

Increased blood viscosity in young women using oral contraceptives, by G. D. Lowe, et al. AMERICAN JOURNAL OF OBSTETRICS AND GYNECOLOGY 137(7):840-842, August 1, 1980.

The increased incidence of renal stones in women with spontaneous abortion: a retrospective study, by L. H. Honore. AMERICAN JOURNAL OF OBSTETRICS AND GYNECOLOGY 137(1):145-146, May 1, 1980.

Increased occurrence of ectopic pregnancy. A relation to the contraceptive practice?, by M. Onsrud. TIDSSKRIFT FOR DEN NORSKE LAEGEFORENING 100(14):944-947, May 20, 1980.

Indications for ovulation inhibitors. Recommendations of the Swiss Society for Family Planning. THERAPIE DER GEGENWART 119(3):297-299, March, 1980.

Individual needs in oral contraception, by E. Weisberg. AUSTRALIAN FAMILY PHYSICIAN Suppl:20-24, February, 1980.

Induced abortion after feeling fetal movements: its causes and emotional consequences, by C. Brewer. JOURNAL OF BIOSOCIAL SCIENCE 10(2):203-208, April, 1978.

Induced abortion followed by pelvic osteomyelitis, by S. Yadav, et al. JOURNAL OF THE INDIAN MEDICAL ASSOCIATION 73(9-10):168-169, November, 1979.

Induced abortion: free freedom to abort for whom? SYGEPLEJERSKEN 80(4):4-6, January 23, 1980.

—. We meet the patients once the decision for abortion has been

made, by K. Hindberg. SYGEPLEJERSKEN 80(12):17,
March 19, 1980.

Induced abortion from a social point of view, by Y. Kadman. SO-
CIETY AND WELFARE 2(3):320-329, 1979.

Induced abortion in 1-day patients, by M. Anderer. ARCHIVES
OF GYNECOLOGY 228(1-4):385-386, July 20, 1979.

Induced abortion in primigravidae and subsequent pregnancy,
with particular consideration of underweight, by B. Grindel,
et al. ZENTRALBLATT FUR GYNAEKOLOGIE 101(16):
1009-1014, 1979.

Induced abortion in rural villages of Cavite, the Phillipines: knowledge, attitudes, and practice, by J. M. Flavier, et al. STUD-
IES IN FAMILY PLANNING 11(2):65-71, February, 1980.

Induced abortion in the Wessex Health Region, England, UK, by
J. R. Ashton. EPIDEMIOLOGY AND COMMUNITY
HEALTH 33(2):168, 1979.

Induced abortion, 1979, by C. Tietze. POPULATION COUNCIL
1979.

Induced abortion—psychological implications, by M. Golomb.
SOCIETY AND WELFARE 2(3):311-319, 1979.

Induced abortion with prostaglandin gel in the 1st pregnancy trimester, by H. Kühnle, et al. ARCHIVES OF GYNECOLOGY
228(1-4):414, July 20, 1979.

Induced abortions and their complications, by S. Yarkoni, et al.
HAREFUAH 96(11):603-607, June 1, 1979.

Induction of abortion by intramuscular administration of (15S)-
15-methyl PGF2 alpha. An overview of 815 cases, by P. C.
Schwallie, et al. JOURNAL OF REPRODUCTIVE MEDI-
CINE 23(6):289-293, December, 1979.

Induction of aryl hydrocarbon hydroxylase by lymphocytes
from women taking oral contraceptives, by D. R. Nash, et al.

CONTRACEPTION 20(3):297-302, September, 1979.

Induction of first and second-trimester abortion by the extra-amniotic administration of a prostaglandin E2-derivate, by J. Kunz, et al. GEBURTSHILFE UND FRAUENHEILKUNDE 39(9):798-808, September, 1979.

Induction of therapeutic abortion with intravenous administration of prostaglandin F2-alpha, by A. Nasi, et al. MINERVA GINECOLOGIA 31(12):927-931, December, 1979.

Infant mortality, birth order and contraception in India, by S. K. B. Pathak. JOURNAL OF FAMILY WELFARE 25:12-21, June, 1979.

Infectious complications following abortion, by U. Hoyme, et al. ARCHIVES OF GYNECOLOGY 228(1-4):379, July 20, 1979.

Influence of age, cigarette smoking and the oral contraceptive on plasma concentrations of clomipramine, by D. K. Luscombe, et al. POSTGRADUATE MEDICAL JOURNAL 56 Suppl 1: 99-102, 1980.

Influence of HLA types on carbohydrate effects of a low-estrogen oral contraceptive, by W. N. Spellacy, et al. FERTILITY AND STERILITY 33(5):506-509, May, 1980.

Influence of parents, peers, and partners on the contraceptive use of college men and women, by L. Thompson, et al. JOURNAL OF MARRIAGE AND THE FAMILY 40(3):481-492, August, 1978.

Influence of sterilization methods and medium composition on the growth of Brucella abortus strain 19 in shake-flasks, by O. Y. Yantorno, et al. REVISTA DE LA ASOCIACION ARGENTINA DE MICROBOLOGIA 10(3):83-93, 1978.

The influence of sulprostone upon platelet function: in vitro and in vivo studies, by R. C. Briel, et al. ADVANCES IN PROSTAGLANDIN AND THROMBOXANE RESEARCH 6:351-353, 1980.

Information in matters of contraception: a role for the nurse [editorial], by C. Kurz. SOINS 25(8):2, April 20, 1980.

Initial pill selection and managing the contraceptive pill patient, by R. P. Dickey. INTERNATIONAL JOURNAL OF GYNAECOLOGY AND OBSTETRICS 16(6):547-555, 1978-1979.

Injectable contraceptive synthesis: an example of international cooperation, by P. Crabbe, et al. SCIENCE 209(4460):992-994, August 29, 1980.

Injectable non-occlusive chemical contraception in the male-I, by M. Misro, et al. CONTRACEPTION 20(5):467-473, November, 1979.

Injustices of the court rule Hyde constitutional [McRae v. Harris], by M. Rylance. OFF OUR BACKS 8:2, August-September, 1980.

Inmate abortions—the right to government funding behind the prison gates. FORDHAM LAW REVIEW 48:550-567, March, 1980.

Insertion of a coil (Gravigard) in induced abortion, by S. Olsen, et al. UGESKRIFT FOR LAEGER 142(13):820-822, March 24, 1980.

Intact pregnancy of 7 weeks' duration with an intrauterine pessary in place, by A. Feige. MEDIZINISCHE KLINIK 75(2): 54+, January 18, 1980.

Integration of nutrition and family planning into primary health care [news]. WHO CHRONICLES 34(2):77, February, 1980.

Intensive control of pregnancy. Comparison of plasma and urine estriol, by R. Göser, et al. ARCHIVES OF GYNECOLOGY 228(1-4):229, July 20, 1979.

Interaction between anticoagulants and contraceptives: an unsuspected finding, by E. de Teresa, et al. BRITISH MEDICAL JOURNAL 2(6200):1260-1261, November 17, 1979.

The interaction between legalization of abortion and contraception in Denmark, by P. C. Matthiessen. WORLD HEALTH STATISTICS QUARTERLY 32(4):246-256, 1979.

Interaction between oral contraceptives and other drugs [letter], by H. M. Burt. BRITISH MEDICAL JOURNAL 280(6225): 1230, May 17, 1980.

An interdisciplinary approach to population dynamics and family planning, by C. Adick. DIE DRITTE WELT 6(3-4):345-356, 1978.

Intermenstrual hemorrhage from the taking of oral contraceptives, by T. P. Barkhatova. FEL'DSHER I AKUSHERKA 44 (9):52-55, September, 1979.

Internal sterilization using the Falope ring, by P. H. Roberts. TRANSACTIONS OF THE PACIFIC COAST OBSTETRICAL AND GYNECOLOGICAL SOCIETY 46:72-76, 1979.

Interruptio—conventional or durg induced? A report on 58 abortions using intramuscular injections of sulproston, by K. Schlüter, et al. MEDIZINISCHE WELT 31(10):370-373, March 7, 1980.

Interruption of early pregnancy with Enzaprost-F, by P. Mocsary. THERAPIE HUNGARICA 27(2):84-86, 1979.

Interruption of early stages of pregnancy (menstrual regulation, mini-interruption), by F. Havranek, et al. CESKOSLOVENSKA GYNEKOLOGIE 44(8):561-566, September, 1979.

Interruption of pregnancy based on prenatal diagnosis, by J. D. Murken, et al. HAUTARZT 31 Suppl 4:25-30, 1980.

Interruption of pregnancy in the I. and II. trimester and its relationship to the woman's health, by M. Chalupa. SBORNIK VEDECKYCH PRACI LEKARSKE FAKULTY KARLOVY UNIVERZITY V HRADCI KRALOVE [Suppl] 23(1):1-73, 1980.

Interruption of pregnancy. Use of prostaglandins in the gynecology-obstetrics service of CHUV, Lausanne, by P. De Grandi. REVUE MEDICALE DE LA SUISSE ROMANDE 99(9):665-670, September, 1979.

Interruption of pregnancy with vaginal suppositories containing 16,16-dimethyl-trans-delta 2-prostaglandin E1 methyl ester, by T. Wagatsuma, et al. CONTRACEPTION 19(6):591-597, June, 1979.

Inter-spousal communication and practice of contraception in India, by J. C. Bhatia, et al. JOURNAL OF FAMILY WELFARE 26:18-30, June, 1980.

Interval mini-laparotomy: an alternative to laparoscopic sterilization?, by H. W. Foster, Jr. JOURNAL OF THE NATIONAL MEDICAL ASSOCIATION 72(6):567-570, June, 1980.

Intimacy and human sexuality: a challenge to the consensus on contraception, by L. B. Porter. COMMUNIO 7:269-277, Autumn, 1980.

Intra-abdominal foreign bodies sequelae from attempted abortion, by E. Maggiore, et al. ANNALI ITALIANI DI CHIRURGIA 49(1-6):219-225, 1975-1976.

Intracellular relationships of the rat uterine estrogen receptor: Alteration by intra-uterine devices, by L. Myatt, et al. CANCER TREATMENT REPORTS 63(7):1164, 1979.

Intrahepatic cholestasis and thromboembolism disease due to oral contraceptives, by M. Del Pilar Pla, et al. GEN 33(2): 213-219, April-June, 1979.

Intramural-intrauterine administration of prostaglandin E2 derivative for abortion induction in semi-hospitalized care in the operating room, by H. Wiechell. ARCHIVES OF GYNECOLOGY 228(1-4):409-410, July 20, 1979.

The intra-operative proof of occlusion of the tubes in tubal sterilizations, by B. Henkel. GEBURTSHILFE UND FRAUEN-HEILKUNDE 39(8):682-686, August, 1979.

Intrauterine contraception: a combined histologic and cytologic study, by M. L. Carneiro de Moura, et al. PATHOLOGY, RESEARCH AND PRACTICE 165(1/2):73, 1979.

Intrauterine devices, by D. R. Mishell. CLINICAL OBSTETRICS AND GYNAECOLOGY 6(1):27-38, 1979.

Intrauterine devices: a story of pain—and risk, by C. Dreifus. REDBOOK 154:67+, March, 1980.

Intrauterine microbial flora in septic abortion, with special reference to anaerobic germs, by R. Valle Ponce, et al. REVISTA CHILENA DE OBSTETRICIA Y GINECOLOGIA 43(3):137-139, 1978.

Intravaginal and intracervical devices for the delivery of fertility regulating agents. JOURNAL OF STEROID BIOCHEMISTRY 11(1B):461-467, July, 1979.

Intravaginal contraception with the synthetic progestin, R2010, by J. Toivonen. CONTRACEPTION 20(5):511-518, November, 1979.

An investigation of the association between cervical cancer and oral contraceptive use, by R. A. Willis. FEDERATION PROCEEDINGS 39(3):3250, 1980.

Involuntary sterilization of the mentally retarded: blessing or burden?. SOUTH DAKOTA LAW REVIEW 25:55-68, Winter, 1980.

Involving young men in family planning: an evaluation of a sex education project for men, by S. M. Moore. DISSERTATION ABSTRACTS INTERNATIONAL 40(09):4901-A, 1979.

Involvement of the private physician to the family planning programs: pilot study, by J. Campos, et al. GINECOLOGIA Y OBSTETRICIA DE MEXICO 45(267):11-23, January, 1979.

Involvement of vasectomy in endocrine aspects of aging, by G. Kinson. FERTILITY AND STERILITY 32(2):247-248, 1979.

The Irish solution: an account of the novel legislation on family planning which has been introduced in the Republic of Ireland, by D. Nowlan. POPULI 7(2):8-15, 1980.

Is a fetus a person?, by C. Donovan. SCIENCE FOR THE PEOPLE 12:9-11, November-December, 1980.

Is the pill natural?, by M. Potts. POPULI 7(1):12-17, 1980.

Is today's condom better than its reputation?, by G. K. Doring. FORTSCHRITTE DER MEDIZIN 98(4):113-117, January 31, 1980.

James Mackenzie Lecture 1979. The happiness pill?, by C. R. Kay. JOURNAL OF THE ROYAL COLLEGE OF GENERAL PRACTITIONERS 30(210):8-19, January, 1980.

Japan: 7 in 10 married women want no more children; fertility falls [news]. FAMILY PLANNING PERSPECTIVES 12(1): 52-53, January-February, 1980.

The jargon of hypocrisy, by J. Noonan, Jr. NEW COVENANT 10:12-16, October, 1980.

Jaundice from troleandomycin and oral contraceptives [letter], by J. P. Miguet, et al. ANNALS OF INTERNAL MEDICINE 92(3):434, March, 1980.

Jaundice in women taking both troleandomycin and oral contraceptives, an outbreak in France, by J. P. Miguet, et al. GASTROENTEROLOGIE CLINIQUE ET BIOLOGIQUE 4(6-7): 420-424, June-July, 1980.

Je choisis la pauvrete des pauvres gens, by T. Boyaxhiu. LA DOCUMENTATION CATHOLIQUE 77:234-236, March 2, 1980.

Judge Dooling's decision: '...allied to her right to be', by J. I. Rosoff. FAMILY PLANNING PERSPECTIVES 12(1):4+, January-February, 1980.

The juridical status of the fetus: a proposal for legal protection

104

of the unborn, by P. A. King. MICHIGAN LAW REVIEW 77 (7):1647-1687, August, 1979.

Karyotype, toxoplasma investigation, and the LAI gest in women with spontaneous abortions, by B. Mejsnarova, et al. CESKO-SLOVENSKA GYNEKOLOGIE 44(10):741-742, December, 1979.

Keep the official flag flying over birth control services, by A. Leathard. HEALTH AND SOCIAL SERVICE JOURNAL 90 (4695):704-707, May, 1980.

Kenya's maternal, child health/family planning programme, by S. Kanani. EAST AFRICAN MEDICAL JOURNAL 57(2): 80-86, February, 1980.

Kinemometric study of the Achilles reflex during normal pregnancy, abortions and early and late toxicoses, by N. Nedev, et al. AKUSHERSTVO I GINEKOLOGIIA 18(4):246-253, 1979.

Label game: views of D. Callahan on Medicaid funding. COMMONWEAL 106:614-615, November 9, 1979.

Lactational amenorrhoea, prolactin and contraception [editorial], by P. W. Howie, et al. EUROPEAN JOURNAL OF CLINICAL INVESTIGATION 9(4):237-238, August, 1979.

Laparoscopic sterilization, by M. Eskes. NEDERLANDS TIJDSCHRIFT VOOR GENEESKUNDE 124(19):729-734, May 10, 1980.

Laparoscopic sterilization with the aid of the Yoon ring, by F. Zabransky. CESKOSLOVENSKA GYNEKOLOGIE 45(4): 231-233, May, 1980.

Laparoscopic sterilization with electrocautery, silastic bands and spring-loaded clips: report of our experience with 790 patients, by P. Buytaert, et al. EUROPEAN JOURNAL OF OBSTETRICS, GYNECOLOGY AND REPRODUCTIVE BIOLOGY 10(2):109-118, February, 1980.

Laparoscopic sterilization with the Falopr ring, by B. L. Hejl, et al. UGESKRIFT FOR LAEGER 142(7):429-430, February 11, 1980.

Laparoscopic sterilization with Hulka-Clemens clips. A technical modification with a preliminary assessment, by P. Ladehoff, et al. UGESKRIFT FOR LAEGER 142(31):1998-1999, July 28, 1980.

Laparoscopic sterilization with a silicone rubber ring (Falope-ring), by P. Hansen, et al. UGESKRIFT FOR LAEGER 142 (7):438-440, February 11, 1980.

Laparoscopic sterilization with the spring clip: instrumentation development and current clinical experience, by J. F. Hulka, et al. AMERICAN JOURNAL OF OBSTETRICS AND GY-NAECOLOGY 135(8):1016-1020, December 15, 1979.

Laparoscopic tubal ligation. A follow-up report on the Yoon falope ring methodology, by I. Yoon, et al. JOURNAL OF REPRODUCTIVE MEDICINE 23(2):76-80, August, 1979.

Laparoscopic tubal sterilization by bipolar electrocoagulation, by K. Decker, et al. ARCHIVES OF GYNECOLOGY 228(1-4): 278, July 20, 1979.

Laparoscopic tubal sterilization: postoperative follow-up and late gynecological complaints, by P. Buytaert, et al. EURO-PEAN JOURNAL OF OBSTETRICS, GYNECOLOGY AND REPRODUCTIVE BIOLOGY 10(2):119-124, February, 1980.

Laparoscopic tubal sterilization under local anesthesia, by H. A. Hirsch, et al. ARCHIVES OF GYNECOLOGY 228(1-4):282-283, July 20, 1979.

Laparoscopic tubal sterilization using thermal coagulation, by J. E. Gunning, et al. OBSTETRICS AND GYNECOLOGY 54 (4):505-509, October, 1979.

Laparoscopy and Minilaparotomy: two major advances in female sterilization, by M. F. McCann, et al. STUDIES IN FAMILY

PLANNING 11(4):119, April, 1980.

Laparoscopy in Southland, by G. T. Thomas, et al. NEW ZEA-
LAND MEDICAL JOURNAL 91(651):10-12, January 9,
1980.

Laparoscopy or minilaparotomy for sterilization of women, by
A. T. Letchworth, et al. OBSTETRICS AND GYNECOLOGY
56(1):119-121, July, 1980.

Late effects of induced abortion: hypothesis or knowledge, by
W. Cates, Jr. JOURNAL OF REPRODUCTIVE MEDICINE
22(4):207-212, 1979.

Later hospitalizations of tubal sterilization patients, by P. A.
Poma. JOURNAL OF THE NATIONAL MEDICAL ASSOCI-
ATION 71(11):1085-1089, November, 1979.

Law requiring doctor to notify parents in minor's abortion valid.
FAMILY LAW REPORTER: COURT OPINIONS 6(10):
2153-2154, January 15, 1980.

Left ventricular size and function in women receiving oral contraceptives, by K. M. Kessler, et al. OBSTETRICS AND GYNE-
COLOGY 55(2):211-214, February, 1980.

Legal abortion in England and Wales 1968-1978, by T. L. Lewis.
BRITISH MEDICAL JOURNAL 280(6210):295-296, February 2, 1980.

Legal abortion: questions of law from practice, by E. W. Hanack,
et al. ARCHIVES OF GYNECOLOGY 228(1-4):331-343,
July 20, 1979.

Legal abortions and trends in fetal and infant mortality rates in
the United States, by K. E. Bauman, et al. AMERICAN
JOURNAL OF OBSTETRICS AND GYNECOLOGY 136(2):
194-202, January 15, 1980.

Legal aspects. Mental deficiency and sterilization: the case of
Eve, by C. L. Sklar. INFIRMIERE CANADIENNE 22(6):30-
32, June, 1980.

Legal blow to abortion [Supreme Court decision in favor of the Hyde amendment], by C. Fox. MACLEANS 93:33-34, July 14, 1980.

Legal termination of pregnancy. Economic and social aspects, by A. Delachaux, et al. REVUE MEDICALE DE LA SUISSE ROMANDE 99(12):913-919, December, 1979.

Legalised, or just localised? ECONOMIST 276:41, August 9, 1980.

Legalization of abortion in India, by N. L. Pande, et al. THE EASTERN ANTHROPOLOGIST 32(1):55-57, January-March, 1979.

Legislation on abortion in the countries of the world (a review of the literature), by V. K. Kuznetsov, et al. ZDRAVOOKHRANENIYE ROSSIISKOL FEDERATZII (5):37-40, 1980.

Legislation, public opinion, and the press: an interrelationship reflected in the New York Times' reporting of the abortion issue, by N. Buutap. DISSERTATION ABSTRACTS INTERNATIONAL 40(10):5599-A, 1979.

Let only two children bloom. SCIENTIFIC AMERICAN 242:64, April, 1980.

Let them eat cake, says the Supreme Court [Harris vs McRae decision; Hyde Amendment and Medicaid], by D. M. Kelley. CHRISTIAN CENTURY 97:820-824, August 27-September 3, 1980.

A life, a life style, and the way of life; cond from The Florida Catholic, February 2, 1980, by T. Grady. CATHOLIC DIGEST 44:34-36, June, 1980.

Life risks associated with reversible methods of fertility regulation, by C. Tietze, et al. INTERNATIONAL JOURNAL OF GYNAECOLOGY AND OBSTETRICS 16(6):456-459, 1978-1979.

Limiting public funds for abortions: state response to Congressional action. SUFFOLK UNIVERSITY LAW REVIEW 13: 923-959, Summer, 1979.

Liver and the contraceptive pill, by S. P. Dixit. CANADIAN JOURNAL OF SURGERY 23(3):222-227+, May, 1980.

Liver and ovulation inhibitors. Effects on liver function of estrogen-progestagen containing steroid oral contraceptives, by J. Eisenburg, et al. NATURWISSENSCHAFTEN 66(10):489-497, October, 1979.

Liver cancer and oral contraceptives [letter], by R. L. Goldman. AMERICAN JOURNAL OF SURGICAL PATHOLOGY 4 (2):208, April, 1980.

Liver cell tumor induction by oral contraceptives, by K. J. Gräf, et al. DEUTSCHE MEDIZINISCHE WOCHENSCHRIFT 105 (2):61-65, January 11, 1980.

Liver tumours and the contraceptive pill: controversies in aetiology, diagnosis and management, by J. Terblanche, et al. SOUTH AFRICAN MEDICAL JOURNAL 56(22):932-940, November 24, 1979.

Liber tumors and contraceptive steroids, by E. D. Nissen. CANCER TREATMENT REPORTS 63(7):1204, 1979.

Liver tumours and oral contraceptives [letter], by J. Borst. LANCET 1(8167):549, March 8, 1980.

Lobbyist quits: abortion issue cited, by M. Papa. NATIONAL CATHOLIC REPORTER 17:7, November 7, 1980.

Local antifertility effect of luteinizing hormone-releasing hormone (LRH), by R. C. Jones. CONTRACEPTION 20(6):569-578, December, 1979.

Local versus general anesthesia: which is safer for performing suction curettage abortions?, by D. A. Grimes, et al. AMERICAN JOURNAL OF OBSTETRICS AND GYNECOLOGY 135(8):1030-1035, December 15, 1979.

Locus of control and contraceptive knowledge, attitudes and practice, by I. Blignault, et al. BRITISH JOURNAL OF MEDICAL PSYCHOLOGY 52(4):339-345, December, 1979.

Locus-of-control, perceived susceptibility to pregnancy and choice of contraceptive among college students, by M. B. Dignan. PERCEPTUAL AND MOTOR SKILLS 48(3 Pt 1): 782, June, 1979.

Long-acting, more effective copper T IUDs [intrauterine devices] : a summary of U.S. experience, 1970-1975, by I. Sivin, et al. STUDIES IN FAMILY PLANNING 10:263-281, October, 1979.

A long-lasting effect of oral contraceptives on the excretion of urinary steroids: an implication of heaptic dysfunction in pill-users, by T. Kodama, et al. CANCER TREATMENT REPORTS 63(7):1205, 1979.

The long-term effect of various hormonal contraceptives on the excretion of sodium, potassium, calcium, magnesium, chloride, phosphorus, uric acid, oxalic acid, citric acid, sulfate and lysozyme in the 24 hour urine, by G. Klinger, et al. ZEITSCHRIFT FUR UROLOGIE UND NEPHROLOGIE 72 (6):393-398, June, 1979.

Long-term effects of interval laparoscopic sterilization by electrocoagulation on menstruation, by A. Weil, et al. ARCHIVES OF GYNECOLOGY 227(2):141-146, August, 1979.

Long-term outcome of sterlization as a function of the indication, marital status, age, number of children and concurrently performed therapeutic abortions, by U. Bänninger, et al. GEBURTSHILFE UND FRAUENHEILKUNDE 39(6):492-496, June, 1979.

Low birthrate a problem in France. OUR SUNDAY VISITOR 69:2, July 20, 1980.

McRae decision on abortion: seizing the moral imperative [ruling on constitutionality of Hyde amendment by Judge J. F. Dooling], by M. Thom. MS MAGAZINE 8:22-24, April, 1980.

Macroscopic and microscopic studies of fallopian tube after laparoscopic sterilization, by J. Donnez, et al. CONTRACEPTION 20(5):497-509, November, 1979.

Major British study finds no association between use of the pill and development of breast cancer [news] . FAMILY PLANNING PERSPECTIVES 11(5):311+, October, 1979.

Male contraception; synergism of gonadotropin-releasing hormone analog and testosterone in suppressing gonadotropin, by D. Heber, et al. SCIENCE 209(4459):936-938, August 22, 1980.

Male juvenile delinquints: birth control knowledge, practice and attitudes, by J. Bingham, et al. CLINICAL RESEARCH 27 (1):134A, 1979.

Male responsibility in sexual activity and family planning: perspectives of a college mental health professional, by A.Roach. JOURNAL OF THE AMERICAN COLLEGE HEALTH ASSOCIATION 28(3):173-175, December, 1979.

Male sterilization, by J. E. Davis. CLINICAL OBSTETRICS AND GYNAECOLOGY 6(1):97-108, 1979.

Malignant group B streptococcal endocarditis associated with saline-induced abortion, by J. G. Jemsek, et al. CHEST 76 (6):695-697, December, 1979.

Malnutrition, fertility and family planning, by P. N. Gupta. JOURNAL OF THE INDIAN MEDICAL ASSOCIATION 72 (8):194-199, April 16, 1979.

The management of early pregnancy: Colombian folk concepts of fertility control, by C. Browner. SOCIAL SCIENCE AND MEDICINE 14B(1):25-32, February, 1980.

Management of first trimester pregnancy termination failures, by R. F. Valle, et al. OBSTETRICS AND GYNECOLOGY 55 (5):625-629, May, 1980.

Management of intrauterine fetal death with prostaglandin E2 vaginal suppositories, by N. H. Lauersen, et al. AMERICAN JOURNAL OF OBSTETRICS AND GYNECOLOGY 137(7): 753-757, August 1, 1980.

Management of threatened abortion with real-time sonography, by S. G. Anderson. OBSTETRICS AND GYNECOLOGY 55 (2):259-262, February, 1980.

Managing oral contraception, by M. D. Read. PRACTITIONER 224(1340):179-181, February, 1980.

Many ways of looking at an IUD, by A. Kessler, et al. WORLD HEALTH p18-19, April, 1980.

Margaret Sanger: birth control's successful revolutionary, by D. Wardell. AMERICAN JOURNAL OF PUBLIC HEALTH 70 (7):736-742, July, 1980.

Marked preference for female sterilization in a semirural squatter settlement, by L. Gulati. STUDIES IN FAMILY PLANNING 10(11-12):332-336, November-December, 1979.

The Marquis de Sade and induced abortion, by A. D. Farr. JOURNAL OF MEDICAL ETHICS 6(1):7-10, March, 1980.

Masculinity-femininity and the desire for sexual intercourse after vasectomy: a longitudinal study, by D. Williams, et al. SOCIAL PSYCHOLOGY QUARTERLY 43:347-352, September, 1980.

Massive arterial thrombosis and oral contraception [letter], by S. Adam, et al. BRITISH MEDICAL JOURNAL 280(6210): 332, February 2, 1980.

Maternal age, stillbriths, abortions and factors related to maternal blood groups: a hospital survey from Lahore (Punjab, Pakistan), by S. A. Shami, et al. JPMA: JOURNAL OF THE PAKISTAN MEDICAL ASSOCIATION 30(2):27-34, February, 1980.

Maternal hormone therapy and congenital heart disease, by C. Ferencz, et al. TERATOLOGY 21(2):225-239, April, 1980.

Maternal plasma alpha-feto-protein in missed abortion, by Z. Habib. BIOLOGY OF THE NEONATE 35(5-6):264-267, 1979.

Maternal reactions to involuntary fetal/infant death, by L. G. Peppers, et al. PSYCHIATRY 43(2):155-159, May, 1980.

The Matlab family planning-health services project [project to distribute oral contraceptives and condoms in 150 villages in rural Bangladesh], by S. Bhatia, et al. STUDIES IN FAMILY PLANNING 11:202-212, June, 1980.

Maturation of the cervix by prostaglandins before inducing termination of pregnancy, in the first trimester, by B. Bourrit, et al. JOURNAL DE GYNECOLOGIE OBSTETRIQUE ET BIOLOGIE DE LA REPRODUCTION 8(6):567-570, 1979.

Mean cell volume in a working population: the effects of age, smoking, alcohol and oral contraception, by D. M. Chalmers, et al. BRITISH JOURNAL OF HAEMATOLOGY 43(4):631-636, December, 1979.

Measuring contraceptive efficacy and side effects, by I. Sivin. INTERNATIONAL JOURNAL OF GYNAECOLOGY AND OBSTETRICS 16(6):460-465, 1978-1979.

Mechanism of action of intrauterine devices, by S. Correu, et al. GINECOLOGIA Y OBSTETRICIA DE MEXICO 45(271): 419-428, May, 1979.

The mechanism of action of a new low-dosed combined oral contraceptive, by J. S. Dericks-Tan, et al. ARCHIVES OF GYNECOLOGY 229(2):107-114, 1980.

Mechanism of single-stitch failure of tubal ligation: a morphologic appraisal, by P. V. Mehta, et al. OBSTETRICS AND GYNECOLOGY 54(4):509-512, October, 1979.

Media treatment of life march 'terrible', by F. Franzonia. OUR SUNDAY VISITOR 68:3, February 10, 1980.

Medical risks of abortion, by C. Berman. GOOD HOUSEKEEP-

ING 191:230, October, 1980.

Medicine and killing: the CAtholic view, by R. R. Roach. JOURNAL OF MEDICAL PHILOSOPHY 4(4):383-397, 1979.

Medicolegal aspects of abortion, by W. Spann. HAUTARZT 31 (Suppl 4):3-7, 1980.

Medico-legal aspects of family planning, by I. E. Black. LEGAL MEDICAL QUARTERLY 2(3):198-203, 1978.

Medroxyprogesterone acetate in depot form for contraception, by I. Mark. UGESKRIFT FOR LAEGER 141(29):1965-1968, July 16, 1979.

Meeting special needs. NURSING ADMINISTRATION QUARTERLY 4(4):61-74, Summer, 1980.

Menarcheal age and spontaneous abortion: a causal connection?, by K. Liestol. AMERICAN JOURNAL OF EPIDEMIOLOGY 111(6):753-758, June, 1980.

Menstrual cycle after artificial abortion, by Z. Pavlic, et al. JUGOSLAVENSKA GINEKOLOGIJA I OPSTETRICIJA 19 (1-2):59-66, 1979.

Menstrual induction in preference to abortion [letter], by A. I. Csapo, et al. LANCET 1(8159):90-91, January 12, 1980.

Menstrual regulation and the law, by J. M. Paxman, et al. INTERNATIONAL JOURNAL OF GYNAECOLOGY AND OBSTETRICS 17(5):493-503, March-April, 1980.

Menstrual regulation clients in a village-based family planning programme, by S. Bhatia, et al. JOURNAL OF BIOSOCIAL SCIENCE 12(1):31-39, January, 1980.

Mental health consequences of abortion and refused abortion, by W. W. Watter. CANADIAN JOURNAL OF PSYCHIATRY 25 (1):68-73, February, 1980.

The metabolic effects of contraception with estrogen-progesto-

114

gen products, by J. Heim. JOURNAL DE GYNECOLOGIE OBSTETRIQUE ET BIOLOGIE DE LA REPRODUCTION 8(8):745-749, 1979.

Metabolic effects of oral contraceptives containing 30 micrograms of oestrogen, by A. L. Nash, et al. MEDICAL JOURNAL OF AUSTRALIA 2(6):277-281, September 22, 1979.

The metabolism of 3-amino-1-chloropropan-2-o1 in relation to its antifertility activity in male rats, by A. R. Jones, et al. XENOBIOTICA 9(4):253-261, April, 1979.

Method, age, education, and race influence success in contraceptive use. FAMILY PLANNING PERSPECTIVES 12:266-267, September-October, 1980.

Methodical aspects and results of studies into motivations for induced termination of pregnancy and the wish to have a child, by G. Henning, et al. ZENTRALBLATT FUR GYNAEKOLOGIE 101(10):666-672, 1979.

Microanalysis of lipids in discrete brain areas of the rabbit following intramuscular administration of steroid conttraceptive, by F. Islam, et al. CONTRACEPTION 21(4):434-442, April, 1980.

Microbiological aspects of the clinical features of puerperal infections and post-septic abortion with special reference to anaerobic bacteria, by C. M. Ulson, et al. REVISTA DO INSTITUTO DE MEDICINA TROPICAL DE SAO PAULO 21 (4 Suppl 3):24-66, July-August, 1979.

Microsurgical tubal anastomosis in the rabbit following three types of sterilization procedure, by O. M. Petrucco. CONTRACEPTION 20(1):55-60, July, 1979.

A middle ground on abortion [replies to Mc. C. Segers, "Abortion politics and policy", Christianity and Crisis February 18, 1980; rejoinder], by J. W. Dellapenna, et al. CHRISTIANITY AND CRISIS 40:70-80, March 31, 1980.

Midtrimester abortion by dilatation and evacuation versus intra-amniotic instillation of prostaglandin F2 alpha: a randomized clinical trial, by D. A. Grimes, et al. AMERICAN JOURNAL OF OBSTETRICS AND GYNECOLOGY 137(7):785-790, August 1, 1980.

Midtrimester dilatation and evacuation abortion, by D. A.Grimes, et al. SOUTHERN MEDICAL JOURNAL 73(4):448-451, April, 1980.

Minilaparotomy and salpingoclasia. Modification of the instruments, by J. Casasola Garcia, et al. GINECOLOGIA Y OBSTETRICIA DE MEXICO 47(281):181-190, March, 1980.

Mini-laparotomy for bilateral tubal ligation in lithotomy position, by W. E. Byrd. SOUTHERN MEDICAL JOURNAL 72 (12):1554-1556, December, 1979.

Minilaporotomy provides safety and savings [interview] , by E. Hakim-Elahi. SAME-DAY SURGERY 3(7):88+, July, 1979.

Minilaparotomy under local anesthesia for outpatient sterilization: a preliminary report, by R. B. Lee, et al. FERTILITY AND STERILITY 33(2):129-134, February, 1980.

Minnesota abortion statute held unconstitutional. FAMILY LAW REPORTER: COURT OPINIONS 6(13):2194-2195, February 5, 1980.

Minor consent in birth control and abortion: Part 1, by D. Trandel-Korenchuk, et al. NURSE PRACTITIONER 5(2): 47+, March-April, 1980.

—. Part 2, by D. Trandel-Korenchuk, et al. NURSE PRACTITIONER 5(3):48+, May-June, 1980.

Minor's right to abortion and contraception: prospects for invalidating less than absolute restrictions, by D. Klassel, et al. WOMEN'S RIGHTS LAW REPORTER 4(3):165-183, Spring, 1978.

Miscarriage, by C. Rankovic. SAINT ANTHONY MESSENGER 87:28-33, February, 1980.

Misscarriage: the fears and the facts, by M. Hewson. MCCALLS 107:41-42, July, 1980.

Miscarriages and DES daughters [research of L. Cousins]. SCIENCE NEWS 117:69, February 2, 1980.

Missed tubal abortion, by S. Burrows, et al. AMERICAN JOURNAL OF OBSTETRICS AND GYNECOLOGY 136(5):691-692, March 1, 1980.

Missouri abortion statute struck down on equal protection grounds. FAMILY LAW REPORTER: COURT OPINIONS 6 (13):2193-2194, February 5, 1980.

Missouri abortion statute unconstitutional in part. CRIMINAL LAW REPORTER: COURT DECISIONS AND PROCEEDINGS 26(23):2503-2505, March 12, 1980.

Missouri law regulating abortions declared unconstitutional. FAMILY LAW REPORTER: COURT OPINIONS 6(16): 2262-2264, February 26, 1980.

Mode of action of DL-norgestrel and ethinylestradiol combination in postcoital contraception, by W. Y. Ling, et al. FERTILITY AND STERILITY 32(3):297-302, September, 1979.

Modern contraception, by E. Paterok, et al. ZFA. ZEITSCHRIFT FUR ALLGEMEINMEDIZIN 55(29):1603-1604, October 20, 1979.

The modern indications for abortion, by D. Stucki. PRAXIS 69 (2):38-41, January 15, 1980.

Modes of male contraception: vasectomy and non-hormonal drug sterilization, by J. L. Alloza y Gascon-Molins, et al. MEDICINA CLINICA 73(5):209-214, September 15, 1979.

Modification by oral contraceptives in rat of 14C acetate incorporation into platelet lipids, by M. Ciavatti, et al. HORMONE AND METABOLIC RESEARCH 11(7):441-444, July, 1979.

Morbidity following vaginal tubal ligation, by I. Gupta, et al.

INDIAN JOURNAL OF MEDICAL RESEARCH 69:770-775, May, 1979.

More than just a packet of pills, by K. Margolis. GUARDIAN p10, November 17, 1980.

A morning-after double, by C. Doyle. OBSERVER p48, April 27, 1980.

Morphological alterations of rabbit oviducts following ligature of the tubal isthmus, by D. Bernhardt-Huth, et al. VIRCHOWS ARCHIV 384(2):195-211, 1979.

Morphological changes of the Shwartzman type in endotoxic shock after abortion, by D. Alessandrescu, et al. MORPHO-LOGIE ET EMBRYOLOGIE 26(1):41-45, January-March, 1980.

Most French back 1975 abortion law; birthrate decline worries many [news]. FAMILY PLANNING PERSPECTIVES 12 (3):158-159, May-June, 1980.

Mother Teresa: abortion greatest misery of our time. OUR SUNDAY VISITOR 69:7, August 17, 1980.

Mother Teresa: abortion makes rich nations poor. OUR SUNDAY VISITOR 68:7, December 23, 1979.

Motherhood and the flag of dissent [the growing conflict between pro- and anti-abortion forces; emphasis on Georgia], by M. Green. ATLANTIC MONTHLY 18:42-44+, February, 1979.

Mr. Hyde; Medicaid funds, by R. Becker. NEW REPUBLIC 181: 10-11, November 17, 1979.

Multidimensional investigations to elucidate relationships between case histories of interruption of pregnancy and premature deliveries and low birth weight, by C. Zwahr, et al. ZEN-TRALBLATT FUR GYNAEKOLOGIE 101(23):1502-1509, 1979.

Multiple births in former oral contraceptive users, by S. Harlap. BRITISH JOURNAL OF OBSTETRICS AND GYNAECOLOGY 86(7):557-562, July, 1979.

Mycoplasmas and ureaplasmas in infertility and abortion, by J. Friberg. FERTILITY AND STERILITY 33(4):351-359, April, 1980.

NAF sets sights on quality care, by D. Maine. FAMILY PLANNING PERSPECTIVES 11(5):303-307, October, 1979..

NCCB issues statement on tubal ligation. HOSPITAL PROGRESS 61:18-19, August, 1980.

NCCB statement on tubal ligation: issued July 9. ORIGINS 10: 175, August 28, 1980.

N.D. law barring funds to abortion referral agency is unconstitutional. FAMILY LAW REPORTER: COURT OPINIONS 6(32):2562, June 17, 1980.

NOR activity in two families with balanced D;D translocations and numerous consecutive miscarriages, by N. Gahmberg, et al. HEREDITAS 92(2):217-221, 1980.

National program of the Plan of Education for Family Planning, by M. Urbina Fuentes. GINECOLOGIA Y OBSTETRICIA ET MEXICO 46(278):475-481, December, 1979.

The National Reporting System for Family Planning Services—a new look, by J. G. Dryfoos. FAMILY PLANNING PERSPECTIVES 12:193-201, July-August, 1980.

Natural family planning, by C. Anthony. OUR SUNDAY VISITOR 69:6-7, November 30, 1980.

—, by C. A. Lanctot. CLINICAL OBSTETRICS AND GYNAECOLOGY 6(1):109-128, 1979.

— [editorial], by J. J. Billings. PAPAU NEW GUINEA MEDICAL JOURNAL 21(4):286-287, December, 1978.

Natural family planning. II. Basal body temperature and estimated time of ovulation, by T. W. Hilgers, et al. OBSTETRICS AND GYNECOLOGY 55(3):333-339, March, 1980.

—: a case history, by J. Margeot. ORIGINS 10:282-283, October 16, 1980.

—: the couple to couple approach, by E. Barkley. COLUMBIA 60:8-17, September, 1980.

Natural family planning in Australia: accidental pregnancies, discontinuation frequent. FAMILY PLANNING PERSPECTIVES 12:214-218, July-August, 1980.

Natural family planning in the past and present, by A. Löfström. LAKARTIDNINGEN 76(34):2779-2780, August 22, 1979.

Natural family planning: unlocking the mystery of woman, by T. Flynn. LIGUORJAN 68:16-19, March, 1980.

New abortion bill for old, by J. Turner. NEW SOCIETY p62, January 10, 1980.

New approaches to immunological contraception, by P. Matangkasombut. CLINICAL OBSTETRICS AND GYNAECOLOGY 6(3):531-548, December, 1979.

A new breed of right-to-lifers. NATIONAL CATHOLIC REPORTER 16:23, July 18, 1980.

New considerations in therapeutic abortions using a second generation prostaglandins, by H. Steiner, et al. GEBURTSHILFE UND FRAUENHEILKUNDE 39(6):464-469, June, 1979.

New context for contraception teaching, by J. Quinn. ORIGINS 10:263-267, October 9, 1980.

New effects from old ginseng. MMW 122(13):50, March 28, 1980.

A new non-steroidal drug for long-acting contraception, by P. C. Das, et al. ACTA PHYSIOLOGICA POLONICA 30(3):389-391, March-April, 1979.

New poll shows most want abortion law left along, by P. Kellner, et al. SUNDAY TIMES p3, February 3, 1980.

New right exploits abortion, by J. M. Wall. CHRISTIAN CENTURY 97:852+, September 10-17, 1980.

New risks in abortion plans, by A. Coote. NEW STATESMAN 98:616, October 26, 1979.

A new technique for minilaparotomy, by B. Palaniappan. INTERNATIONAL JOURNAL OF GYNAECOLOGY AND OBSTETRICS 17(3):260-262, November-December, 1979.

A new therapeutic approach for terminating intact and disturbed pregnancies: three years of experience with the prostaglandin E2-derivative sulprostone (SHB 286), by K. Schmidt-Gollwitzer, et al. GEBURTSHILFE UND FRAUENHEILKUNDE 39(8):667-675, August, 1979.

A new therapeutic possibility of abortion in 2d trimester using intravenous administration of sulprostone, by K. Schmidt-Gollwitzer, et al. ARCHIVES OF GYNECOLOGY 228(1-4): 402-403, July 20, 1979.

Nineteen-eighty presidential campaign: abortion question poses constant concern, by L. B. Weiss. CONGRESSIONAL QUARTERLY WEEKLY REPORT 38:733-734, March 15, 1980.

No association between oral contraceptives and malignant melanomas [letter], by R. G. Stevens, et al. NEW ENGLAND JOURNAL OF MEDICINE 302(17):966, April 24, 1980.

The no-birth bonus scheme: the use of savings accounts for family planning in South India [offers a deferred payment, in effect an old-age pension, to couples who limit their family size], by R. G. Ridker. POPULATION AND DEVELOPMENT REVIEW 6:31-46, March, 1980.

No case for an abortion Bill [editorial]. BRITISH MEDICAL JOURNAL 2(7184):230, July 28, 1979.

121

Norplant: reversible implant contraception, by I. Sivin, et al. STUDIES IN FAMILY PLANNING 11(7-8):227-235, July-August, 1980.

Norwegian Christians and abortion [in Norway], by F. Hale. DIAL 19:45-50, Winter, 1980.

Not free to choose [Harris vs McRae decision; Hyde Amendment and Medicaid]. NATION 231:33, July 12, 1980.

Notes on moral theology, 1978: Humanae vitae and the Magisterium, by R. A. McCormick. THEOLOGICAL STUDIES 40: 80-97, March, 1979.

The nurse and contraception for adolescents, by R. Gagne. INFIRMIERE CANADIENNE 22(1):18-22, January, 1980.

Nurse's role in voluntary pregnancy interruption and contraception, by A. Vogogne. SOINS 25(8):25-29, April 20, 1980.

OSHA cites Cyanamid on pigments operation. CHEMICAL MARKETING REPORTER 216:3+, October 15, 1979.

OSHA cites Cyanamid on sterilization issue. CHEMICAL AND ENGINEERING NEWS (57):7-8, October 22, 1979.

Observation on the new abortion offenses, by R. Spizuoco. GIUSTIZIA PENALE 84(3):174-175, 1979.

Observations on family planning acceptors in Papua New Guinea, by A. M. Saloheimo. PAPAU NEW GUINEA MEDICAL JOURNAL 21(4):299-305, December, 1978.

Obstetricians' attitudes and hospital abortion services, by C. A. Nathanson, et al. FAMILY PLANNING PERSPECTIVES 12 (1):26-32, January-February, 1980.

Obstruction of the axillary artery: cervical rib or adverse effects of oral contraceptives in the young woman? [letter], by M. Salzmann, et al. NOUVELLE PRESEE MEDICALE 8(24): 2023, June 2, 1979.

Obstructionist activities at abortion clinics: a framework for remedial litigation. NEW YORK UNIVERSITY REVIEW OF LAW AND SOCIAL CHANGE 8:325-360, 1978-1979.

Of feminism and birth control propaganda (1790-1840), by N. Weiner. INTERNATIONAL JOURNAL OF WOMEN'S STUDIES 3:411-430, September-October, 1980.

Office of Human Development Services—service programs for families and children, individuals and families, and aged, blind, or disabled persons; federal financial participation in state claims for abortions. FEDERAL REGISTER 44(209): 61599-61600, October 26, 1979.

On allocating resources for fertility reduction in developing countries, by B. Berelson, et al. POPULATION STUDIES 34:227-237, July, 1980.

On being a certifying abortion consultant: an ethical dilemma [editorial], by S. E. Clarkson. NEW ZEALAND MEDICAL JOURNAL 91(659):346-347, May 14, 1980.

On the efficient allocation of resources for fertility reduction, by B. Berelson, et al. INTERNATIONA FAMILY PLANNING PERSPECTIVES 5:133-142, December, 1979.

On impoverished spirits [judicial appointment plank of Republican Party platform], by W. F. Buckley, Jr. NATIONAL REVIEW 32:1041, August 22, 1980.

On the protection of the life of the child, by B. Arthadeva. CHRIST TO THE WORLD 24:401-405, November-December, 1979.

One is best, two is most, by B. Beedham, et al. ECONOMIST 273:24-25, December 29, 1979.

One is fine, two is more than adequate, by S. E. Fraser. FAR EASTERN ECONOMIC REVIEW 106:61-62, October 5, 1979.

One thousand march against Right-to-Life [Anaheim, California,

June 28, 1980], by R. Katz. OFF OUR BACKS 8:3, August-September, 1980.

Open letter to participants in the 1980 Synod of Bishops, by A. Zimmerman. LINACRE 47:171-181, May, 1980.

Operation methods in early and late abortion, by M. Bygdeman. LAKARTIDNINGEN 77(7):546-548+, February 13, 1980.

Oral contraception, by W. C. Andrews. CLINICAL OBSTETRICS AND GYNAECOLOGY 6(1):3-26, April, 1979.

—, by J. C. Guillat. SOINS 25(8):9-12, April 20, 1980.

—, by N. B. Loudon. PRACTITIONER 223(1337):641-645, November, 1979.

Oral contraception and depression, by J. L. Garrison. SOCIAL WORK 24(2):162-163, March, 1979.

Oral contraception and neoplasia, by G. Huggins, et al. FERTILITY AND STERILITY 32(1):1-23, 1979.

Oral contraception and oral mucosa, by P. Delaunay, et al. ACTUAL ODONTOSTOMATOL 34(129):149-156, 1980.

Oral contraception: candidates for the pill, by D. Hamilton. NURSING MIRROR 150(9):43-45, February 28, 1980.

Oral contraception in a regional centre. Variation in age profile and profesion, from 21,000 case notes in 5 years (1973-1977), by J. H. Soutoul, et al. JOURNAL DE GYNECOLOGIE, OBSTETRIQUE ET BIOLOGIE DE LA REPRODUCTION 8(3):193-199, April-May, 1979.

Oral contraception, mechanical contraception, and carbohydrate and lipid metabolism: a two-year study, by V. Pribicevic, et al. INTERNATIONAL JOURNAL OF FERTILITY 24(2): 114-119, 1979.

Oral contraception with an associated therapeutic action using a progestational method at two levels, by J. H. Soutoul, et al.

JOURNAL DE GYNECOLOGIE, OBSTETRIQUE ET BI-
OLOGIE DE LA REPRODUCTION 8(6):561-565, 1979.

Oral-contraceptive-associated liver tumours [letter], by Q. B.
Emerson, et al. LANCET 1(8180):1251, June 7, 1980.

—: occurrence of malignancy and difficulties in diagnosis, by J.
Neuberger, et al. LANCET 1(8163):273-276, February 9,
1980.

Oral contraceptive hypertension and thromboembolism, by W.
B. Kannel. INTERNATIONAL JOURNAL OF GYNAECOL-
OGY AND OBSTETRICS 16(6):466-472, 1978-1979.

Oral contraceptive-induced ischemic bowel disease, by W. A.
Parker, et al. AMERICAN JOURNAL OF HOSPITAL PHAR-
MACY 36(8):1103-1107, August, 1979.

Oral contraceptive pills and endometrial cancer [letter], by L. S.
Acheson. ANNALS OF INTERNAL MEDICINE 91(5):793,
November, 1979.

Oral contraceptive steroids: effects on iron and zinc levels and on
tryptophan pyrrolase and alkaline phosphatase activities in
tissues of iron-deficient anemic rats, by Y. Kanke, et al. A-
MERICAN JOURNAL OF CLINICAL NUTRITION 33(6):
1244-1250, June, 1980.

Oral-contraceptive use and bacteriuria in a community-based
study, by D. Evans, et al. NEW ENGLAND JOURNAL OF
MEDICINE 299:536-537, September 7, 1978.

Oral contraceptive use and vitamin nutrition status of malnourished women—effects of continuous and intermittent vitamin
supplements, by M. S. Bamji, et al. JOURNAL OF STEROID
BIOCHEMISTRY 11(1B):487-491, July, 1979.

Oral contraceptive use, cigarette smoking and myocardial infarction, by C. H. Hennekens. CLINICAL RESEARCH 28(2):
226A, 1980.

Oral contraceptive use in relation to nonfatal myocardial infarc-

tion, by L. Rosenberg, et al. AMERICAN JOURNAL OF
EPIDEMIOLOGY 111(1):59-66, January, 1980.

Oral contraceptives, by I. Lejins. AUSTRALIAN NURSES
JOURNAL 9(2):23-25, August, 1979.

Oral contraceptives according to the normophasic principle, by
N. E. Borglin, et al. ARZNEIMITTEL FORSCHUNG 28
(12):2354-2357, 1978.

Oral contraceptives and birth defects, by K. Rothman. NEW
ENGLAND JOURNAL OF MEDICINE 299:522-524, September 7, 1978.

Oral contraceptives and endometrial cancer [editorial], by P.
Cole. NEW ENGLAND JOURNAL OF MEDICINE 302(10):
575-576, March 6, 1980.

Oral contraceptives and fatal subarachnoid haemorrhage, by W.
H. Inman. BRITISH MEDICAL JOURNAL 6203:1468-1470,
December 8, 1979.

Oral contraceptives and hepatic vein thrombosis, by D. R. Kent.
CANCER TREATMENT REPORTS 63(7):1205, 1979.

Oral contraceptives and physiological variables, by L. D. Ostrander, Jr., et al. JAMA 244(8):677-679, August 15, 1980.

Oral contraceptives and pituitary adenomas, by S. J. Wingrave,
et al. BRITISH MEDICAL JOURNAL 280(6215):685-686,
March 8, 1980.

Oral contraceptives and plasma protein metabolism, by M. H.
Briggs, et al. JOURNAL OF STEROID BIOCHEMISTRY 11
(1B):425-428, July, 1979.

Oral contraceptives and prolactin-producing hypophyseal tumors, by S. W. Lamberts. NEDERLANDS TIJDSCHRIFT
VOOR GENEESKUNDE 124(4):111-113, January 26,
1980.

Oral contraceptives and the prothrombin time [letter], by J.

Pangrazzi, et al. BRITISH MEDICAL JOURNAL 280(6210): 332-333, February 2, 1980.

Oral contraceptives and the risk of thrombosis [letter], by J. Dommisse. SOUTH AFRICAN MEDICAL JOURNAL 56 (20):786, November 10, 1979.

Oral contraceptives and sex hormone binding globulin capacity, by K. G. Masurkar, et al. INDIAN JOURNAL OF MEDICAL RESEARCH 71:221-224, February, 1980.

Oral contraceptives and thromboembolic disease: effects of lowering oestrogen content, by L. E. Böttiger, et al. LANCET 1(8178):1097-1101, May 24, 1980.

Oral contraceptives and trisomy 21. A retrospective study of 730 cases, by J. Lejeune, et al. ANNALES DE GENETIQUE 22 (2):61-66, June, 1979.

Oral contraceptives, antithrombin III and deep vein thrombosis, by S. Kakkar, et al. THROMBOSIS AND HAEMOSTASIS 42 (1):26, 1979.

Oral contraceptives: cardiovascular complications and additional risk factors, by C. Herzog. PRAXIS 68(41):1321-1329, October 9, 1979.

Oral contraceptives in otosclerosis? [letter], by D. Plester. DEUTSCHE MEDIZINISCHE WOCHENSCHRIFT 104(39): 1368, September 28, 1979.

Oral contraceptives in women over 40, by J. A. Desrosiers. UNION MEDICALE DU CANADA 108(8):909-918, August, 1979.

Oral contraceptives: mechanisms in thromboembolism [editorial]. LANCET 1(8178):1118-1119, May 24, 1980.

Oral contraceptives, norethindrone and mestranol: effect on serum vitamin A, retinol-binding protein and prealbumin in women, by V. K. Nonavinakere, et al. FEDERATION PROCEEDINGS 39(3): Abstract 908, 1980.

Oral contraceptives raise the cholesterol saturation of bile by increasing biliary cholesterol secretion, by L. J. Bennion, et al. METABOLISM 29(1):18-22, January, 1980.

Organization of specialized care in miscarriage, by L. G. Kovtunova, et al. AKUSHERSTVO I GINEKOLOGIIA (5):13-16, May, 1980.

Organized family planning services in the United States, 1976-1977, by A. Torres. FAMILY PLANNING PERSPECTIVES 11:342-347, November-December, 1979.

Origin of triploidy in spontaneous abortuses, by J. G. Lauritsen, et al. ANNALS OF HUMAN GENETICS 43(1):1-6, July, 1979.

Other right-to-lifers, by M. Meehan. COMMONWEAL 107:13-16, January 18, 1980.

Otolaryngologic effects of 'the pill', by S. W. Coulthard. OTOLARYNGOLOGY AND HEAD AND NECK SURGERY 87 (5):555-556, September-October, 1979.

Ought we to try to save aborted fetuses?, by D. I. Wikler. ETHICS 90:58-65, October, 1979.

Our experience with the early termination of unwanted pregnancy by Karman's method, by A. Khubenov. AKUSHERSTVO I GINEKOLOGIIA 18(5):385-388, 1979.

Our experience with intrauterine devices (IUD) for birth control, by J. J. Vidal, et al. ACTA OBSTETRICA Y GINECOLOGICA HISPANA-LUSITANA 28(2):87-94, February, 1980.

Our purpose is to fight for life. OUR SUNDAY VISITOR 68:3, February 3, 1980.

Outcome of the delivery following an induced or spontaneous abortion, by S. C. Schoenbaum, et al. AMERICAN JOURNAL OF OBSTETRICS AND GYNECOLOGY 136(1):19-24, January 1, 1980.

128

The outcome of pregnancies subsequent to induced and spontaneous abortion, by A. U. Oronsaye. INTERNATIONAL JOURNAL OF GYNAECOLOGY AND OBSTETRICS 17(3): 274-277, November-December, 1979.

Outcome of pregnancy after spontaneous abortion, by T. J. David, et al. BRITISH MEDICAL JOURNAL 280(6212): 447-448, February 16, 1980.

Outcome of pregnancy in women using different methods of contraception, by M. Vessey, et al. BRITISH JOURNAL OF OBSTETRICS AND GYNAECOLOGY 86(7):548-556, July, 1979.

An outpatient approach to female sterilization with methylcyanoacrylate, by R. S. Neuwirth, et al. AMERICAN JOURNAL OF OBSTETRICS AND GYNECOLOGY 136(7):951-956, April 1, 1980.

Outpatient laparoscopy with local anesthesia, by H. Zevallos, et al. INTERNATIONAL JOURNAL OF GYNAECOLOGY AND OBSTETRICS 17(4):379-381, January-February, 1980.

Outpatient termination of early pregnancies using syringe and plastic cannula, by B. R. Marshall, et al. WESTERN JOURNAL OF MEDICINE 132(3):186-188, March, 1980.

Outreach education: a possible preventer of teenage pregnancy, by R. W. Block, et al. ADOLESCENCE 15:657-660, Fall, 1980.

Ovarian ectopic pregnancy in association with a copper 7 intrauterine device in situ, by A. Chidiac, et al. FERTILITY AND STERILITY 32(1):127-129, 1979.

Ovarian pregnancy and the intrauterine device: report of a case and review of the literature, by S. J. Wilson, et al. MT. SINAI JOURNAL OF MEDICINE 46(1):15-20, 1979.

Ovulation following spontaneous abortion (a histological and cytological study, by E. I. Efiong. NIGER MEDICAL JOURNAL 9(3):357-359, March, 1979.

Ovulation inhibition with a combined oral contraceptive containing 20 micrograms ethinyl estradiol and 250 micrograms levonorgestrel. Serum levels of the active ingredients and FSH, LH, estradiol 17-beta and progesterone, by N. O. Lunell, et al. ACTA OBSTETRICIA ET GYNECOLOGICA SCANDINAVICA [Suppl] 88:17-21, 1979.

Paediatric aspects of family planning, by B. N. Walia, et al. JOURNAL OF THE INDIAN MEDICAL ASSOCIATION 73 (1):21-22, July 1, 1979.

Pain during laparoscopic sterilization least likely with clips, three-country study finds [news]. FAMILY PLANNING PERSPECTIVES 12(1):56-57, January-February, 1980.

The paper 'pill': an acceptability study in Thai women, by S. Koetsawang, et al. JOURNAL OF THE MEDICAL ASSOCIATION OF THAILAND 62(11):605-610, November, 1979.

Paradoxical embolism associated with oral contraceptives: an underdiagnosed lesion?, by J. de Swiet. POSTGRADUATE MEDICAL JOURNAL 55(644):419-420, June, 1979.

Parasitism and contraceptives: a preliminary survey of the effect on haemoglobin levels, by E. A. Imohiosen, et al. NIGERIAN MEDICAL JOURNAL 9(4):487-491, April, 1979.

Parent, child, and the decision to abort: a critique of the Supreme Court's statutory proposal in Bellotti v. Baird (99 Sup Ct 3035). SOUTHERN CALIFORNIA LAW REVIEW 52: 1869-1915, September, 1979.

Parental notice statutes: permissible state regulation of a minor's abortion decision. FORDHAM LAW REVIEW 49:81-111, October, 1980.

Parental notification as a prerequisite for minors' access to contraceptives: a behavioral and legal analysis, by M. N. Finger. UNIVERSITY OF MICHIGAN JOURNAL OF LAW REFORM 13:196-223, Fall, 1979.

Parental origin of triploidy and D and G trisomy in spontaneous

130

abortions, by B. G. Brennan, et al. JOURNAL OF MEDICAL GENETICS 16(4):285-287, August, 1979.

Parents and teens agree: teenagers should get birth control information—from parents primarily [news]. FAMILY PLANNING PERSPECTIVES 11(3):200-201, May-June, 1979.

Parents' social status found to play key role in daughters' sexual activity, contraceptive use. FAMILY PLANNING PERSPECTIVES 12:208-209, July-August, 1980.

Parliament overrules churches on abortion, by T. Beeson. CHRISTIAN CENTURY 97:461-462, April 23, 1980.

Participation of community members in family planning programs, by E. S. Cruz Zapata. REVISTA DEL COLEGIO NACIONAL DE ENGERMERAS 24-25(101):7, September-February, 1978.

Pathogenesis of late spontaneous abortions of phenotypically normal fetuses, by T. V. Zhurkova, et al. VOPROSY OKHRANY MATERINSTVA I DETSTVA 24(12):48-50, December, 1979.

Pathologist links IUDs worn for years with infertility risk. MEDICAL WORLD NEWS 21:50-51, April 14, 1980.

The patient's choice in contraception, by R. A. Kinch. INTERNATIONAL JOURNAL OF GYNAECOLOGY AND OBSTETRICS 16(6):561-563, 1978-1979.

Patterns of discussion and decision-making amongst abortion patients, by J. R. Ashton. JOURNAL OF BIOSOCIAL SCIENCE 12:247-260, July, 1980.

Patterns of family building and contraceptive use of middle-class couples, by D. Woodward, et al. JOURNAL OF BIOSOCIAL SCIENCE 10(1):39-58, January, 1978.

Peeling off the labels [Canada's youth], by J. Timson. MACLEANS 93:40-41, March 31, 1980.

Peptide hormones tested as contraceptives. CHEMICAL AND ENGINEERING NEWS 58:18+, February 11, 1980.

Peptides could be contraceptives and fertility promoters. CHEMISTRY AND INDUSTRY p298, April 19, 1980.

Perspectives on fertility control, by M. Potts. INTERNATIONAL JOURNAL OF GYNAECOLOGY AND OBSTETRICS 16(6): 449-455, 1978-1979.

Pharmacokinetics and pharmacodynamics of sustained release systems, by K. Fotherby. JOURNAL OF STEROID BIOCHEMISTRY 11(1B):457-459, July, 1979.

Phenobarbitone interaction with oral contraceptive steroids in the rabbit and rat, by D. J. Back, et al. BRITISH JOURNAL OF PHARMACOLOGY 69(3):441-452, July, 1980.

A physician's lament, by R. White. JOURNAL OF THE AMERICAN COLLEGE HEALTH ASSOCIATION 28(3):191-192, December, 1979.

Phytoestrol in the hormone-free interval during administration of contraceptives, by M. Mettenleiter. FORTSCHRITTE DER MEDIZIN 98(13):498-500, April 3, 1980.

The pill, by C. Anthony. OUR SUNDAY VISITOR 68:6-7, April 6, 1980.

—, by H. P. Zahradnik. ZFA. ZEITSCHRIFT FUR ALLGEMEINMEDIZIN 55(26):1410-1412, September 20, 1979.

The pill and cardiovascular disease [letter], by V. Beral, et al. FAMILY PLANNING PERSPECTIVES 11(3):205-206, May-June, 1979.

The pill and thromboembolism. 1. Thrombogenesis and additional risk factors. A review of the literature, by C. Herzog, et al. THERAPIE DER GEGENWART 118(10):1550-1574, October, 1979.

—. 2. Pathogenesis and additional risk factors. Review of the lit-

132

erature, by C. Herzog, et al. THERAPIE DER GEGENWART 118(11):1722-1744, November, 1979.

Pill, IUD users run no increased risk of ectopics, malformation, miscarriage in planned pregnancies [news]. FAMILY PLANNING PERSPECTIVES 12(3):156-157, May-June, 1980.

The pill, mesenteric vein thrombosis and the short, short bowel syndrome, by A. A. Barros D'Sa. BRITISH JOURNAL OF CLINICAL PRACTICE 34(2):47-52, February, 1980.

Pill power for nurses?, by A. Shevas. NURSING MIRROR 150 (9):9, February 28, 1980.

Pill use in pregnancy not strongly linked to infants' heart defects. FAMILY PLANNING PERSPECTIVES 11(4):260, July-August, 1979.

Pituitary adenoma and contraceptives [letter], by M. Batrinos. FERTILITY AND STERILITY 32(6):711, December, 1979.

Pituitary and ovarian function in women receiving hormonal contraception, by B. L. Cohen, et al. CONTRACEPTION 20(5): 475-487, November, 1979.

Pituitary and ovarian responsiveness to a graded gonadotropin releasing factor stimulation test in women using a low-estrogen or a regular type of oral contraceptive, by W. N. Spellacy, et al. AMERICAN JOURNAL OF OBSTETRICS AND GYNECOLOGY 137(1):109-115, May 1, 1980.

Placental lactogen content in women with habitual abortion, by L. I. Tereshchenko. VOPROSY OKHRANY MATERINSTVA I DETSTVA February, 1980.

Planned parenthood charges its opponents with acts of violence. SECURITY SYSTEMS DIGEST 11(15):10, July 16, 1980.

Plasma alpha-feto protein levels and its relation to duration of oral contraceptive use, by S. Babu, et al. CONTRACEPTION 21(1):53-60, January, 1980.

Plasma hormone concentrations in abortion induction using sulprostone, a prostaglandin E2 derivative, by H. O. Hoppen, et al. ARCHIVES OF GYNECOLOGY 228(1-4):399-400, July 20, 1979.

Plasma levels of active ingredients after single and repeated administration of a new oral contraceptive containing 2 mg of cyproterone acetate and 50 micrograms of ethinyl estradiol (DIANE) to five young women, by B. Düsterberg, et al. ACTA OBSTETRICIA ET GYNECOLOGICA SCANDINAVICA [Suppl] 88:27-31, 1979.

Plasma levels of fifteen (S) 15-methyl-PGF 2 alpha-methyl ester following vaginal administration for induction of abortion in women, by A. Bhaskar, et al. CONTRACEPTION 20(5):519-531, November, 1979.

Plasma lipids and high density lipoproteins during oral contraception with different combinations of ethinyl estradiol and levonorgestrel, by U. Larsson-Cohn, et al. HORMONE AND METABOLIC RESEARCH 11(7):437-440, July, 1979.

Plasma lipids, lipoproteins, and blood pressure in female adolescents using oral contraceptives, by R. B. Wallace, et al. JOURNAL OF PEDIATRICS 95(6):1055-1059, December, 1979.

Plasma lipoprotein changes during oral contraception, by M. H. Briggs, et al. CURRENT MEDICAL RESEARCH AND OPINION 6(4):249-254, 1979.

Plasma progesterone levels in normal and pregnant Chinese women and effects of contraceptives on them, by Z. P. Gu, et al. CHINESE MEDICAL JOURNAL 93(8):523-527, August, 1980.

Plasma renin activity, reactivity, concentration and substrate following hypertension during pregnancy. Effect of oral contraceptive agents, by T. A. Kotchen, et al. HYPERTENSION 1 (4):355-361, July-August, 1979.

Plasma Xa inhibitory activities and plasma concentrations of norgestrel and ethinyloestradiol in women on oral contraceptive steroids, by D. J. Back, et al. BRITISH JOURNAL OF CLINICAL PHARMACOLOGY 8(5):505-506, November, 1979.

Plasmatic coagulation and thrombocyte function in abortion induction with prostaglandin E2 derivative sulprostone, by K. Schander, et al. ARCHIVES OF GYNECOLOGY 228(1-4): 635-637, July 20, 1979.

Platelet function, coagulation and fibrinolysis during termination of missed abortion and missed labor by PGF2 alpha and oxytocin, by R. C. Briel, et al. ACTA OBSTETRICIA ET GYNECOLOGICA SCANDINAVICA 58(4):361-364, 1979.

Political developments in the abortion area, by J. L. Robinson. CATHOLIC LAWYER 25:319-326, Autumn, 1980.

The political parties on abortion: Democrats ambivalent, by T. Blackburn. NATIONAL CATHOLIC REPORTER 16:11, October 17, 1980.

—:Republicans consistent, by S. Valentine. NATIONAL CATHOLIC REPORTER 16:11, October 17, 1980.

Politics of abortion, by S. Flynn, et al. WORKING WOMEN 5: 47-49, August, 1980.

The politics of abortion in the House of Representatives in 1976, by M. A. Vinovskis. MICHIGAN LAW REVIEW 77(7):1790-1827, August, 1979.

Politics of abortion stalls exemptions from OSHA visits. BUSINESS INSURANCE 13:28, November 12, 1979.

The politics of contraception: the view from Beijing, by C. Djerassi. NEW ENGLAND JOURNAL OF MEDICINE 303: 334-346, August 7, 1980.

The poor have rights. ECONOMIST 274:38, January 26, 1980.

Pope and the pill [Synod of Bishops meeting], by K. L. Woodward, et al. NEWSWEEK 96:85, October 13, 1980.

Pope asks 'self-mastery' in marital sex, by P. Hebblethwaite. NA-
TIONAL CATHOLIC REPORTER 16:20, November 16,
1979.

Pope critics debate Italy's abortion law, by P. Hebblethwaite.
NATIONAL CATHOLIC REPORTER 16:4, October 3, 1980.

Population and family planning, by H. Romero. REVISTA MED-
ICA DE CHILE 105(12):946-950, December, 1977.

Population and family planning programs: a compendium of data
through 1978, by D. L. Nortman, et al. POPULATION
COUNCIL 1980.

Population dip dangerous, economist warns. OUR SUNDAY
VISITOR 69:2, July 6, 1980.

The population problem and the Synod on the family, by a. Mc-
Cormack. CLERGY REVIEW 65:328-338, September, 1980.

Population processes in rural Yemen: temporary emigration,
breastfeeding, and contraception, by C. Myntti. STUDIES IN
FAMILY PLANNING 20(10):282-289, October, 1979.

A position paper on the relation between oral contraceptives and
blood coagulation, by H. Ludwig. CONTRACEPTION 20
(3):257-261, September, 1979.

Possible landmark abortion case faces Supreme Court, by F.
Franzonia. OUR SUNDAY VISITOR 69:3, November 2,
1980.

Possible relationship between lupus inhibitor and recurrent abortion in young women [letter], by B. G. Firkin, et al. LAN-
CET 2(8190):366, August 16, 1980.

Post-abortion attitudes and patterns of birth control, by M.
Abrams, et al. JOURNAL OF FAMILY PRACTICE 9(4):
593-599, October, 1979.

Postabortion depressive reactions in college women, by N. B.
Gould. JOURNAL OF THE AMERICAN COLLEGE

HEALTH ASSOCIATION 28(6):316-320, June, 1980.

Post-coital contraception. DRUG AND THERAPEUTICS BUL-
LETIN 18(2):5-7, January 18, 1980.

Postcoital contraception, by A. A. Yuzpe. INTERNATIONAL
JOURNAL OF GYNAECOLOGY AND OBSTETRICS 16(6):
497-501, 1978-1979.

Postcoital estrogens win backing of FDA advisors. MEDICAL
WORLD NEWS 21:26+, May 26, 1980.

Post-operative analgesia following laparoscopic sterilization, by I.
T. Leggat, et al. SCOTTISH MEDICAL JOURNAL 24(3):
220, July, 1979.

Postovulatory and post-implantation inhibition of fertility—general account, by M. Oettel, et al. ZENTRALBLATT FUR
GYNAEKOLOGIE 101(21):1381-1392, 1979.

Postpartum sterilization, by L. R. Green, et al. CLINICAL OB-
STETRICS AND GYNECOLOGY 23(2):647-659, June,
1980.

Post-bill amenorrhea. Analysis of the literature and a clinical
contribution, by E. Zanardi, et al. REVISTA ITALIANA DI
GINECOLOGIA 58(4):223-241, July-August, 1977.

Post-pill amenorrhea and drugs, by P. Grella. REVISTA ITALI-
ANA DI GINECOLOGIA 58(4):243-246, July-August, 1977.

Post-pill amenorrhea and prolactin, by A. Volpe, et al. RIVISTA
ITALIANA DI GINECOLOGIA 58(4):247-252, July-August,
1977.

Poststerilization pain: a comparison of band versus clip, by M. A.
Cognat, et al. JOURNAL OF REPRODUCTIVE MEDICINE
25(1):29-30, July, 1980.

The potential for an androgen male contraceptive, by G. R. Cunningham, et al. JOURNAL OF CLINICAL ENDOCRINOL-
OGY AND METABOLISM 49(4):520-526, October, 1979.

Precocious pregnancies: patterns of sexuality among white adolescent women in the rural south, by K. P. J. Fischer. DISSERTATION ABSTRACTS INTERNATIONAL 40(12): 6346-A, 1979.

Predicting the psychological consequences of abortion, by L. R. Shusterman. SOCIAL SCIENCE AND MEDICINE 13A(6): 683-689, November, 1979.

The prediction of adoption and continued practice of contraception among enrolees in family planning clinics: 1972, by Z. Zablan. PHILIPPINE SOCIOLOGICAL REVIEW 23(1-4): 29-54, January-October, 1975.

Preferences for sweet in relationship to use of oral contraceptives and pregnancy, by R. L. Dippel, et al. HORMONES AND BEHAVIOR 14(1):1-6, March, 1980.

Pregnancies associated with sperm concentrations below 10 million/ml in clinical studies of a potential male contraceptive method, monthly depot medroxyprogesterone acetate and testosterone esters, by A. Barfield, et al. CONTRACEPTION 20(2):121-127, August, 1979.

Pregnancy after laparoscopic sterilization, by F. D. Loffer, et al. OBSTETRICS AND GYNECOLOGY 55(5):643-648, May, 1980.

Pregnancy after oral contraception [news], by C. Colas. PRESSE MEDICALE 8(48):3986, December 10, 1979.

Pregnancy attributable to interaction between tetracycline and oral contraceptives, by J. F. Bacon, et al. BRITISH MEDICAL JOURNAL 280(6210):293, February 2, 1980.

Pregnancy complications following legally induced abortion, by E. B. Obel. ACTA OBSTETRICIA ET GYNECOLOGICA SCANDINAVICA 58(5):485-490, 1979.

Pregnancy complications following legally induced abortion: an analysis of the population with special reference to prematurity, by E. B. Obel. DANISH MEDICAL BULLETIN 26

(4):192-199, July, 1979.

Pregnancy following laparoscopic sterilization, by W. NEDERLANDS TIJDSCHRIFT VOOR GENEESKUNDE 124(19):727-729, May 10, 1980.

Pregnancy in IUD in situ—abortion from clinical-bacteriological viewpoint?, by G. E. Feichter, et al. ARCHIVES OF GYNE-COLOGY 228(1-4):396, July 20, 1979.

Pregnancy in a non-communicating, rudimentary uterine horn. A reason for failed therapeutic second trimester abortion, by R. Kirschner, et al. ACTA OBSTETRICIA ET GYNECOLOGI-CA SCANDINAVICA 58(5):499-501, 1979.

Pregnancy outcome after previous induced abortion, by M. Mandelin, et al. ANNALES CHIRURGIAE ET GYNAECOLO-GIAE 68(5-6):147-154, 1979.

Pregnant low-income teenagers: a social structural model of the determinants of abortion-seeking behavior, by R. Dworkin. YOUTH AND SOCIETY 11(3):295-309, March, 1980.

Premarital contraceptive usage among male and female adoles-cents, by J. P. Hornick. FAMILY COORDINATOR 28:181-190, April, 1979.

Premier in storm over tough new abortion law, by D. Reinhardt. SUNDAY TIMES p8, May 4, 1980.

Prenatal diagnosis, selective abortion, and the Abortion (Amend-ment) Bill, by K. M. Laurence. LANCET 1(8162):249-250, February 2, 1980.

Preoperative prostaglandin administration, for avoidance of dilatation-caused damages in induced abortion, by S. Heinzl, et al. ARCHIVES OF GYNECOLOGY 228(1-4):422-423, July 20, 1979.

Prescribing an oral contraceptive for the individual woman, by P. Chick. AUSTRALIAN FAMILY PHYSICIAN Suppl: 8-12, February, 1980.

Pressure politics revisited: the anti-abortion campaign [emphasis on Pennsylvania], by M. Margolis, et al. POLICY STUDIES JOURNAL 8:698-716, Spring, 1980.

Prevalence of acne [letter], by P. V. Harrison, et al. BRITISH MEDICAL JOURNAL 2(6188):495, August 25, 1979.

The prevalence of actinomycete-like organisms found in cervico-vaginal smears of 300 intrauterine device wearers, by M. Jones, et al. ACTA CYTOLOGICA 23(4):282-286, 1979.

Prevalence of premalignant lesions of the cervix uteri. Comparative study between a female population using contraceptives, by J. M. Arizaga Cruz, et al. GINECOLOGIA Y OBSTETRICIA DE MEXICO 46(273):37-44, July, 1979.

Prevention of recurrent menstrual psychosis by an oral contraceptive, by A. R. Felthous, et al. AMERICAN JOURNAL OF PSYCHIATRY 137(2):245-246, February, 1980.

Prevention of respiratory distress in premature infants through pernatal treatment with betamethasone, by L. Di Meglio, et al. MINERVA GINECOLOGICA 31(7-8):557-562, July-August, 1979.

Previous induced abortion and antenatal depression in primiparae: preliminary report of a survey of mental health in pregnancy, by R. Kumar, et al. PSYCHOLOGICAL MEDICINE 8(4):711-715, November, 1978.

Primary abdominal pregnancy associated with the intrauterine device (2 cases), by D. Muzsnai, et al. EUROPEAN JOURNAL OF OBSTETRICS, GYNECOLOGY AND REPRODUCTIVE BIOLOGY 10(4):275-278, 1980.

Primary liver cancer in a woman taking oral contraceptives [letter], by H. Slaoui, et al. NOUVELLE PRESSE MEDICALE 9(7):456, February 9, 1980.

The probability of side effects with ovral, norinyl 1/50 and norlestrin, by G. S. Berger, et al. CONTRACEPTION 20(5):447-453, November, 1979.

Problem pregnancy and abortion counseling with teenagers, by J. S. Chesler, et al. SOCIAL CASEWORK 61:173-179, March, 1980.

Problems arising from the interruption of pregnancy, by F. Zimmer. HAUTARZT 31(Suppl 4):31-35, 1980.

Problems of fertility in women with a history of induced abortion in the 1st pregnancy, by S. Lembrych, et al. GINEKOLOGIA POLSKA 50(8):669-673, August, 1979.

Problems of implementation and consequences of the 1975 provisional law to liberalize abortion in France, by J. H. Soutoul, et al. INTERNATIONAL JOURNAL OF GYNAECOLOGY AND OBSTETRICS 16(6):505-508, 1978-1979.

Problems posed by birth control in cardiac and hypertensive patients, by J. H. Soutoul, et al. ANNALES DE CARDIOLOGIE ET D'ANGEIOLOGIE 28(6):419-422, November, 1979.

Proceedings of Natural Family Planning Meeting. LINACRE 45: 327-422, November, 1978.

Procreative rights and the sterilization of the retarded: with special reference to Roman Catholic theory of human rights, by R. Sherlock. HARVARD THEOLOGICAL REVIEW 71:324-325, July-October, 1978.

Profile of family planning service personnel for barrier method acceptability study [Egypt], by M. T. Hassouna, et al. POPULATION STUDIES p24-39, January-March, 1980.

The progestational activity of different gestagens used for human contraception in the beagle bitch, by S. Beier, et al. CONTRACEPTION 20(6):533-548, December, 1979.

Progestational potency of oral contraceptives: a polemic, by R. A. Edgren. INTERNATIONAL JOURNAL OF FERTILITY 23(3):162-169, 1978.

Progesterone and human chorionic gonadotrophin in serum and pregnandiol in urine in threatened abortion, by J. B. Hertz,

et al. ACTA OBSTETRICIA ET GYNECOLOGICA SCANDI-
NAVICA 59(1):23-27, 1980.

Progestogens and cardiovascular reactions associated with oral
contraceptives and a comparison of the safety of 50- and 30-
microgram oestrogen preparations, by T. W. Meade, et al.
BRITISH MEDICAL JOURNAL 280(6224):1157-1161,
May 10, 1980.

Prognosis in threatened abortion evaluated by hormone assays
and ultrasound scanning, by P. S. Eriksen, et al. OBSTE-
TRICS AND GYNECOLOGY 55(4):435-438, April, 1980.

Prognostic significance of maternal serum beta1-glycoprotein determination using LC partigen plates in threatened abortion
in early pregnancy, by W. Eiermann, et al. ARCHIVES OF
GYNECOLOGY 228(1-4):231-232, July 20, 1979.

Prognostic value of pregnancy-specific serum beta glycoprotein
in threatened abortion, by N. Karg, et al. ORVOSI HETILAP
121(16):939-941, April 20, 1980.

Program of family planning in the United Kingdom, West Germany, Denmark and Sweden and its repercussions in Canada,
by E. S. Smith. BOLETIN DE LA OFICINA SANITARIA
PANAMERICAN 87(1):35-49, July, 1979.

A progressive rise in serum copper levels in women taking oral
contraceptives: a potential hazard?, by Y. Rubinfeld, et al.
FERTILITY AND STERILITY 32(5):599-601, November,
1979.

Pro-life means more than anti-abortion, by J. Garvey. US CATH-
OLIC 45:35-37, March, 1980.

The prolife movement and the new right, by G. Higgins. AMERI-
CA 143:107-110, September 13, 1980.

Pro-life: not a Catholic monopoly, by T. O'Reilly. LIGUORIAN
68:11-13, January, 1980.

Pro-life PAC eyes 1980 races. CONSERVATIVE DIGEST 6:12+,

January, 1980.

Pro-life ready to reap seeds sown since 1973, by F. Franzonia. OUR SUNDAY VISITOR 68:3, January 20, 1980.

Pro-life squabble follows Marx's leave of absence. NATIONAL CATHOLIC REPORTER 17:3+, December 5, 1980.

Pro-life violence. OUR SUNDAY VISITOR 67:2, January 14, 1979.

Pro-lifer's cross-country march may end in jail, by P. Cullen. OUR SUNDAY VISITOR 68:8, January 20, 1980.

Pro-lifers look to final victory, by B. Kenkelen. NATIONAL CATHOLIC REPORTER 16(2):1+, July 18, 1980.

Prolongation of normotest clotting times in rats on the pill, by M. C. Roncaglioni, et al. THROMBOSIS AND HAEMOSTA-SIS 43(1):73, February 29, 1980.

Prolonged amenorrhea and oral contraceptives, by G. Tolis, et al. FERTILITY AND STERILITY 32(3):265-268, September, 1979.

Prophylactic vasectomy, by A. Kambal. BRITISH JOURNAL OF UROLOGY 51(4):310-311, 1979.

Proposition of a method to evaluate the prognosis of threatening premature labor and the possibility of success in the treatment. Tocolytic index, by M. Pommier, et al. GINECOLO-GIA Y OBSTETRICIA DE MEXICO 46(275):173-181, September, 1979.

A prospective, randomized study of oral contraceptives: the effect of study design on reported rates of symptoms, by P. P. Talway, et al. CONTRACEPTION 20(4):329-337, October, 1979.

Prospective studies of the gonadotropin responses to graded injections of gonadotopin-releasing factor in women using a low-estrogen type oral contraceptive for three months, by W.

143

N. Spellacy, et al. FERTILITY AND STERILITY 32(6):661-663, December, 1979.

A prospective study of the effects of the progestagen content of oral contraceptives on measures of affect, automatization, and perceptual restructuring ability, by A. Worsley. PSYCHOPHARMACOLOGY 67(3):289-296, 1980.

Prospective study of oral contraceptives effects on platelets and blood clotting: a preliminary report, by R. Abbate, et al. THROMBOSIS AND HAEMOSTASIS 42(1):393, 1979.

Prospective study of the Social Medical Service of the University Gynecological Hospital Basel on induced abortion, by M. Mall-Haefeli, et al. ARCHIVES OF GYNECOLOGY 228(1-4):389-391, July 20, 1979.

A prospective study of spontaneous fetal losses after induced a-bortions, by S. Harlap, et al. NEW ENGLAND JOURNAL OF MEDICINE 301(13):677-681, September 27, 1979.

Prospects for improved contraception, by L. Atkinson, et al. FAMILY PLANNING PERSPECTIVES 12:173-175+, July-August, 1980.

Prostaglandin as an abortifacient agent, by M. Bygdeman. LAKARTIDNINGEN 77(7):549-551, February 13, 1980.

Prostaglandin biosynthesis and catabolism in fetal and neonatal tissues, by R. Skidgel. 40(07):3117-B, 1979.

Prostaglandin E2 for abortion and labor induction in pregnancies with fetal death, by J. H. Duenhoelter. ARCHIVES OF GYNECOLOGY 228(1-4):407-408, July 20, 1979.

Prostaglandin E2 vaginal suppositories in pregnancy with an a-nencephalic fetus, by F. H. Boehm, et al. OBSTETRICS AND GYNECOLOGY 55(6):758-760, June, 1980.

Prostaglandin F2 alpha for interrupting pregnancy, managing intrauterine death and molar pregnancy and inducing labor, by H. de Gezelle, et al. INTERNATIONAL JOURNAL OF

GYNAECOLOGY AND OBSTETRICS 17(4):362-367, January-February, 1980.

Prostaglandin F2 alpha for oestrus synchronisation or abortion in Polwarth ewes, by R. N. Reid, et al. AUSTRALIAN VETERINARY JOURNAL 56(1):22-24, January, 1980.

Prostaglandins in gynecology and obstetrics. Prostaglandins offer new methods for abortion, anticonception and regulating fertility, by M. Bygdeman. NORDISK MEDICIN 94(8-9): 217-219, September, 1979.

Psychiatric aspects in rejection of family planning, by R. Taufa. PAPAU NEW GUINEA MEDICAL JOURNAL 21(3):264-266, September, 1978.

Psychiatric aspects of oral contraceptive use, by D. Sheehan, et al. PSYCHIATRIC ANNALS 6(10):500-508, October, 1976.

Psychiatric aspects of sterilization: a prospective survey, by A. H. Smith. BRITISH JOURNAL OF PSYCHIATRY 135:304-309, October, 1979.

Psychiatric problems presented at abortion, by C. Protheroe. CONFRONTATION PSYCHIATRIQUES (16):125-148, 1978.

The psychoanalytic approach to contraception today, by M. Bydlowski, et al. JOURNAL DE GYNECOLOGIE, OBSTETRIQUE ET BIOLOGIE DE LA REPRODUCTION 8(6): 527-531, 1979.

Psychological and situation-specific correlates of contraceptive behavior among university women, by W. A. Fisher, et al. JOURNAL OF SEX RESEARCH 15(1):38-55, February, 1979.

Psychological factors in IUD case: a review, by A. E. Reading, et al. JOURNAL OF BIOSOCIAL SCIENCE 9(3):317-323, July, 1977.

Psychological factors involved in request for elective abortion, by

M. Blumenfield. JOURNAL OF CLINICAL PSYCHIATRY 39(1):17-25, January, 1978.

Psychological resistance of women to the principal feminine contraception methods: toward a clinical calssification, by M. C. Wauty-Dancot, et al. ACTA PSYCHIATRICA BELGICA 75 (1):49-73, January, 1975.

Psychological sequelae of the termination of pregnancy and their prevention, by P. A. Gloor. REVUE MEDICALE DE LA SUISSE ROMANDE 99(12):901-904, December, 1979.

Psychosocial aspects of abortion, by J. A. Nunez-Lopez. BOLE-TIN-ASOCIACION MEDICA DE PUERTO RICO 71(5):178-181, May, 1979.

Public health need for abortion statistics, by J. Smith. PUBLIC HEALTH REPORTS 43(2):194-197, March-April, 1978.

Public support for pro-choice abortion policies in the nation and states: changes and stability after the Roe and Doe decisions, by E. M. Uslaner, et al. MICHIGAN LAW REVIEW 77(7): 1772-1789, August, 1979.

Puerperal laparoscopic sterilization, by C. F. McDonnell, Jr. A-MERICAN JOURNAL OF OBSTETRICS AND GYNECOL-OGY 137(8):910-913, August 15, 1980.

Puerto Rico: recent trends in fertility and sterilization, by H. B. Presser. FAMILY PLANNING PERSPECTIVES 12(2):102-106, March-April, 1980.

The purchase of contraceptives by college students, by D. Kallen, et al. FAMILY RELATIONS 29(3):358-363, July, 1980.

Putting a better cap on the cervix [news], by G. McBride. JAMA 243(16):1617-1618, April 25, 1980.

Qualitative study of prostaglandins in pregnant uterine tissues, effects of estradiol-17 beta and betamethasone, by F. E. Lima, et al. PROSTAGLADINS AND MEDICINE 3(6):387-393, December, 1979.

Quality of life and factors affecting the response to hysterectomy, by N. C. Roeske. JOURNAL OF FAMILY PRACTICE 7 (3):483-488, September, 1978.

Quality of life: from Toe to Quinlan and beyond, by J. Cincotta. CATHOLIC LAWYER 25:13-31, Winter, 1979.

Quantitative aspects of marriage, fertility and family limitation in nineteenth century America: another application of the Coale specifications, by W. C. Sanderson. DEMOGRAPHY 16:339-358, August, 1979.

Questions of bio-ethics in the termination of pregnancy in the second and third trimester of pregnancy for eugenic indications, by F. K. Beller, et al. GEBURTSHILFE UND FRAUENHEILKUNDE 40(2):142-144, February, 1980.

Quick cut straight to the heart (vasectomy), by S. Zwarun. MACLEAN'S 93:58-60, October, 20, 1980.

Quinacrine hydrochloride. Review and mode of action of an antimalarial, used as an occlusive agent for transvaginal human sterilization, by E. Patek. ACTA OBSTETRICIA ET GYNECOLOGICA SCANDINAVICA 58(6):561-564, 1979.

Race, motherhood, and abortion, by C. Clark. DISSERTATION ABSTRACTS INTERNATIONAL 40(10):5606-A, 1979.

Racism and the availability of family planning services in the United States, by G. C. Wright, Jr. SOCIAL FORCES 56: 1087-1098, June, 1978.

A randomized double blind study of two oral contraceptives, by H. Sanhueza, et al. CONTRACEPTION 20(1):29-48, July, 1979.

Rare position of transcervically penetrated IUP DANA-Super in intact gravidity, by H. H. Fröhlich. ZENTRALBLATT FUR GYNAEKOLOGIE 101(18):1200-1202, 1979.

Rate of Rh immunization after induced abortion, by I. Simonovits, et al. VOX SANGUINIS 38(3):161-164, 1980.

Re-acutized latent toxoplasmosis as a demonstrated cause of current abortion and probable cause of preceding abortive pregnancies and fetal death. Study of a case, by S. Deragna, et al. MINERVA GINECOLOGIA 32(1-2):43-47, January-February, 1980.

A reappraisal of abortion as a method of fertility control, by J. Barnes. INTERNATIONAL JOURNAL OF GYNAECOLOGY AND OBSTETRICS 16(6):502-504, 1978-1979.

Reason for nonuse of contraception by sexually active women aged 15-19, by M. Zelnik, et al. FAMILY PLANNING PERSPECTIVES 11:289-296, September-October, 1979.

Rebirth of the abortion furore [right to life groups in Canada], by A. Grescoe. MACLEANS 93:46-47, June 2, 1980.

Recent changes in the emotional reactions of therapeutic abortion applicants, by S. Meikle, et al. CANADIAN PSYCHIATRIC ASSOCIATION JOURNAL 22(2):67-70, March, 1977.

A recent experiment the author conducted on US Senators revealed a wide variety of strategies used to answer constituent letters from single-issue voters; in the case of the experiment, the Senators were asked to state their position on abortions, by M. Feldstein. WASHINGTON MONTHLY 11(8):41-48, 1979.

Recent trends in fertility, abortion and contraception in Cuba, by P. E. Hollerbach. FAMILY PLANNING PERSPECTIVES 6:97-106, September, 1980.

Reclaiming reproductive control: a feminist approach to fertility consciousness, by S. Bell, et al. SCIENCE FOR THE PEOPLE 12:6-9+, January-February, 1980.

Recommendations of the swiss family planning association regarding the indications for oral contraceptives. PRAXIS 68 (41):1330-1332, October 9, 1979.

Recovery for wrongful conception: who gets the benefit—the parents or the public?. NEW ENGLAND LAW REVIEW 14:

784-811, Spring, 1979.

Recurrent abortions associated with Robertsonian translocation (22/22) in a male carrier, by P. Temperani, et al. CLINICAL GENETICS 17(1):90, 1980.

Recurrent jaundice in the course of natural and iatrogenic estrogen metabolism disorders, by G. Mach, et al. POLSKI TYGODNIK LEKARSKI 34(49):1923-1924, December 3, 1979.

Recurrent miscarriage in a patient with chromosomal translocation—karyotype 46,XX,t(10;11) (q21;q23), by K. Boczkowski, et al. GINEKOLOGIA POLSKA 50(7):627-630, July, 1979.

Reduction of maternal mortality due to post-abortion septic shock, by medical and surgical treatment, by S. Iturriaga Ruiz, et al. REVISTA CHILENA DE OBSTETRICIA Y GINECOLOGIA 43(6):330-343, 1978.

Regulating abortion services [letter], by M. B. Kapp. NEW ENGLAND JOURNAL OF MEDICINE 302(6):350, February 7, 1980.

—, by V. P. Riggs. NEW ENGLAND JOURNAL OF MEDICINE 302(6):350, February 7, 1980.

Regulation of abortion services—for better or worse?, by W. Cates, Jr., et al. NEW ENGLAND JOURNAL OF MEDICINE 301(13):720-723, September 27, 1979.

Regulation of epididymal function and sperm maturation—endocrine approach to fertility control in male, by B. S. Setty. ENDOKRINOLOGIE 74(1):100-117, April, 1979.

Regulation of fecundity. Knowledge, attitude and opinions of French-speaking female Belgian university students, by G. Rucquoy, et al. ACTA PSYCHIATRICA BELGICA 78(6): 869-1166, November-December, 1978.

Regulations on the interruption of pregnancy in current German criminal law, by P. Bockelmann. HAUTARZT 31(Suppl 4):

41-45, 1980.

Regressive ischemia of the small intestine and contraceptives, by C. L'Hermine, et al. LILLE MEDICAL 24(9):693-696, November, 1979.

Relation between hepatic lesions and use of oral contraceptives, by M. J. Wexler. CANADIAN JOURNAL OF SURGERY 23 (3):216-217, May, 1980.

Relationship between abortion and child abuse, by P. Ney. CANADIAN JOURNAL OF PSYCHIATRY 24(7):610-620, November, 1979.

Relationship of estrogens and oral contraceptives to endometrial cnacer in animals and women, by V. A. Drill. JOURNAL OF REPRODUCTIVE MEDICINE 24(1):5-13, January, 1980.

The relationship of knowledge to perceived benefits and risks of oral contraceptives among college women, by B. T. Lively. DISSERTATION ABSTRACTS INTERNATIONAL 40(12): 6159-A, 1979.

Relative sensitivity of postpartum gestational diabetic women to oral contraceptive agents and other metabolic stress, by R. K. Kalkhoff. DIABETES CARE 3(3):421-424, May-June, 1980.

The relative value of two concentrations of hypertonic saline for midtrimester abortion, by A. K. Ghosh, et al. INTERNATIONAL JOURNAL OF GYNAECOLOGY AND OBSTETRICS 17(4):368-371, January-February, 1980.

Renal artery thrombosis: systemic contraceptive-induced or spontaneous? [letter], by J. Montoliu. ANNALS OF INTERNAL MEDICINE 91(4):657, October, 1979.

Repeat abortion and self-reported contraceptive behavior [letter], by R. D. Gillette. AMERICAN JOURNAL OF PUBLIC HEALTH 70(6):637, June, 1980.

Repeat abortions: blaming the victims, by B. Howe, et al. AMERICAN JOURNAL OF PUBLIC HEALTH 69:1242-1246,

December, 1979.

Repeat induced abortion: single, married and divorced women, by B. E. Aguirre. JOURNAL OF BIOSOCIAL SCIENCE 12: 275-286, July, 1980.

Repeated abortions and histocompatibility antigens. Can HLA antigen restricted gene dose effects influence the feto-maternal relationship?, by L. Komlos, et al. MEDICAL HYPOTHESES 5(8):901-908, August, 1979.

Reply to paper by Dr. Edgren on 'progestational potency of oral contraceptives: a polemic', by R. P. Dickey. INTERNATIONAL JOURNAL OF FERTILITY 23(3):170-174, 1978.

Report of National Conference on Abortion. Abortion debaters urged to cease shouting match and to listen and learn, by R. J. Stephens. HOSPITAL PROGRESS 60(11):18-19, November, 1979.

Reproductive performance of women following end-to-end anastomosis of fallopian tubes after previous sterilization, by J. J. Marik. FERTILITY AND STERILITY 32(4):497, 1979.

Research note: study of women seeking abortion, by K. Sidenius. SOCIAL SCIENCE AND MEDICINE 12(5):423-424, 1978.

Research on birth control technology, by A. Kessler. INTERDISCIPLINARY SCIENCE REVIEWS 3(3):196-201, 1978.

Resources from the community; planned parenthood of Toronto. ORBIT 11(2):27, April, 1980.

Restatement on tubal ligation confuses policy with normative ethics, by R. McCormick. HOSPITAL PROGRESS 61:40, September, 1980.

Restoration of ovarian function byprogesterone administration following copper intrauterine device insertion in rats, by S. K. Nayyar. IRCS MEDICAL SCIENCE LIBRARY 7(4):175, 1979.

Restoration of ovarian function following prostaglandin F-2L administration in copper intrauterine device-bearing rats, by S. K. Nayyar, et al. IRCS MEDICAL SCIENCE LIBRARY 7(6):305, 1979.

Restrictive regulations for Medicaid, by C. D. Davis. TEXAS HOSPITALS 36(2):57, July, 1980.

Results of a structurized discussion within the framework of a-bortion with particular reference to problems of pregnancy, conflict and related topics, by W. Woynar, et al. OEFFENT-LICHE GESUNDHEITSWESEN 42(2):51-54, February, 1980.

Results of treatment of threatened abortion with synthetic ACTH, by R. Klimek, et al. GINEKOLOGIA POLSKA Suppl:254-256, 1979.

Retinal migraine and the pill, by E. Byrne. MEDICAL JOURNAL OF AUSTRALIA 2(12):659-660, December 15, 1979.

A retrospective clinical study of a vaginal contraceptive supposi-tory, by J. Squire, et al. JOURNAL OF REPRODUCTIVE MEDICINE 22(6):319-323, 1979.

Return of ovulation after the cessation of depot-medroxy proges-terone acetate treatment in Thai women, by B. N. Saxena, et al. JOURNAL OF THE MEDICAL ASSOCIATION OF THAILAND 63(2):66-69, February, 1980.

Reversible sterilization; socio-ethical considerations, by G. Largey. SOCIAL BIOLOGY 25:143-144, Summer, 1978.

A review: adverse effects of oral contraceptives, by S. H. Tsung, et al. JOURNAL OF THE INDIANA STATE MEDICAL AS-SOCIATION 72(8):578-580, August, 1979.

Review of abortions at Kenyatta National Hospital, Nairobi, by V. P. Aggarwal, et al. EAST AFRICAN MEDICAL JOUR-NAL 57(2):138-143, February, 1980.

Riboflavin nutritional status and absorption in oral contraceptive users and nonusers, by P. J. Carrigan, et al. AMERICAN JOURNAL OF CLINICAL NUTRITION 32(10):2047-2051, October, 1979.

Riboflavin nutriture of oral contraceptive users, by S. C. Vir, et al. INTERNATIONAL JOURNAL FOR VITAMIN AND NUTRITION RESEARCH 49(3):286-290, 1979.

The right takes aim. ECONOMIST 277:27+, October 4, 1980.

Right to abortion: the courts versus the legislatures, by A. H. Bernstein. HOSPITALS 54(1):30-34, January 1, 1980.

Right-to-life head finds facts of life hard to live with, by R. McClory. NATIONAL CATHOLIC REPORTER 16:1+, June 20, 1980.

Right to life homily, by H. Ratner. LINACRE 47:110-113, May, 1980.

Right to life/women's death, by R. Katz, et al. OFF OUR BACKS 10:11+, June, 1980.

Right-to-lifers fear being pushed to wall by courts, by R. Shaw. OUR SUNDAY VISITOR 68:7, February 17, 1980.

Right-to-lifers waging tough battle for Senate seats, by F. Franzonia. OUR SUNDAY VISITOR 69:6, October 19, 1980.

The right to private and public dissent from specific pronouncements of the ordinary magisterium, by R. M. Gula. EGLISE ET THEOLOGIE 9:319-343, May, 1978.

Rights of religion. COMMONWEAL 107:100, February 29, 1980.

Ring-like chromosome 18 and osteogenesis imperfecta in a family in which spontaneous abortions appear, by S. Markovic, et al. SRPSKI ARHIV ZA DELOKUPNO LEKARSTVO 107(3): 245-252, March, 1979.

Risk, fertility, and family planning in a Bangladesh village, by M. Cain. STUDIES IN FAMILY PLANNING 11:219, June,

1980.

Risk of spontaneous abortion following legally induced abortion, by E. B. Obel. ACTA OBSTETRICIA ET GYNECOLOGICA SCANDINAVICA 59(2):131-135, 1980.

Risking jail for a backstreet job, by J. Flint. NEW STATESMAN 98:763, November 16, 1979.

The role of age, smoking habits, and oral contraceptives in the frequency of myocardial infarction in young women, by J. W. Goldzieher. REPRODUCTION 4(1):21-27, January-March, 1980.

Role of catecholamines in the central and peripheral actions of steroidal contraceptives, by M. L. Gupta, et al. ARCHIVES INTERNATIONALES DE PHARMACODYNAMIE ET DE THERAPIE 243(2):284-291, February, 1980.

The role of community health nurses in family health education at home in a southern province of Iran, by M. K. Jinadu. INTERNATIONAL JOURNAL OF NURSING STUDIES 17 (1):47-53, 1980.

Role of the family planning counselor in French Switzerland, by V. Champod, et al. REVUE MEDICALE DE LA SUISSE ROMANDE 99(12):931-934, December, 1979.

The role of hormones in the etiology of breast and endometrial cancer, by R. D. Gambrell. ACTA OBSTETRICIA ET GYNECOLOGICA SCANDINAVICA [Suppl] 88:73-81, 1979.

The role of a long-acting vaginal suppository of 15-ME-PGF2 alpha in first and second trimester abortion, by N. H. Lauersen, et al. ADVANCES IN PROSTAGLANDIN AND THROMBOXANE RESEARCH 8:1435-1441, 1980.

The role of oral contraceptives in cervical infection with sexually transmitted diseases, by J. Gardner. DISSERTATION ABSTRACTS INTERNATIONAL 40(12):5619-B, 1980.

Role of physician for promoting the involvement of other health

154

personnel and auxiliaries in implementing programmes of fertility regulation and family, by A. Chandy. NURSING JOURNAL OF INDIA 70(10):269-271, October, 1979.

Role of the prenatal consultation in controlling spontaneous a-bortions and the results of the measures taken, by I. Vasileva. AKUSHERSTVO I GINEKOLOGIIA 19(3):209-214, 1980.

Role of prostagladins in endotoxic abortion and intrauterine fetal death, by R. C. Skarnes, et al. TOXICON 17(Suppl 1):173, 1979.

The role of psycho-social factors in intrauterine device continuation, by A. Reading. SOCIAL SCIENCE AND MEDICINE 13 (6):631-640, 1979.

The role of traditional birth attendants in family planning programs in Southeast Asia, by J. Y. Peng. INTERNATIONAL JOURNAL OF GYNAECOLOGY AND OBSTETRICS 17 (2):108-113, September-October, 1979-1980.

Roles for non-physicians in fertility regulation: an international overview of legal obstacles and solutions, by J. M. Paxman. AMERICAN JOURNAL OF PUBLIC HEALTH 70(1):31-39, January, 1980.

Romania raises birthrate by restricting abortion, birth control access [news]. FAMILY PLANNING PERSPECTIVES 11 (5):317-318, October, 1979.

Rubella and oral contraceptives [letter], by H. P. Dunn. NEW ZEALAND MEDICAL JOURNAL 91(654):154, February 27, 1980.

Rubella vaccination and unnecessary abortions [letter], by J. W. Peters, et al. BRITISH MEDICAL JOURNAL 2(6204):1588-1589, December 15, 1979.

Ruby v. Massey (452 F Supp 361): sterilization of the mentally retarded. CAPITOL UNIVERSITY LAW REVIEW 9:191-206, 1979.

Rupture of the uterus during prostaglandin-induced abortion [letter], by G. J. Jarvis, et al. BRITISH MEDICAL JOURNAL 2(6191):671, September 15, 1979.

STS 557, a new orally active progestin with antiprogestational and contragestational properties in rabbits, by M. Oettel, et al. CONTRACEPTION 21(1):61-69, January, 1980.

Safety of legal abortion [letter], by W. Cates, Jr., et al. LANCET 2(8161):198-199, January 26, 1980.

Safety of modern contraceptive technology. Current status, by S. K. Khoo. AUSTRALIAN FAMILY PHYSICIAN Suppl:3-7, February, 1980.

Safety of post-abortion sterilization [letter], by G. Chamberlain. LANCET 2(8150):1020, November 10, 1979.

Safety of postabortion sterilization compared with interval sterilization. A controlled study, by M. C. Cheng, et al. LANCET 2(8144):682-685, September 29, 1979.

Saline-instillation abortion with laminaria and megadose oxytocin, by M. Hachamovitch, et al. AMERICAN JOURNAL OF OBSTETRICS AND GYNECOLOGY 135(3):327-330, October 1, 1979.

The scandle that grew up to respectability, by P. Chorlton. GUARDIAN (8):8, July, 1980.

Scarlet letter [pastoral letter published by H. Medeiros], by E. J. Dionne, Jr. COMMONWEAL 107:554-555, October 10,1980.

School nurse helps develop new program, by R. Laidlaw. ARIZONA NURSE 33(3):11, May-June, 1980.

Scraping out the pregnant uterus using suction curette compared to treatment with stump curette, by K. W. Schweppe, et al. ARCHIVES OF GYNECOLOGY 228(1-4):386-387, July 20, 1979.

Screening for gonorrhoea, trichomoniasis and candidosis in women presenting for termination of pregnancy, by H. S. Singha, et al. BRITISH JOURNAL OF CLINICAL PRACTICE 33(6):163-164, June, 1979.

The second national family planning and population survey in Singapore 1977, by A. J. Chen, et al. NURSING JOURNAL OF SINGAPORE 19(2):67-71, December, 1979.

Second pregnancies to premaritally pregnant teenagers, 1976 and 1971, by M. Aelnik. FAMILY PLANNING PERSPECTIVES 12(2):69-76, March-April, 1980.

Second-trimester abortion deaths—a clarification [letter], by J. M. Benditt. FAMILY PLANNING PERSPECTIVES 12(1): 5+, January-February, 1980.

Second trimester abortion in the United States, by J. Benditt. FAMILY PLANNING PERSPECTIVES 11:358-362, November-December, 1979.

Second trimester abortion with prostaglandin F2 alpha, by T. K. Chatterjee, et al. INTERNATIONAL JOURNAL OF GYNAECOLOGY AND OBSTETRICS 17(4):357-361, January-February, 1980.

Second-trimester D & E [letter], by L. Iffy, et al. OBSTETRICS AND GYNECOLOGY 55(6):766-767, June, 1980.

Secondary effects of oral contraceptives, by E. Yeun, et al. SOUTH AFRICAN JOURNAL OF SCIENCE 75(7):319, 1979.

Selecting the optimum method of contraception for each patient, by J. Gavin. INTERNATIONAL JOURNAL OF GYNAECOLOGY AND OBSTETRICS 16(6):542-546, 1978-1979.

Self-ownership, abortion and infanticide, by E. F. Paul, et al. JOURNAL OF MEDICAL ETHICS 5(3):133-138, September, 1979.

Semen analysis & hormonal levels in bonnet macaques administered Embelia ribes berries, an indigenous plant having con-

traceptive activity, by T. V. Purandare, et al. INDIAN JOUR-
NAL OF EXPERIMENTAL BIOLOGY 17(9):935-936, September, 1979.

Septic abortion. Complications and therapeutic considerations,
by E. Canas, et al. MEDICINA CLINICA 74(2):43-47, January 25, 1980.

The sequelae of female sterilization in one general practice, by D.
M. Curtis. JOURNAL OF THE ROYAL COLLEGE OF GEN-
ERAL PRACTITIONERS 29(203):366-369, June, 1979.

Sequence of fibrinogen proteolysis and platelet release after intrauterine infusion of hypertonic saline, by H. L. Nossel, et
al. JOURNAL OF CLINICAL INVESTIGATION 64(5):
1371-1378, November, 1979.

Sequential analysis of spontaneous abortion [letter], by W. H.
James. FERTILITY AND STERILITY 32(3):350-351, September, 1979.

Seropositivity to toxoplasma in 3,455 women. Its role in abortion and evaluation of some probable risk factors, by C.
Amici, et al. ANNALI SCLAVO 21(3):264-271, May-June,
1979.

Serum bile acids in women taking combination contraceptives,
by U. M. Donde, et al. CONTRACEPTION 20(6):479-583,
December, 1979.

Serum copper and zinc in hormonal contraceptive users, by K.
Prema, et al. FERTILITY AND STERILITY 33(3):267-271,
March, 1980.

Serum levels of FSH, LH, estradiol-17 beta and progesterone following the administration of a combined oral contraceptive
containing 20 micrograms ethinylestradiol, by K. Carlström,
et al. GYNECOLOGIC AND OBSTETRIC INVESTIGATION
9(6):304-311, 1978.

Serum vitamin A and retinol-binding protein in malnourished women treated with oral contraceptives: effects of estrogen dose

and duration of treatment, by M. Mohan Ram, et al. AMERI-
CAN JOURNAL OF OBSTETRICS AND GYNECOLOGY
135(4):470-472, October 15, 1979.

Service availability and the unmet need for contraceptive and
sterilization services in Sao Paulo State, Brazil. INTERNA-
TIONAL FAMILY PLANNING PERSPECTIVES 6:10-19,
March, 1980.

Service statistics: aid to more effective FP program management,
by H. Elkins, et al. POPULATION REPORTS (17):321-337+,
November, 1977.

Seth Low Junior College of Columbia University: a case study on
an abortive experiment, by B. Carron. DISSERTATION AB-
STRACTS INTERNATIONAL 40(09):4072-B, 1979.

Sex education and contraceptive practice amongst abortion patients, by J. R. Ashton. JOURNAL OF BIOSOCIAL SCI-
ENCE 12(2):211-217, April, 1980.

Sex, sin, and abortion, by J. Lifrieri. HERESIES 9:68-69, 1980.

Sexual activity, contraceptive use and pregnancy among metro-
politan area teenagers—1971-1979, by M. Zelnik, et al. FAM-
ILY PLANNING PERSPECTIVES 12:230-237, September-
October, 1980.

Sexual behaviour and contraceptive practice of undergraduates
at Oxford University, by P. Anderson, et al. JOURNAL OF
BIOSOCIAL SCIENCE 10(3):277-286, July, 1978.

Sexual experience and family planning among freshmen, by K.
Starke. AERZTLICHE JUGENDKUNDE 70(3):210-217,
June, 1979.

Sexual experience and responses to a birth control film, by E.
S. Herold, et al. JOURNAL OF SCHOOL HEALTH 50(2):
66-73, February, 1980.

Sexual knowledge and attitudes of adolescents: relationship to
contraceptive use, by C. C. Nadelson, et al. OBSTETRICS

AND GYNECOLOGY 55(3):340-345, March, 1980.

Sexual misunderstanding: the true cause of the Magisterium's ban on contraception, by F. Price. CLERGY REVIEW 65:157-163, May, 1980.

The short term effects of psychological preparation for surgery, by A. E. Reading. SOCIAL SCIENCE AND MEDICINE 13A (6):641-654, November, 1979.

Side effects of oral contraceptives, by K. Dawson. NURSE PRACTITIONER 4(6):53-55+, November-December, 1979.

Side effects of oral contraceptives from a dermatological viewpoint, by S. Marghescu. THERAPIE DER GEGENWART 118 (8):1230-1243, August 17, 1979.

Significance of preoperative diagnosis in induced abortion, by H. Wilken, et al. ARCHIVES OF GYNECOLOGY 228(1-4):379-381, July 20, 1979.

Significance of T mycoplasma and actinomycetales in intrauterine device and nonintrauterine device wearing women, by C. D. Graben, et al. ANNALS OF CLINICAL AND LABORATORY SCIENCE 9(5):434, 1979.

A significant association between spontaneous abortion and tubal, ectopic pregnancy, by L. H. Honore. FERTILITY AND STERILITY 32(4):401-402, October, 1979.

Signing away their birth rights: women are often given little choice but to be sterilised, by M. Bailey, et al. NEW STATESMAN p5, August 29, 1980.

Silymarin in pregnancy and during hormonal contraceptive treatment. Blood chemistry and ultrastructural findings in the experimental model, by G. Martines, et al. ARCHIVIO PER LE SCIENZE MEDICHE 136(3):443-454, July-September, 1979.

The single child family—China's prospects for the 1980's: sexual restraint, birth control or both, by S. E. Fraser. JOURNAL

OF FAMILY WELFARE 26:3-12, March, 1980.

Single-issue voting: interview of C. Anthony, by D. O'Brien. OUR SUNDAY VISITOR 69:4-5, September 7, 1980.

Sister-chromatid exchanges in oral contraceptive users, by P. B. Murthy, et al. MUTATION RESEARCH 68(2):149-152, October, 1979.

Situational, attitudinal and normative determinants of coital, contraceptive and conceptive behavioral intentions: an integration of social exchange theory and the fishbein model, by R. Venjohn. DISSERTATION ABSTRACTS INTERNATIONAL 40(09):4574-B, 1979.

Six in ten U.S. Catholic hospitals provide family planning: one in five offers medical sterilization [news]. FAMILY PLANNING PERSPECTIVES 11(5):308-309, October, 1979.

Six score and then..., by J. Robertson. OBSERVER p46, February 10, 1980.

Skin and genital diseases of the mother as indications for induced abortion, by G. W. Korting. HAUTARZT 31(Suppl 4):9-12, 1980.

A small but significant pro-life victory, by R. McMinn. OUR SUNDAY VISITOR 68:5, December 9, 1979.

Smoking, age and the pill, by J. McEwan. INTERNATIONAL JOURNAL OF GYNAECOLOGY AND OBSTETRICS 16 (6):529-534, 1978-1979.

Social and individual responsibility in premature termination of pregnancy, by J. Rothe. MEDIZIN UND GESELLSCHAFT (3):90-96, 1978.

Social and psychological correlates of pregnancy resulution among adolescent women: a review, by L. Olson. AMERICAN JOURNAL OF ORTHOPSYCHIATRY 50(3):432-445, July, 1980.

Social characteristics of diaphragm users in a family planning clinic, by J. McEwan. JOURNAL OF BIOSOCIAL SCIENCE 10(2):159-167, April, 1978.

Social marketing: does it work?, by D. L. Altman, et al. POPULATION REPORTS (21):393-434, January, 1980.

Social security and public welfare—federal assistance and state cooperation, statutes, and regulations in general—statute disallowing payment of Medicaid funds for therapeutic abortions held invalid. NORTH DAKOTA LAW REVIEW 56:289-299, 1980.

Social workers and family planning [developing countries], by A. H. Reda. POPULATION STUDIES p1-13, April-June, 1979.

Sociodemographic and psychological aspects of contraceptive practice. SOINS 25(8):15-18, April 20, 1980.

Socio-demographic characteristics of early and late adopters of family planning, by P. Kumar. ASIAN JOURNAL OF PSYCHOLOGY AND EDUCATION 3(3):12-15, November, 1978.

Socio-personal variables associated with attitudes of Tharus toward birth control, by M. Seth, et al. JOURNAL OF FAMILY WELFARE 25:34-39, June, 1979.

Some estrogenic effects of two oral contraceptives consisting of norgestrel and two different doses of ethynylestradiol, by J. F. Miller, et al. CONTRACEPTION 20(1):5-10, July, 1979.

Some pathologic findings in spontaneous abortions, by J. Byrne, et al. BIRTH DEFECTS 15(5A):137-147, 1979.

Some practical aspects of contraception, by R. J. Beard. CLINICAL OBSTETRICS AND GYNAECOLOGY 6(1):157-170, April, 1979.

Some thoughts on the epidemiology of cardiovascular disease, (with special reference to women 'on the pill'). Role of ascorbic acid, by C. A. Clemetson. MEDICAL HYPOTHE-SES 5(8):825-934, August, 1979.

Sonography in 74 abortions using prostaglandin F2alpha gel, by R. Ulbrich, et al. ARCHIVES OF GYNECOLOGY 228(1-4):421-422, July 20, 1979.

The South African gynaecologists' attitude to the present abortion law, by J. Dommisse. SOUTH AFRICAN MEDICAL JOURNAL 57(25):1044-1045, June 21, 1980.

Special project: survey of abortion law. Introduction. History of abortion law. Perspectives of viability. Federal funding of abortion. Appendix: the impact of changes in Arizona's abortion funding—a statistical analysis. Epilogue. ARIZONA STATE LAW JOURNAL 1980:70-216, 1980.

Special reasons for abortion, by L. Sundström-Feigenberg. LA-KARTIDNINGEN 77(7):558-559, February 13, 1980.

Spontaneous abortion, by F. Willgeroth. ZFA. ZEITSCHRIFT FUR ALLGEMEINMEDIZIN 55(29):1625-1627, October 20, 1979.

Spontaneous abortion and grieving, by J. M. Stack. AMERICAN FAMILY PHYSICIAN 21(5):99-102, May, 1980.

Spontaneous abortion rates, gravidity and neural tube defectes, by W. James. EARLY HUMAN DEVELOPMENT 2(3):291-296, 1978.

Spontaneous abortions among female chemical workers in Finland, by K. Hemminki, et al. INTERNATIONAL AR-CHIVES OF OCCUPATIONAL AND ENVIRONMENTAL HEALTH 45(2):123-126, February, 1980.

Spontaneous abortions and chromosomal anomalies: current questions, by A. Boue, et al. CLINICAL GENETICS 17(1): 57, 1980.

Spontaneous abortions and terminations of pregnancy: histo-

163

logical differences, by A. S. Bodey. MEDICAL JOURNAL OF AUSTRALIA 2(13):709-710, December 29, 1979.

Spontaneous mesenteric venous thrombosis, a rare complication of oral contraceptives, by F. Hofbauer, et al. WIENER KLINISCHE WOCHENSCHRIFT 92(6):191-194, March 14, 1980.

Spread of the use of modern contraceptive methods in France: 1971-1978, by P. Collomb. POPULATION 34:1045-1066, November-December, 1979.

St. Louis pro-lifers sued for $1 million. OUR SUNDAY VISITOR 69:2, May 4, 1980.

State-funded abortions: judicial acquiescence in the sanctity of a physician's medical judgment, by T. D. Harper. JOURNAL OF THE MEDICAL ASSOCIATION OF GEORGIA 69(4):313-315, April, 1980.

State implementation of Supreme court decisions: abortion rates since Roe v. Wade, by S. B. Hanse. JOURNAL OF POLITICS 42:372-395, May, 1980.

State regulation of late abortion and the physician's duty of care to the viable fetus, by M. A. Wood, et al. MISSOURI LAW REVIEW 45:394-422, Summer, 1980.

Statement on abortion: Australian Episcopal Conference. L'OSSERVATORE ROMANO 27(640):19-20, July 7, 1980.

Statistical studies on complications following abortion in the Federal Republic of Germany, by H. H. Bräutigam, et al. ARCHIVES OF GYNECOLOGY 228(1-4):344-348, July 20, 1979.

Statistico epidemiological study of changes in the vaginal flora of contraceptive pill users in Alexandria, by E. Fares, et al. JOURNAL OF THE EGYPTIAN PUBLIC HEALTH ASSOCIATION 54(1-2):49-63, 1979.

Statistics on abortion and reproduction in the county of Rostock during the period 1972-1977, by K. H. Mehlan, et al. DEUTSCHE GESUNDHEITSWESEN 34(14):665-670, 1979.

Status of humoral immunity in threatened abortion, by K. N. Prozorovskaia, et al. AKUSHERSTVOI GINEKOLOGIIA (11):57, November, 1979.

Sterilization abuse: current state of the law and remedies for abuse. GOLDEN GATE UNIVERSITY LAW REVIEW 10: 1147-1189, Summer, 1980.

Sterilization abuse: a proposed regulatory scheme. DEPAUL LAW REVIEW 28:731-768, Spring, 1979.

Sterilization and the birth rate, by D. L. Nortman. STUDIES IN FAMILY PLANNING 11:286-300, September-October, 1980.

Sterilization ban draws ire, by B. Kankelen. NATIONAL CATHOLIC REPORTER 16:20, September 12, 1980.

Sterilization by cesarean hysterectomy, by J. J. Britton. AMERICAN JOURNAL OF OBSTETRICS AND GYNECOLOGY 137(8):887-892, August 15, 1980.

Sterilization: a comparative review, by J. D. Keeping, et al. AUSTRALIAN AND NEW ZEALAND JOURNAL OF OBSTETRICS AND GYNAECOLOGY 19(4):193-202, November, 1979.

Sterilization concurrent with abortion is as safe as interval sterilization. FAMILY PLANNING PERSPECTIVES 12:213-214, July-August, 1980.

The sterilization decision: a socio-demographic and fertility profile of the Indian woman, by S. A. Jamshedji, et al. JOURNAL OF FAMILY WELFARE 26:27-41, March, 1980.

Sterilization: the dilemma of Catholic hospitals, by C. Bayley, Sr., et al. AMERICA 143:222-225, October 18, 1980.

Sterilization in family planning. The psychology of voluntary sterilization, by P. Petersen. MMW 122(15):557-559, April 11, 1980.

Sterilization is becoming a leading method of birth control. Here's a look at the trend, by T. Moon. AIR FORCE TIMES 41:53-54, December 15, 1980.

Sterilization issues [letter], by L. Gostin. LANCET 2(8148): 909-910, October 27, 1979.

Sterilization of the female by tubal ligation and by inserting the Fallopian tube ring of Yoon, by H. Toumi. TUNISIE MEDICALE 56(4):359-365, July-August, 1978.

Sterilization of the mentally handicapped [letter], by J. Dunelm. LANCET 2(8151):1081, November 17, 1979.

Sterilization of the mentally handicapped. Working group in current medical/ethical problems. LANCET 2(8144):685-686, September 29, 1979.

Sterilization of the mentally retarded—parents of mentally retarded children found to have no stututory right to consent to sterilization of child. State statute providing only for sterilization of inmates of certain state institutions held u under-inclusive and violative of the equal protection clause of the fourteenth amendment. JOURNAL OF FAMILY LAW 17:834-841, August, 1979.

Sterilization of women, by W. P. Black. PRACTITIONER 223 (1337):627-632, November, 1979.

—, by P. E. Treffers. NEDERLANDS TIJDSCHRIFT VOOR GENEESKUNDE 124(19):748-749, May 10, 1980.

—: benefits vs risks, by J. E. Rioux. INTERNATIONAL JOURNAL OF GYNAECOLOGY AND OBSTETRICS 16(6):488-492, 1978-1979.

Sterilization of women by laparoscopic electrocoagulation of the ovarian duct, by E. Pitner, et al. JUGOSLAVENSKA

KINEKOLOGIJA I OPSTETRICIJA 18(5-6):411-415, 1978.

Sterilization of women. A five year material, by P. E. Bordahl, et al. UGESKRIFT FOR LAEGER 142(7):431-433, February 11, 1980.

Sterilization of women—not as effective or harmless as assumed, by J. F. Larsen. UGESKRIFT FOR LAEGER 142(7):467-468, February 11, 1980.

Sterilization performed in connection with induced abortion, by F. Hald, et al. UGESKRIFT FOR LAEGER 142(5):321, January 28, 1980.

Sterilization services at Planned Parenthood of Maryland, by F. H. Trimble. MARYLAND STATE MEDICAL JOURNAL 29 (5):68-69, May, 1980.

Sterilization via the mini-laparotomy technique, by L. Weinstein. CLINICAL OBSTETRICS AND GYNECOLOGY 23 (1):273-280, March, 1980.

Sterilization—where mentally retarded and presumable fertile daughter cannot understand or exercise her constitutional right to voluntary sterilization, equity court has jurisdiction to empower parents to exercise right on her behalf. JOURNAL OF FAMILY LAW 18:648-653, April, 1980.

Sterilization: who says it's anti-life. NATIONAL CATHOLIC REPORTER 16:2, August 1, 1980.

Sterilizing the mentally-handicapped: who can give consent? CANADIAN MEDICAL ASSOCIATION JOURNAL 122 (2):234-236+, January 26, 1980.

Steroid and nonsteroid postcoital contraceptives, by V. V. Korkhov, et al. FARMAKOLOGIYA I TOKSIKOLOGIYA 43(1):94-96, January-February, 1980.

Steroid contraception and cancer, by L. Andolsek. JUGOSIA-VENSKA, GINEKOLOGIJA I OPSTETRICIJA 18(2):193-

199, March-April, 1978.

Strategies of despair: abortion in America and in American medicine, by J. B. Imber. DISSERTATION ABSTRACTS INTERNATIONAL 40(10):5617-A, 1979.

Strategy for human life amendment announced. OUR SUNDAY VISITOR 69:2, July 13, 1980.

The strategy of communication [how family planning information is relayed in rural India], by M. Chadda. POPULI 7(1-2):30-37; 24-31, 1980.

Strokes and contraceptive medication, by J. N. Currie, et al. MEDICAL JOURNAL OF AUSTRALIA 1(2):58, January 26, 1980.

Structural chromosomal aberrations in parents with spontaneous abortions, by S. Adzic, et al. JUGOSLAVENSKA GINEKOLOGIJA I OPSTETRICIJA 18(3-4):295-302, May-August, 1978.

Studies on liver functions under the effect of sequence drugs, by E. Brugmann, et al. MATERIA MEDICA POLONA 11(1):47-50, January-March, 1979.

Studies on a peerless contraceptive, by J. S. Greenstein. CHEMICAL TECHNOLOGY 9:217-221, April, 1979.

Studies on phenotype, development, and viability of human spontaneous abortuses with acrocentric trisomies and polyploidies: with reference to the relationship of the viability to the origin of extrachromosomes, by N. Niikawa. HOKKAIDO IGAKU ZASSHI 54(3):235-244, May, 1979.

Studies with cyproterone acetate for male contraception, by S. Roy, et al. JOURNAL OF STEROID BIOCHEMISTRY 11 (1 Part B):675-680, 1979.

A study of determinants and impact of the vasectomy programme in a rural community block of Madhya-Pradesh, by D. P. Akhand, et al. JOURNAL OF FAMILY WELFARE 26:

41-53, September, 1979.

A study of investigations used to predict outcome of pregnancy after threatened abortion, by G. B. Duff, et al. BRITISH JOURNAL OF OBSTETRICS AND GYNAECOLOGY 87 (3):194-198, March, 1980.

A study of the spontaneous abortions in rural community, by K. N. Yadava, et al. INDIAN JOURNAL OF PUBLIC HEALTH 23(2):100-102, April-June, 1979.

A study of spontaneously aborted twins, by J. E. Livingston, et al. TERATOLOGY 21(2):139-148, April, 1980.

Study of a topical antibacterial, contraceptive, antifungal and anti-venereal pharmacological combination. III. Post-coital test of the spermicidal action of a combination of oxyquinoline sulfate, copper sulfate and lactic acid, by F. Franchi, et al. MINERVA GINECOLOGIA 31(6):483-486, June, 1979.

Study on induced abortion in married women in an urban area, by C. Bose. JOURNAL OF FAMILY WELFARE 26:40-49, June, 1980.

Subcutaneous steroid hormone capsules. The future contraception?, by M. Osler. UGESKRIFT FOR LAEGER 141(45): 3097-3099, November 5, 1979.

Subdermal norethindrone pellets—a method for contraception?, by V. Odlind, et al. CONTRACEPTION 19(6):639-648, June, 1979.

Successful control of refractory ventricular premature beat with an estrogen-progesterone compound, by K. Ishikawa, et al. JAPANESE CIRCULATION JOURNAL 44(2):146-150, February, 1980.

A successful pregnancy following total hysterectomy, by P. Jackson, et al. BRITISH JOURNAL OF OBSTETRICS AND GYNAECOLOGY 87(5):353-355, May, 1980.

Successful pregnancy in an abortion-prone woman: prostaglandin and hormone levels during implantation, gestation and lactation, by M. Korteweg, et al. PROSTAGLANDINS & MEDICINE 4(3):185-192, March, 1980.

Sugar tolerance test in the clinical investigation of the etiology of spontaneous and habitual abortions, by D. Popovic, et al. SRPSKI ARHIV ZA CELOKUPNO LEKARSTVO 107(9): 469-475, September, 1979.

Suitability of the beagle dog as a test model for the tumorigenic potential of contraceptive steroids. 'A short review', by M. F. Etreby, et al. CONTRACEPTION 20(3):237-256, September, 1979.

Sulprostone, an uterospecific prostaglandin E2 derivative. Significance for abortion with special reference to various administration forms, by M. Schmidt-Gollwitzer, et al. ARCHIVES OF GYNECOLOGY 228(1-4):403, July 20, 1979.

Supportive hormone therapy and birth defects [letter], by D. T. Janerich. TERATOLOGY 20(3):483-486, December, 1979.

Suppression of human spermatogenesis by depot androgen: potential for male contraception, by R. S. Swerdloff, et al. JOURNAL OF STEROID BIOCHEMISTRY 11(1 Part B): 663-670, 1979.

Suprapubic endoscopy for internal female sterilization, by L. E. Laufe. AMERICAN JOURNAL OF OBSTETRICS AND GYNECOLOGY 136(2):257-259, 1980.

The Supreme Court and abortion: the irrelevance of medical judgment, by G. J. Annas. HASTINGS CENTER REPORT 10:23-24, October, 1980.

Supreme Court and a minor's abortion decision, by N. Dembitz. COLUMBIA LAW REVIEW 80:1251-1263, October, 1980.

Supreme Court Report: abortion...minors, by R. L. Young. AMERICAN BAR ASSOCIATION JOURNAL 65:1388-1389, September, 1979.

Supreme Court ruling a victory for unborn life, by F. Franzonia. OUR SUNDAY VISITOR 69:3, July 13, 1980.

Supreme court upholds Hyde amendment [prohibiting federal funding of most abortions], by K. A. Weiss. CONGRESSIONAL QUARTERLY WEEKLY REPORT 38:1860-1862, July 5, 1980.

The Supreme Court's Hyde Amendment ruling: Medicaid abortion restrictions, by P. Stewart. ORIGINS 10:113+, July 17, 1980.

Surgical abortion, by W. Lichtenegger, et al. ARCHIVES OF GYNECOLOGY 228(1-4):397, July 20, 1979.

Survey findings on family planning program effects in the Philippines, 1968-1973, by J. Laing, et al. PHILIPPINE SOCIOLOGICAL REVIEW 23(1-4):91-99, January-October, 1975.

Survey of abortion law [United States]. ARIZONA STATE LAW JOURNAL 1980:67-216, 1980.

A survey of sterilization acceptors in a family planning program in rural Bangladesh, by S. Bhatia, et al. INTERNATIONAL JOURNAL OF GYNAECOLOGY AND OBSTETRICS 17 (3):268-273, November-December, 1979.

Survey on family planning, by J. Berzosa, et al. ACTA OBSTETRICIA Y GINECOLOGICA HISPANA-LUSITANA 28(2): 97-126, February, 1980.

Symposium on adolescent gynecology and endocrinology. Part III: Veneral diseases in adolescents and contraception in teenagers, by P. A. Oill, et al. WESTERN JOURNAL OF MEDICINE 132(1):39-48, January, 1980.

Sumposium on the law and politics of abortion, by M. A. Vinovskis, ed. MICHIGAN LAW REVIEW 77:1569-1827, August, 1979.

Taking the pledge for just one child, by T. Munford. DAILY TELEGRAPH p15, October 21, 1980.

Taking the real worry out of being close [spermicides], by V. Ross. MACLEAN'S 93:48, March 3, 1980.

The teaching of family planning in the medical schools of Mexico, by S. C. Azcona, et al. GINECOLOGIA Y OBSTETRICIA DE MEXICO 46(278):465-474, December, 1979.

Techniques of induced abortion, their health implications and service aspects: a review of the literature, by K. Edström. WHO BULLETIN 57(3):481-497, 1979.

Teen clinics get good rating in HEW survey; teens want confidentiality, treatment as adults [news]. FAMILY PLANNING PERSPECTIVES 11(4):248-251, July-August, 1979.

Teenagers and contraception, by H. Rozenbaum. INTERNATIONAL JOURNAL OF GYNAECOLOGY AND OBSTETRICS 16(6):564-567, 1978-1979.

Teenagers and health care: a growing right to choose. INTERNIST 20(8):13, October, 1979.

Tell tale signs, by H. Franks. GUARDIAN p8, February 25, 1980.

The ten years of Humanae vitae: tr and cond from Moralia: revista de ciencas morales 1:2'79, by F. Elizari. THEOLOGICAL DIGEST 28:33-37, September, 1980.

Termination of pregnancy by medical induction: new DHSS guidelines. MIDWIVES CHRONICLE 93(1107):112-113, March, 1980.

Termination of pregnancy by vaginal administration of prostaglandin F2 alpha, by L. Matadial, et al. WEST INDIAN MEDICAL JOURNAL 29(1):57-59, March, 1980.

Termination of pregnancy complicated by anencephaly with intra-amniotic prostaglandin F2 alpha, by M. L. Schwartz, et al. AMERICAN JOURNAL OF OBSTETRICS AND GYNECOLOGY 136(2):203-204, January 15, 1980.

172

Termination of pregnancy in adolescents in Vaud, by P. A. Michaud, et al. REVUE MEDICALE DE LA SUISSE RO-MANDE 99(12):921-929, December, 1979.

Testing the quantity-quality fertility model: the use of twins as a natural experiment, by M. R. Rosenzweig, et al. ECONO-METRICA 48:227-240, January, 1980.

Thailand's continuing reproductive revolution [declining fertility and increasing contraceptive use], by J. Knodel, et al. IN-TERNATIONAL FAMILY PLANNING PERSPECTIVES 6: 84-96, September, 1980.

That the fetus should be considered a legal person, by J. M. Boyle. AMERICAN JOURNAL OF JURISPRUDENCE 24: 59-71, 1979.

Therapeutic abortion data from the Wergelandsveiens Clinic in Oslo, by K. K. Klem. TIDSSKRIFT FOR DEN NORSKE LAEGEFORENING 99(28):1418-1421, October 10, 1979.

Therapeutic management of post-pill amenorrhea, by F. Bottig-lioni, et al. RIVISTA ITALIANA DI GINECOLOGIA 58(4): 253-273, July-August, 1977.

Therapeutic procedure in acute renal insufficiency developing after septic abortion, by V. L. Cherniakov, et al. AKU-SHERSTVO I GINEKOLOGIIA (7):32-34, July, 1979.

Therapeutic value of indomethacin in threatened abortion, by A. R. Souka, et al. PROSTAGLANDINS 19(3):457-460, March, 1980.

Threatened abortion, hormone therapy and malformed embryos [letter], by G. P. Oakley. TERATOLOGY 20(3):481-482, December, 1979.

Threatened abortion studied by estradiol-17 beta in serum and ultrasound, by J. B. Hertz, et al. OBSTETRICS AND GYNE-COLOGY 55(3):324-328, March, 1980.

Three thousand interviews before elective interruption of pregnancy, by A. Monsaingeon, et al. ACADEMIE NATIONALE DE MEDECINE. BULLETIN 163(7):674-679, October, 1979.

Thrombocyte aggregation in pregnancy termination in first trimester, by E. Kidess, et al. ARCHIVES OF GYNECOLOGY 228(1-4):629-630, July 20, 1979.

Thrombocyte function in relation to the long term application of medroxyprogesterone acetate as a female contraceptive agent, by L. Mettler, et al. JOURNAL OF POSTGRADUATE MEDICINE 25(3):154-157, July, 1979.

Thrombotic thrombocytopenic purpura, cholangiocarcinoma, and oral contraceptives [letter], by V. Caggiano, et al. LANCET 2(8190):365, August 16, 1980.

Thyroid function in women taking oral contraceptives, by N. Juras, et al. LIJECNICKI VJESNIK 102(1):19-21, January, 1980.

Thyroid gland activity and the state of the thiol compounds in early spontaneous abortions, by V. I. Kachala, et al. VOPROSY OKHRANY MATERINSTVA I DETSTVA 24(7): 52-54, July, 1979.

Timing of laparoscopic sterilization in abortion patients, by H. M. Kwak, et al. OBSTETRICS AND GYNECOLOGY 56(1): 85-89, July, 1980.

The tiniest humans, by D. Dooley. TABLET 233:1116-1117, November 17, 1979.

Tomorrow's contraceptives—yesterday's problem [editorial]. BRITISH MEDICAL JOURNAL 2(6196):951, October 20, 1979.

Tonometric studies on the pregnant cervix uteri in abortion before and after intracervical administration of prostaglandin F2 gel, by W. Rath, et al. ARCHIVES OF GYNECOLOGY 228(1-4):416-417, July 20, 1979.

Torts, wrongful conception, measuring the damages incurred by the parents of an unplanned child. DEPAUL LAW REVIEW 28:249-258, Fall, 1978.

Torts—wrongful pregnancy—when defendent's negligence or breach of contract in a sterilization procedure allows the conception and birth of a healthy child, damages may be recovered in an action for wrongful pregnancy without reduction for the value of the benefits derived from the child. UNIVERSITY OF DETROIT JOURNAL OF URBAN LAW 57: 184-201, Fall, 1979.

Toward a predictive model of family planning, by S. Pick-Deweiss. REVISTA LATINOAMERICANA DE PSICOLOGIA 12(1):119-126, 1980.

Toxic hepatitis and spontaneous abortions in female anesthesiologists: 2 cases, by S. Popova, et al. KHIRURGIIA 33(2): 118-120, 1980.

Traditional midwives and family planning. POPULATION REPORTS 8(3):52, May, 1980.

Training developing-world personnel in family planning and population: accomplishments and patterns, by T. L. Hall, et al. STUDIES IN FAMILY PLANNING 11(5):167-177, May, 1980.

Transcortin as an indicator of estrogenic potency in oral contraceptives, by W. Carol, et al. ENDOKRINOLOGIE 75(2):167-172, 1980.

Transferrin C subtypes and spontaneous abortion, by G. Beckman, et al. HUMAN HEREDITY 30(5):316-319, 1980.

Treatment of rhesus monkeys (Macaca mulatta) with intravaginal rings loaded with levonorgestrel, by P. F. Wadsworth, et al. CONTRACEPTION 20(6):559-567, December, 1979.

Treatment of spontaneous abortions with the preparation, Provera, by D. Despodova, et al. AKUSHERSTVO I GINEKOLOGIIA 18(6):457-461, 1979.

The trend and pattern in attitudes toward abortion in the United States, 1965-1977, by M. Evers, et al. SOCIAL INDICATORS RESEARCH 7:251-267, January, 1980.

Trends in the indications for termination of pregnancy in the last 10 years in Switzerland, by D. Stucki. REVUE MÉDICALE DE LA SUISSE ROMANDE 99(12):857-871, December, 1979.

Trends in mideco-legal aspects of contraception, by J. Gardner. CLINICAL OBSTETRICS AND GYNAECOLOGY 6(1):185-195, April, 1979.

Tubal anastomosis in the New Zealand White rabbit using a circular suturing instrument, by P. J. Taylor, et al. FERTILITY AND STERILITY 33(2):204-206, February, 1980.

Tubal ligation and medical indications, by M. Reidy. IRISH THEOLOGICAL QUARTERLY 46(2):88-98, 1979.

Tubal ligations: a review of three years' work by a medical axuiliary, by P. R. Crouch. TROPICAL DOCTOR 9(4):189-191, October, 1979.

Tubal occlusion via laparoscopy in Latin America: an evaluation of 8186 cases, by L. P. Cole, et al. INTERNATIONAL JOURNAL OF GYNAECOLOGY AND OBSTETRICS 17 (3):253-259, November-December, 1979.

Tubal occlusion with silicone rubber: an update, by T. P. Reed, et al. JOURNAL OF REPRODUCTIVE MEDICINE 25(1): 25-28, July, 1980.

Tuboovarian abscess following laparoscopic sterilization with silicone rubber bands, by R. H. Glew, et al. OBSTETRICS AND GYNECOLOGY 55(6):760-762, June, 1980.

The Tunisian experience in legal abortion, by I. Nazer. INTERNATIONAL JOURNAL OF GYNAECOLOGY AND OBSTETRICS 17(5):488-492, March-April, 1980.

Twelve years of legal abortions: the facts, by O. Gillie, et al.

SUNDAY TIMES p6, January 27, 1980.

Twenty-seven strategies for teaching contraception to adolescents, by J. Chesler. JOURNAL OF SCHOOL HEALTH 50 (1):18-21, January, 1980.

A twenty-year prospective follow-up study of 2164 cases at the child guidance clinics in Stockholm, by I. Nylander. ACTA PAEDIATRICA SCANDINAVICA [Suppl] 276:1-45, 1979.

Twinning in postpill spontaneous abortions [letter], by L. H. Honore. AMERICAN JOURNAL OF OBSTETRICS AND GYNECOLOGY 135(5):700-701, November 1, 1979.

Twinning rates and the 'pill' [letter], by W. H. James. AMERICAN JOURNAL OF OBSTETRICS AND GYNECOLOGY 135(5):699-700, November 1, 1979.

Two methods of natural family planning [letter], by T. W. Hilgers. AMERICAN JOURNAL OF OBSTETRICS AND GYNECOLOGY 136(5):696-697, March 1, 1980.

Two Princeton scholars cast a cold eye on the Supreme Court's abortion ruling: nobody wins [Hyde Amendment ruling; interview by R. K. Rein], by J. Trussell, et al. PEOPLE 14: 77-78+, July 21, 1980.

Typical complications of tubal ligation by laparoscopy with the tupla-clip and measures to avoid these complications, by B. Henkel. GEBURTSHILFE UND FRAUENHEILKUNDE 39 (10):892-896, October, 1979.

U.S. bishops cite dissent: ask contraception review, by P. Hebblethwaite. NATIONAL CATHOLIC REPORTER 16:1+, October 10, 1980.

U.S. bishops: contraceptive sterilization immoral. OUR SUNDAY BISITOR 69:6, July 20, 1980.

U.S. Supreme Court affirms society's interest in 'potential life', by P. Geary. HOSPITAL PROGRESS 61(8):22-24, August, 1980.

U.S.A.: a legal blow to abortion, by C. Fox. MACLEAN'S 93: 33-34, July 14, 1980.

U.S.A. Volunatry sterilization is legal [news], by E. Roseau. NOUVELLE PRESSE MEDICALE 9(18):1271+, April 19, 1980.

Ultero-abdominal fistula following an induced abortion, by B. Ghosh. JOURNAL OF OBSTETRICS AND GYNECOLOGY OF INDIA 29(4):927-929, 1979.

Ultrasonographic differential diagnosis of imminent abortion, by S. Zanke, et al. ZENTRALBLATT FUR GYNAEKOLOGIE 101(23):1523-1527, 1979.

Unintended pregnancies in the United States, 1970-1972, by C. Tietze. FAMILY PLANNING PERSPECTIVES 11(3):186-188, May-June, 1979.

Unisex birth control chemical [luteinizing hormone-releasing hormone], by J. A. Miller. SCIENCE NEWS 117:331+, May 24, 1980.

Unplanned pregnancies and the pill [letter], by D. C. Boden. MEDICAL JOURNAL OF AUSTRALIA 1(8):391, April 19, 1980.

Unsympathetic attitudes of U.K. physicians limit availability of abortion [news]. FAMILY PLANNING PERSPECTIVES 12 (3):157-158, May-June, 1980.

Unwed adolescent primigravidas identify subject matter for pre-natal classes, by D. Z. Copeland. JOGN NURSING 8(4):248-253, July-August, 1979.

Urinary estrogen excretion and concentration of serum human placental lactogen in pregnancies following legally induced a-bortion, by E. B. Obel, et al. ACTA OBSTETRICIA ET GY-NOCOLOGICA SCANDINAVICA 59(1):37-41, 1980.

Use-effectivness of the copper-7 intrauterine device in a Malay-sian family planning clinic, by G. T. Heng. MEDICAL JOUR-

NAL OF MALAYSIA 33(4):352, June, 1979.

Use of automated record linkage to measure patient fertility after family planning service, by C. A. Burnett 3d, et al. A-MERICAN JOURNAL OF PUBLIC HEALTH 70(3):246-250, March, 1980.

Use of central electroanalgesia for treating threatened abortions, by N. V. Bashmakova. VOPROSY OKHRANY MATER-INSTVA I DETSTVA 25(2):54-56, February, 1980.

Use of contraception among married women in New South Wales, Australia, by F. Yusuf. JOURNAL OF BIOSOCIAL SCIENCE 12(1):41-49, January, 1980.

Use of contraceptives and abortions in Scandinavia. NORDISK MEDICIN 95(5):157-159, May, 1980.

Use of contraceptives prior to and after conception and exposure to other fetal hazards, by P. H. Shino, et al. CONTRACEP-TION 20(2):105-120, August, 1979.

Use of differentiated PGE2, PGF2alpha and prostaglandin-derivative administration for avoidance of complications in abortion induction, by M. Cornely. ARCHIVES OF GYNE-COLOGY 228(1-4):413-414, July 20, 1979.

Use of 15-methyl PGF2-alpha for termination of early pregnancy, by I. A. Manuilova, et al. SOVETSKAIA MEDITSINA (3): 49-53, 1980.

Use of intra-amniotic urea as a second trimester abortifacient, by A. Khare, et al. JOURNAL OF POSTGRADUATE MEDI-CINE 25(3):158-161, July, 1979.

Use of low-dosage oral cyproterone acetate as a male contraceptive, by C. Wang, et al. CONTRACEPTION 21(3):245-272, March, 1980.

The use of oral prostaglandin E2 in the management of intrauterine fetal death, by F. H. Kho, et al. PROSTAGLANDINS 18(4):663-672, October, 1979.

The use of paramedics in family planning services in Iran, by F. S. Ghorbani. INTERNATIONAL JOURNAL OF GYNAE-COLOGY AND OBSTETRICS 17(2):135-138, September-October, 1979-1980.

Use of relaxation training to reduce pain following vaginal hysterectomy, by K. Perri. PERCEPTUAL AND MOTOR SKILLS 48(2):478, April, 1979.

Use of vaginal prostaglandin-E2 suppositories in septic abortion, by C. T. Milano, et al. PROSTAGLANDINS 19(3):455-456, March, 1980.

Use-pattern of oral contraceptive in rural Bangladesh: a case study of Sulla, by F. I. Chowdhury, et al. BANGLADESH DEVELOPMENT STUDIES 6(3):271-300, 1978.

The user perspective: an evolutionary step in contraceptive service programs: implementing the user perspective, by G. Zeidenstein, et al. STUDIES IN FAMILY PLANNING 11(1): 24, January, 1980.

User perferences for contraceptive methods in India, Korea, the Philippines, and Turkey [based on a study conducted by two task forces of the World Health Organization, 1977-1979]. STUDIES IN FAMILY PLANNING 11:267-273, September-October, 1980.

Utah law restricting abortion funding declared unconstitutional. FAMILY LAW REPORTER: COURT OPINIONS 6(22): 2370-2371, April 8, 1980.

Uterine perforation in a legal abortion, by A. Beck, et al. JUGO-SLAVENSKA GINEKOLOGIJA I OPSTETRICIJA 19(1-2): 87-93, 1979.

Uterine rupture as a complication of second trimester abortion using intraamniotic prostaglandin E2 and augmentation with other oxytocic agents, by T. McCarthy, et al. PROSTA-GLANDINS 19(6):849-854, June, 1980.

Uterine rupture caused by midtrimester saline abortion, by T. K.

Bryson, et al. ACTA OBSTETRICIA ET GYNECOLOGICA SCANDINAVICA 58(5):497-498, 1979.

Uterus perforation as complication of legal abortion, by A. Beck, et al. ARCHIVES OF GYNECOLOGY 228(1-4):395, July 20, 1979.

Vacuum aspiration at therapeutic abortion: blood loss at operation in multigravid women, by B. Sandström, et al. GYNECOLOGY AND OBSTETRICS INVESTIGATION 9(6):292-298, 1978.

—: influence of two different negative pressures on blood loss during and after operation, by B. Sandström, et al. GYNECOLOGY AND OBSTETRICS INVESTIGATION 9(6):299-303, 1978.

Vaginal contraceptives: available but—[vaginal spermicides], by A. Hecht. CONSUMER REPORTS 14:29-30, February, 1980.

Vaginal tubal ligation concurrent with medical termination of pregnancy, by I. Gupta, et al. INDIAN JOURNAL OF MEDICAL RESEARCH 70:960-964, December, 1979.

Vaginal tubal ligation—is infection a significant risk?, by R. R. Miesfeld, et al. AMERICAN JOURNAL OF OBSTETRICS AND GYNECOLOGY 137(2):183-188, May 15, 1980.

Value of thyroid function tests after long term hormone therapy, by A. Vucic, et al. JUGOSLAVENSKA GINEKOLOGIJA I OPSTETRICIJA 18(5-6):405-409, 1978.

Values and risks of pregnancy-protecting progesterones, by I. Pazonyi. ORVOSI HETILAP 120(50):3078, December 16, 1979.

Values relating to abortion as expressed by the inner city adolescent girl—report of a physician's experience, by T. J. Silber. ADOLESCENCE 15(57):183-189, Spring, 1980.

Variant chromosome 9 (9qh+) in families with spontaneous abortion, by K. Mijin, et al. SRPSKI ARHIV ZA CELOKUPNO LEKARSTVO 107(10):547-553, October, 1979.

Variations in serum copper and ceruloplasmin activity following a long term intake of combined oral contraceptives in Iranian women, by S. Kamyab, et al. JOURNAL OF ENDOCRINO-LOGICAL INVESTIGATION 3(2):173-175, April-June, 1980.

Varicosity, hormones and pregnancy, by L. Wenner. VASA 8(3): 258-262, 1979.

Various prostaglandins and various administration forms for induced abortion, by H. Steiner, et al. ARCHIVES OF GYNE-COLOGY 228(1-4):404-405, July 20, 1979.

Vasectomy and biochemical composition of human seminal plasma, by R. Mendiratta, et al. INDIAN JOURNAL OF EXPER-IMENTAL BIOLOGY 18(4):409-410, 1980.

Vasectomy and its consequences, by G. Singh. IRCS MEDICAL SCIENCE LIBRARY COMPENDIUM 7(10):488-491, 1979.

Vasectomy in cryosurgery of the prostate, by W. Hiroto, et al. CRYOBIOLOGY 16(6):596, 1979.

Vasectomy may clog up your veins, by R. Hoult. NEW SCIEN-TIST 86:392, June 26, 1980.

Vasectomy: 1980, by L. Lipshultz. UROLOGIC CLINICS OF NORTH AMERICA 7(1):165-169, 1980.

Vasectomy with transurethral resection of prostate, by N. W. Whitlock, et al. UROLOGY 13(2):135-138, 1979.

Vasorasotomy, by S. S. Howards. UROLOGIC CLINICS OF NORTH AMERICA 7(1):165-169, 1980.

Vegetative reaction during pregnancy interruption under general anesthesia, by S. Rajic, et al. SRPSKI ARHIV ZA CELO-KUPNO LEKARSTVO 107(4):387-390, April, 1979.

Vermont's voluntary sterilization statutes and the rights of the mentally handicapped. VERMONT LAW REVIEW 4:331-352, Fall, 1979.

Vitamin B6 nutriture during pregnancy and lactation. II. The effect of long-term use of oral contraceptives, by J. L. Roepke, et al. AMERICAN JOURNAL OF CLINICAL NUTRITION 32(11):2257-2264, November, 1979.

The vitamin B6 requirement in oral contraceptive users. NUTRITION REVIEWS 37(11):344-345, November, 1979.

Voluntary interruption of pregnancy, by B. Achard. SOINS 25 (8):19-23, April 20, 1980.

Voluntary interruption of pregnancy: admission in the facilities concerned under the application of the legislation. SOINS 25(8):30-32, April 20, 1980.

Voluntary sterilization, by M. S. Morain. HUMANIST 40:51+, July-August, 1980.

—: legal and ethical aspects, by D. I. Wilson. LEGAL MEDICAL QUARTERLY 3(1):13-23, 1979.

—: suggestions for consultation practice, by W. Heidenreich, et al. MEDIZINISCHE KLINIK 74(48):1829-1831, November 30, 1979.

Von Willebrand's disease complicating second-trimester abortion, by J. Sorosky, et al. OBSTETRICS AND GYNECOLOGY 55(2):253-254, February, 1980.

Wallenberg's syndrome in a young woman following long-term use of a contraceptive agent, by G. J. Petten, et al. NEDERLANDS TIJDSCHRIFT VOOR GENEESKUNDE 123(26): 1058-1060, June 30, 1980.

Wardship and abortion prevention, by J. Phillips. Further observations, by N. V. Lowe. LAW QUARTERLY REVIEW 95: 332-335, July, 1979; 96:29-31, January, 1980.

Washington Catholics rap single issue abortion vote, by B. Kenkelen. NATIONAL CATHOLIC REPORTER 16:3+, August 1, 1980.

We need to free our hearts, by C. Gallagher. OUR SUNDAY VISITOR 69:11, May 18, 1980.

The Wessex abortion studies: I. Interdistrict variation in provision of abortion services, by J. R. Ashton, et al. LANCET 1 (8159):82-85, January 12, 1980.

—: II. Attitudes of consultant gynaecologists to provision of abortion services, by J. R. Ashton, et al. LANCET 1(8160): 140-142, January 19, 1980.

What can we learn from the present abortion statistics?, by U. Takman. LAKARTIDNINGEN 77(7):526-530, February 13, 1980.

What did the cardinal really say in controversial letter?, by H. Medeiros. OUR SUNDAY VISITOR 69:8, October 5, 1980.

What do feminists want?, by F. Moira. OFF OUR BACKS 10: 18, January, 1980.

What does seaweed have to do with abortion?, by L. Van Gelder. MS MAGAZINE 9:112-113, November, 1980.

What vasectomy means to a man and his marriage, by J. R. Heilman. READERS DIGEST 116:33-36+, April, 1980.

When does human life begin?, by J. F. Crosby. AMERICAN JOURNAL OF ORTHOPSYCHIATRY 50(2):356-364, April, 1980.

When I was being made in secret, by E. Elliot. CHRISTIAN HERALD 102(2):29-30, November, 1979.

When should contraceptive agents be given to minors? [editorial], by G. Schewe. MMW 122(25):923-924, June 20, 1980.

Where abortion fight goes from here: the high court's new ruling cheered foes of abortion, distressed supporters, now both camps plan to battle even harder. US NEWS AND WORLD REPORT 89:42, July 14, 1980.

Where did you get a cervical cap: a guide to area clinics, by K. J. Littman. BOSTON 72(1):179, June, 1980.

Who should decide? A survey of attitudes about bioethical decision-making, by C. Holmes, et al. ETHICS IN SCIENCE AND MEDICINE 6(3):137-144, 1979.

Why adolescents go to birth-control clinics rather than to their family physicians, by E. S. Herold, et al. CANADIAN JOURNAL OF PUBLIC HEALTH 70(5):317-320, September-October, 1979.

Why natural family planning is different, by H. Klaus. MARRAIGE 62:14-15, April, 1980.

The wider context of abortion, by D. White. NEW SOCIETY p280, February 7, 1980.

Widespread contraceptive use found in Britain: condom popular, two-child families preferred. FAMILY PLANNING PERSPECTIVES 12:108-110, March-April, 1980.

Will High Court usurp Congressional authority? (by overturning the Hyde Amendment which forbids federal money for abortions). HUMAN EVENTS 40:6+, April 26, 1980.

Williams Obstetrics on abortion, by M. E. Bowen. MAN AND MEDICINE 4(3):205-232, 1979.

Women applying for legal abortions and their male partners, by L. Jacobsson, et al. LAKARTIDNINGEN 77(7):537-539+, February 13, 1980.

Women in New Zealand, by D. Black. NEW ZEALAND NURSING JOURNAL 73(5):42, May, 1980.

Worldwide laws and policies on contraception, abortion and sterilization affect service provision. FAMILY PLANNING

PERSPECTIVES 12:210-211, July-August, 1980.

Wrongful conception. WILLIAM MITCHELL LAW REVIEW 5: 464-508, 1979.

Wrongful life: birth control spawns a tort. JOHN MARSHALL LAW REVIEW 13:401-420, Winter, 1980.

You and the law. Consent, sterilization and mental incompetence: the case of 'Eve', by C. Sklar. CANADIAN NURSE 76 (3):14-16+, March, 1980.

Zoning control of abortion clinics. CLEVELAND STATE LAW REVIEW 28:507-527, 1979.

PERIODICAL LITERATURE

SUBJECT INDEX

ABORTION (GENERAL)
Abortion, by L. K. Crockett. CLINICAL OBSTETRICS AND
GYNAECOLOGY 6(1):57-76, 1979.

—, by M. Gould. CHRYSALIS 9:55-57, Fall, 1979.

—, by B. Hayler. SIGNS 5(2):307-323, 1979.

Abortion [letter]. BRITISH MEDICAL JOURNAL 2(6188):
495-496, August 25, 1979.

—, by M. Churchill. BRITISH MEDICAL JOURNAL
2(6191):667, September 15, 1979.

—, by A. K. Clarke. BRITISH MEDICAL JOURNAL
2(6191):666, September 15, 1979.

—, by P. H. Gosling. BRITISH MEDICAL JOURNAL
2(6191):666, September 15, 1979.

—, by B. Johnson. BRITISH MEDICAL JOURNAL 2(6191):
666, September 15, 1979.

—, by D. M. Potts. MEDICAL JOURNAL OF AUSTRALIA
1(5):236, March 8, 1980.

—, by C. P. Rice-Oxley. BRITISH MEDICAL JOURNAL

187

2(6191):667, September 15, 1979.

—, by M. Simms. BRITISH MEDICAL JOURNAL 2(6191): 667, September 15, 1979.

—, by C. P. Wendell-Smith. MEDICAL JOURNAL OF AUS-TRALIA 2(6):313, September 22, 1979.

Abortion: an affirmative public good: USCC brief. ORIGINS 9:534-535, January 31, 1980.

Abortion and plain language [letter], by R. B. Parker. LAN-CET 1(8162):260, February 2, 1980.

Abortion as it is described to us, by M. Six-Quivy, et al. LILLE MEDICAL 25(6):307-310, June-July, 1980.

Abortion: beyond halfway solutions, by M. Papa. NATION-AL CATHOLIC REPORTER 17:12, November 14, 1980.

Abortion compromises wearing thin [news], by J. F. Brazda. HOSPITAL PROGRESS 60(11):20, November, 1979.

Abortion consulting in progress, by K. Sundström-Feigenberg. LAKARTIDNINGEN 77(7):552, February 13, 1980.

Abortion: a convergence of concern, by J. Wallis, ed. SO-JOURNERS 9(3-4):13-25, November, 1980.

Abortion debate continues: a look at laws, regulations, re-strictions and funding, by J. A. Smith. CALIFORNIA NURSE 76(1):8, June, 1980.

The abortion debate: facing up to reality, by T. Ross. NURS-ING MIRROR AND MIDWIVE'S JOURNAL 150(8):40-41, February 21, 1980.

—: life is a serious business, by T. Philpot. NURSING MIR-ROR AND MIDWIVE'S JOURNAL 150(7):34-36, February 14, 1980.

Abortion: the false charges, by R. Butt. TIMES (LONDON) p16, February 7, 1980.

Abortion: an issue that won't go away [views of C. Gerster and F. Wattleton], by H. Epstein. NEW YORK TIMES MAGAZINE p44-46+, March 30, 1980.

Abortion: the last resort, by C. McCray. ESSENCE 10:51-52+, November, 1979.

Abortion: a matter of clinical judgment [editorial]. BRITISH MEDICAL JOURNAL 280(6210):269, February 2, 1980.

Abortion 1979: the concept of viability, by J. M. Healey. CONNECTICUT MEDICINE 43(9):599, September, 1979.

Abortion or contraception, by A. Goldsmith, et al. REPRODUCCION 4(1):55-68, January-March, 1980.

Abortion PRO: the abortion controversy: will it ever disappear? CON: should we change our attitudes about abortion?, by M. S. Burnhill, et al. JOURNAL OF THE MEDICAL SOCIETY OF NEW JERSEY 77(6):450-453, June, 1980.

Abortion: towards continuing the diaglogue, by M. B. Mahowald. CROSS CURRENTS 29:330-335, Fall, 1979.

Abortion: what to expect if you decide to have one. GLAMOUR 77:302+, October, 1979.

Abortion: why the arguments fail, by S. Hauerwas. HOSPITAL PROGRESS 61(1):38-49, January, 1980.

Both sides of the abortion argument, by A. Ferriman.

TIMES (LONDON) p10, February 6, 1980.

Can libertarians support abortion (a libertarian argument against abortion), by E. A. Opitz. HUMAN EVENTS 40:10, March 22, 1980.

Castration of sex offenders: treatment or punishment? A review and critique of recent European literature, by N. Heim. ARCHIVES OF SEXUAL BEHAVIOR 8(3):281-304, May, 1979.

Childbirth and abortion 1975-1978, by L. B. Knudsen, et al. UGESKRIFT FOR LAEGAR 141(31):2134-2135, July 30, 1979.

Containing the discussion: how to argue about abortion: II, by B. Harrison. CHRISTIANITY AND CRISIS 37(21): 311-313, December 26, 1977.

The contraceptive practice of abortion patients, by M. J. Sparrow. NEW ZEALAND MEDICAL JOURNAL 91 (653):104-106, February 13, 1980.

Decision-making regarding abortion: a value x expectancy analysis, by J. G. Smetana, et al. JOURNAL OF POPU-LATION 2(4):338-357, Winter, 1979.

Delayed abortion in an area of easy accessibility, by W. A. Burr, et al. JAMA 244(1):44-48, July 4, 1980.

Facts about abortion, by E. Fein. HARPER'S BAZAAR 113: 75-76, May, 1980.

Fertility following legally induced abortion, by E. B. Obel. ACTA OBSTETRICIA ET GYNECOLOGICA SCANDI-NAVICA 58(6):539-542, 1979.

Has legal abortion replaced other methods of birth control?, by O. Meirik. LAKARTIDNINGEN 77(7):531-532+,

February 13, 1980.

Have the abortions been dedramatized?, by M. Callersten. LAKARTIDNINGEN 77(7):553-554, February 13, 1980.

Legal termination of pregnancy. Economic and social aspects, by A. Delachaux, et al. REVUE MEDICALE DE LA SUISSE ROMANDE 99(12):913-919, December, 1979.

Miscarriage: the fears and the facts, by M. Hewson. MC-CALLS 107:41-42, July, 1980.

The modern indications for abortion, by D. Stucki. PRAXIS 69(2):38-41, January 15, 1980.

Multidimensional investigations to elucidate relationships between case histories of interruption of pregnancy and premature deliveries and low birth weight, by C. Zwahr, et al. ZENTRALBLATT FUR GYNAEKOLOGIE 101(23): 1502-1509, 1979.

New risks in abortion plans, by A. Coote. NEW STATESMAN 98:616, October 26, 1979.

Patterns of discussion and decision-making amongst abortion patients, by J. R. Ashton. JOURNAL OF BIOSOCIAL SCIENCE 12:247-260, July, 1980.

Race, motherhood, and abortion, by C. Clark. DISSERTATION ABSTRACTS INTERNATIONAL 40(10):5606-A, 1979.

A reappraisal of abortion as a method of fertility control, by J. Barnes. INTERNATIONAL JOURNAL OF GYNAE-COLOGY AND OBSTETRICS 16(6):502-504, 1978-1979.

Repeat abortion and self-reported contraceptive behavior [letter], by R. D. Gillette. AMERICAN JOURNAL OF PUBLIC HEALTH 70(6):637, June, 1980.

Report of National Conference on Abortion. Abortion debaters urged to cease shouting match and to listen and learn, by R. J. Stephens. HOSPITAL PROGRESS 60 (11):18-19, November, 1979.

Research note: study of women seeking abortion, by K. Sidenius. SOCIAL SCIENCE AND MEDICINE 12(5): 423-424, 1978.

Results of a structurized discussion within the framework of abortion with particular reference to problems of pregnancy, conflict and related topics, by W. Woynar, et al. OEFFENTLICHE GESUNDHEITSWESEN 42(2):51-54, February, 1980.

Safety of post-abortion sterilization [letter], by G. Chamberlain. LANCET 2(8150):1020, November 10, 1979.

Safety of postabortion sterilization compared with interval sterilization. A controlled study, by M. C. Cheng, et al. LANCET 2(8144):682-685, September 29, 1979.

Screening for gonorrhoea, trichomoniasis and candidosis in women presenting for termination of pregnancy, by H. S. Singha, et al. BRITISH JOURNAL OF CLINICAL PRACTICE 33(6):163-164, June, 1979.

Sex, sin, and abortion, by J. Lifrieri. HERESIES 9:68-69, 1980.

Sterilization concurrent with abortion is as safe as interval sterilization. FAMILY PLANNING PERSPECTIVES 12: 213-214, July-August, 1980.

A successful pregnancy following total hysterectomy, by P.

Jackson, et al. BRITISH JOURNAL OF OBSTETRICS AND GYNAECOLOGY 87(5):353-355, May, 1980.

Three thousand interviews before elective interruption of pregnancy, by A. Monsaingeon, et al. ACADEMIE NATIONALE DE MEDECINE BULLETIN 163(7):674-679, October, 1979.

Timing of laparoscopic sterilization in abortion patients, by H. M. Kwak, et al. OBSTETRICS AND GYNECOLOGY 56(1):85-89, July, 1980.

What do feminists want? Madison Billboard Brigade. Billboard blitz/counter blitz, by F. Moira. OFF OUR BACKS 10:18, January, 1980.

What does seaweed have to do with abortion?, by L. Van Gelder. MS MAGAZINE 9:112-113, November, 1980.

The wider context of abortion, by D. White. NEW SOCIETY p280-281, February 7, 1980.

Williams Obstetrics on abortion, by M. E. Bowen. MAN AND MEDICINE 4(3):205-232, 1979.

Women applying for legal abortions and their male partners, by L. Jacobsson, et al. LAKARTIDNINGEN 77(7):537-539+, February 13, 1980.

AUSTRALIA
Abortion in Queesland [letter], by R. J. Wilson. MEDICAL JOURNAL OF AUSTRALIA 1(5):236, March 8, 1980.

'Inconvenient' babies [letter], by L. Hemingway. AUSTRALIAN FAMILY PHYSICIAN 8(7):800, 1979.

Premier in storm over tough new abortion law, by D. Reinhardt. SUNDAY TIMES p8, May 4, 1980.

CANADA
Abortion referral and MD emigration: areas of concern and study for CMA, by D. A. Geekie. CANADIAN MEDICAL ASSOCIATION JOURNAL 118(2):175+, January 21, 1978.

Abortion repeaters, by A. Lake. MCCALLS 107:58+, September, 1980.

CLC statement on abortion. CANADIAN LABOUR 24:8, December 14, 1979.

Husbands' attitudes towards abortion and Canadian abortion law, by R. W. Osborn, et al. JOURNAL OF BIO-SOCIAL SCIENCE 12:21-30, January, 1980.

THE COMMONWEALTH
Development of Commonwealth abortion laws, by B. M. Dickens, et al. INTERNATIONAL AND COMPARATIVE LAW QUARTERLY 28:424-457, July, 1979.

CUBA
Recent trends in fertility, abortion and contraception in Cuba, by P. E. Hollerbach. FAMILY PLANNING PERSPECTIVES 6:97-106, September, 1980.

DENMARK
The interaction between legalization of abortion and contraception in Denmark, by P. C. Matthiessen. WORLD HEALTH STATISTICS QUARTERLY 32 (4):246-256, 1979.

DEVELOPING COUNTRIES
Dilatation and evacuation for induced abortion in developing countries: advantages and disadvantages, by W. Cates, Jr., et al. STUDIES IN FAMILY PLANNING 11(4):128-133, April, 1980.

EUROPE

EUROPE
Abortion debate, by D. Butler, et al. NEWSWEEK 95:37, January 7, 1980.

FINLAND
Spontaneous abortions among female chemical workers in Finland, by K. Hemminki, et al. INTERNATIONAL ARCHIVES OF OCCUPATIONAL AND ENVIRONMENTAL HEALTH 45(2):123-126, February, 1980.

FRANCE
Analysis of the geographical variations of twinning rate in France. An indirect approach to study spontaneous abortions, by D. Hemon, et al. REVUE D EPIDEMIOLOGIE ET DE SANTE PUBLIQUE 27(2):91-99, September 18, 1979.

Appel aux hommes de bonne volonte au sujet de la loi sur l'avortement, by L. Elchinger. LA DOCUMENTATION CATHOLIQUE 76:890-893, October 21, 1979.

L.Avortement: de quelques stereotypes, by J. Pellet. L'EVOLUTION PSYCHIATRIQUE 42(2):369-374, April-June, 1977.

La denatalite en France et en Occident: ses causes, ses consequences, by P. Chaunu. PAYSANS 23:12-33, February-March, 1979.

Je choisis la pauvrete des pauvres gens, by T. Boyaxhiu. LA DOCUMENTATION CATHOLIQUE 77:234-236, March 2, 1980.

Problems of implementation and consequences of the 1975 provisional law to liberalize abortion in France, by J. H. Soutoul, et al. INTERNATIONAL JOURNAL OF GYNAECOLOGY AND OBSTETRICS 16 (6):505-508, 1978-1979.

GERMANY
Regulations on the interruption of pregnancy in current German criminal law, by P. Bockelmann. HAU-TARZT 31(Suppl 4):41-45, 1980.

Statistical studies on complications following abortion in the Federal Republic of Germany, by H. H. Bräutigam, et al. ARCHIVES OF GYNECOLOGY 228(1-4):344-348, July 20, 1979.

Statistics on abortion and reproduction in the county of Rostock during the period 1972-1977, by K. H. Mehlan, et al. DEUTSCHE GESUNDHEITSWESEN 34(14):665-670, 1979.

GREAT BRITAIN
Abortion and the right to life: a statement by the archbishops of Great Britain. TABLET 234:91-92, January 26, 1980.

Abortion policy in Britain and the United States, by C. Francome. SOCIAL WORK 25(1):5-9, 1980.

Abortion: two steps back [Britain]. ECONOMIST 273: 30-31, October 27, 1979.

Abortion: unhealthy reform [Britain]. ECONOMIST 274:24, February 2, 1980.

Abortion: what the Commons will be deciding today, by M. Phillips. GUARDIAN p8, February 8, 1980.

Abortion: which poll do you read? [Britain]. ECONO-MIST 274:24, February 9, 1980.

The British retrospective and prospective studies, by J. McEwan. INTERNATIONAL JOURNAL OF GY-NAECOLOGY AND OBSTETRICS 16(6):525-528, 1978-1979.

GREAT BRITAIN
Commentary from Westminster. Abortion (Amendment) Bill, by R. Deitch. LANCET 1(8165):433-434, February 23, 1980.

Great Britain: birthrights at the barricades, by M. McDonald. MACLEAN'S 93:40+, March 17, 1980.

Induced abortion in the Wessex Health Region, England, UK, by J. R. Ashton. EPIDEMIOLOGY AND COMMUNITY HEALTH 33(2):168, 1979.

Legal abortion in England and Wales 1968-1978, by T. L. Lewis. BRITISH MEDICAL JOURNAL 280(6210): 295-296, February 2, 1980.

Twelve years of legal abortions: the facts, by O. Gillie, et al. SUNDAY TIMES p6, January 27, 1980.

Unsympathetic attitudes of U.K. physicians limit availability of abortion [news]. FAMILY PLANNING PERSPECTIVES 12(3):157-158, May-June, 1980.

The Wessex abortion studies: I. Interdistrict variation in provision of abortion services, by J. R. Ashton, et al. LANCET 1(8159):82-85, January 12, 1980.

—: II. Attitudes of consultant gynaecologists to provision of abortion services, by J. R. Ashton, et al. LANCET 1(8160):140-142, January 19, 1980.

INDIA
Abortion in India, with particular reference to West Bengal, by R. Dutta. JOURNAL OF BIOSOCIAL SERVICE 12(2):191-200, April, 1980.

Demographic characteristics of acceptors of abortion in selected states of India, by S. B. V. Upadhyay. JOURNAL OF FAMILY WELFARE 25:63-67, June, 1979.

INDIA
Legalization of abortion in India, by N. L. Pande, et al. THE EASTERN ANTHROPOLOGIST 32(1):55-57, January-March, 1979.

Maternal age, stillbriths, abortions and factors related to maternal blood groups: a hospital survey from Lahore (Punjab, Pakistan), by S. A. Shami, et al. JPMA: JOURNAL OF THE PAKISTAN MEDICAL ASSOCIATION 30(2):27-34, February, 1980.

ISRAEL
Illegal abortion in Israel, by P. E. Slater. ISRAEL LAW REVIEW 13(3):411-416, July, 1978.

ITALY
Observation on the new abortion offenses, by R. Spizuoco. GIUSTIZIA PENALE 84(3):174-175, 1979.

Pope, critics debate Italy's abortion law, by P. Hebblethwaite. NATIONAL CATHOLIC REPORTER 16:4, October 3, 1980.

JAPAN
Abortion, contraception, and motherhood in post-war Japan and the United States, by M. M. Franz, et al. INTERNATIONAL JOURNAL OF WOMEN'S STUDIES 3:66-75, January-February, 1980.

KENYA
Review of abortions at Kenyatta National Hospital, Nairobi, by V. P. Aggarwal, et al. EAST AFRICAN MEDICAL JOURNAL 57(2):138-143, February, 1980.

THE NETHERLANDS
The abortion problem in the USA and in the Netherlands. ARS AEQUI 28(6):290-297, 1979.

THE NETHERLANDS
From criminal offense to social service. An analysis of
the social significance of induced abortion in The
Netherlands, by E. Ketting. SAMSOM UITGEVERIJ
39:50, 1978.

NEW ZEALAND
Abortion experiences among New Zealand women, by B.
J. Kirkwood, et al. NEW ZEALAND MEDICAL
JOURNAL 90(645):294-297, October 10, 1979.

Abortion referrals [letter], by L. Bruce. NEW ZEALAND
MEDICAL JOURNAL 90(646):353, October 24,
1979.

Abortion today [letter], by H. Chambers. NEW ZEA-
LAND MEDICAL JOURNAL 90(640):74-75, July
25, 1979.

—, by J. Dobson. NEW ZEALAND MEDICAL JOURNAL
90(640):75, July 25, 1979.

—, by J. V. Hay. NEW ZEALAND MEDICAL JOURNAL
90(639):30, July 11, 1979.

—, by P. Wilcox. NEW ZEALAND MEDICAL JOURNAL
90(641):117, August 8, 1979.

NORWAY
Norwegian Christians and abortion [in Norway], by F.
Hale. DIAL 19:45-50, Winter, 1980.

THE PHILIPPINES
Induced abortion in rural villages of Cavite, the Philippines: knowledge, attitudes, and practice, by J. M.
Flavier, et al. STUDIES IN FAMILY PLANNING 11
(2):65-71, February, 1980.

POLAND

POLAND
Analysis of harmful factors in abortion and premature labor, by J. Kuczynski, et al. GINEKOLOGIA POLS-KA Suppl:95-97, 1979.

RUMANIA
Romania raises birthrate by restricting abortion, birth control access [news]. FAMILY PLANNING PER-SPECTIVES 11(5):317-318, October, 1979.

SCANDINAVIA
Use of contraceptives and abortions in Scandinavia. NOR-DISH MEDICIN 95(5):157-159, May, 1980.

SINGAPORE
Abortion deaths in Singapore (1968-1976), by L. S. Lim, et al. SINGAPORE MEDICAL JOURNAL 20(3):391-394, September, 1979.

SOUTH AFRICA
The South African gynaecologists' attitude to the present abortion law, by J. Dommisse. SOUTH AFRICAN MEDICAL JOURNAL 57(25):1044-1045, June 21, 1980.

SPAIN
Aborto y planificacion familiar: aspectos sociologicos, by H. R. Gerardo. REVISTA ESPANOLA DE INVESTI-GACIONES SOCIOLOGICAS 5:137-163, January-March, 1979.

Aborto y sociologia: en torno a un articulo del Senor Hernandez, by J. de Miguel. REVISTA ESPANOLA DE INVESTIGACIONES SOCIOLOGICAS 4:171-175, October-December, 1978.

Risking jail for a backstreet job, by J. Flint. NEW STATESMAN 98:763, November 16, 1979.

SWEDEN
From the right to live to the right to choose—birth and
legal abortion in Sweden, by H. Sjövall. LAKARTID-
NINGEN 76(48):4380-4386, November 28, 1979.

SWITZERLAND
Trends in the indications for termination of pregnancy in
the last 10 years in Switzerland, by D. Stucki. RE-
VUE MEDICALE DE LA SUISSE ROMANDE 99
(12):857-871, December, 1979.

TUNISIA
The Tunisian experience in legal abortion, by I. Nazer.
INTERNATIONAL JOURNAL OF GYNAECOLO-
GY AND OBSTETRICS 17(5):488-492, March-
April, 1980.

UNITED STATES
APHA recommended program guide for abortion ser-
vices (revised 1979). AMERICAN JOURNAL OF
PUBLIC HEALTH 70:652-656, June, 1980.

Abortion and the presidential election of 1976: a multivariate analysis of voting behavior, by M. A. Vinovskis. MICHIGAN LAW REVIEW 77(7):1750-1771,
1979.

Abortion availability in the United States: eight in ten
U.S. counties had no doctor, clinic or hospital in
1977 that provided any abortions. FAMILY PLAN-
NING PERSPECTIVES 12:88+, March-April, 1980.

Abortion, contraception, and motherhood in post-war
Japan and the United States, by M. M. Franz, et al.
INTERNATIONAL JOURNAL OF WOMEN'S
STUDIES 3:66-75, January-February, 1980.

Abortion in the USA, by J. Deedy. TABLET 234:369-
370, April 19, 1980.

UNITED STATES
Abortion in the United States, 1976-1977, by J. D.
Forrest, et al. FAMILY PLANNING PERSPECTIVES
10(5):271-279, September-October, 1978.

—, 1977-1978, by J. D. Forrest, et al. FAMILY PLAN-
NING PERSPECTIVES 11:329-335+, November-
December, 1979.

—: past, present, and future trends, by R. Krannich.
FAMILY RELATIONS 29(3):365-374, July, 1980.

Abortion—medicaid funding—equal protection. FAMILY
LAW REPORTER: COURT OPINIONS 6(14):2221,
February 12, 1980.

Abortion—Missouri. JUVENILE LAW DIGEST 12(5):
160, May, 1980.

Abortion policy in Britain and the United States, by C.
Francome. SOCIAL WORK 25(1):5-9, January,
1980.

Abortion politics in the United States, by C. Francome.
POLITICAL STUDIES 28:613-621, December, 1980.

The abortion problem in the USA and in the Netherlands.
ARS AEQUI 28(6):290-297, 1979.

Abortion: U.S. case bodes ill for poor, by L. Duncan.
BRANCHING OUT 7(2):54, 1980.

Hospital response to the legalization of abortion in New
York State: an analysis of program innovation, by
J. Miller. JOURNAL OF HEALTH AND SOCIAL BE-
HAVIOR 20:363-375, December, 1979.

Motherhood and the flag of dissent [the growing conflict
between pro- and anti-abortion forces; emphasis on

UNITED STATES
Georgia], by M. Green. ATLANTIC MONTHLY 18:
42-44+, February, 1979.

Rights of religion [ruling by Judge John F. Dooling Jr.
on the unconstitutionality of the Hyde Amendment].
COMMONWEAL 107:100-101, February 29, 1980.

Second trimester abortion in the United States, by J.
Benditt. FAMILY PLANNING PERSPECTIVES 11:
358-362, November-December, 1979.

The trend and pattern in attitudes toward abortion in the
United States, 1965-1977, by M. Evers, et al. SO-
CIAL INDICATORS RESEARCH 7(1-4):251-267,
1980.

ABORTION: ARTIFICIAL
Change in ovarian and adrenal gland function under the effect of artificial abortion, by V. I. Hryshchenko, et al.
PEDIATRIIA AKUSHERSTVO I GINEKOLOGIIA (3):
61-62, 1980.

Conducting delivery in primipara women who interrupted
their first pregnancy by artificial abortion, by T. N.
Kolgushkina, et al. ZDRAVOOKHRANENIYE BELO-
RUSSII 0(9):61-62, 1978.

ABORTION: ATTITUDES
Abortion as 'deviance'. Traditional female roles vs. the fem-
inist perspective, by R. H. Rosen, et al. SOCIAL PSY-
CHIATRY 15(2):103-108, 1980.

Abortion attitudes, 1965-1980: trends and determinants, by
D. Granberg, et al. FAMILY PLANNING PERSPEC-
TIVES 12:250-261, September-October, 1980.

Abortion: how men feel about one of the biggest issues in a
woman's life, by J. L. Collier. GLAMOUR 78:164-165+,

February, 1980.

Abortion: subjective attitudes and feelings, by E. W. Freeman. FAMILY PLANNING PERSPECTIVES 10(3):150-155, 1978.

Aging and conservatism: cohort changes in attitudes about legalized abortion, by S. J. Cutler, et al. JOURNAL OF GERONTOLOGY35:115-123, January, 1980.

Amniocentesis and abortion for sex choice. PROGRESS IN CLINICAL AND BIOLOGICAL RESEARCH 38:75-78, 1980.

—. Case for discussion. PROGRESS IN CLINICAL AND BIOLOGICAL RESEARCH 38:79, 1980.

—. Summary of discussion result. PROGRESS IN CLINICAL AND BIOLOGICAL RESEARCH 38:103-104, 1980.

Attitudes on abortion and firearms control. AMERICAN BAR ASSOCIATION JOURNAL 65:1634-1635, November, 1979.

Attitudes toward abortion: a comparative analysis of correlates for 1973 and 1975, by T. C. Wagenaar. JOURNAL OF SOCIOLOGY AND SOCIAL WELFARE 4(6):927-944, July, 1977.

Attitudes toward abortion have changed little since mid-70s. GALLUP OPINION INDEX p6-7, June, 1980.

Attitudes toward abortion: a pilot cross-cultural comparison, by V. L. Zammuner. GIORNALE ITALIANO DI PSICO-LOGIA 3(1):75-116, April, 1976.

Autoimmune disease and the theory of clonal abortion: is it still relevant, by E. Bitteau. JOURNAL OF PHARMA-

COLOGY 10(1):69-72, 1979.

Beliefs about the permissibility of abortion and their relationship to decisions regarding abortion, by J. G. Smetana. JOURNAL OF POPULATION 2(4:294-305, Winter,
1979.

Changing attitudes toward abortion, by M. Potts. WESTERN
JOURNAL OF MEDICINE 131(5):455-459, November,
1979.

Components of delay amongst women obtaining termination
of pregnancy, by J. R. Ashton. JOURNAL OF BIOSO-
CIAL SCIENCE 12:261-274, July, 1980.

Contact with the hospital service caused helplessness, shame
and guilt, by B. Rennerstedy. LEKARTIDNINGEN 77
(7):533-536, February 13, 1980.

Contraception, abortion and self concept, by R. H. Rosen, et
al. JOURNAL OF POPULATION 2(2):118-139,Sum-
mer, 1979.

Eighty percent of Americans believe abortion should be le-
gal; 70 percent approve Medicaid Funding [news] . FAM-
ILY PLANNING PERSPECTIVES 11(3):189-190, May-
June, 1979.

Even abortionists having second thoughts. (interviews with
4 abortionists), by T. G. Gulick. HUMAN EVENTS 40:
15+, April 12, 1980.

How attitudes toward abortion are changing, by E. F. Jones.
JOURNAL OF POPULATION 1(1):5-21, Spring, 1978.

Induced abortion: free freedom to abort for whom?. SYGE-
PLEJERSKEN 80(4):4-6, January 23, 1980.

—? We meet the patients once the decision for abortion has

been made, by K. Hindberg. SYGEPLEJERSKEN 80 (12):17, March 19, 1980.

Induced abortion from a social point of view, by Y. Kadman. SOCIETY AND WELFARE 2(3):320-329, 1979.

Maternal reactions to involuntary fetal/infant death, by L. G. Peppers, et al. PSYCHIATRY 43(2):155-159, May, 1980.

Mental health consequences of abortion and refused abortion, by W. W. Watter. CANADIAN JOURNAL OF PSYCHIATRY 25(1):68-73, February, 1980.

Methodical aspects and results of studies into motivations for induced termination of pregnancy and the wish to have a child, by G. Henning, et al. ZENTRALBLATT FUR GYNAEKOLOGIE 101(10):666-672, 1979.

New right exploits abortion, by J. M. Wall. CHRISTIAN CENTURY 97:747-748, July 30-August 6, 1980.

Obstetricians' attitudes and hospital abortion services, by C. A. Nathanson, et al. FAMILY PLANNING PERSPECTIVES 12:26-33, January-February, 1980.

Post-abortion attitudes and patterns of birth control, by M. Abrams, et al. JOURNAL OF FAMILY PRACTICES 9 (4):593-599, October, 1979.

Questions of bio-ethics in the termination of pregnancy in the second and third trimester of pregnancy for eugenic indications, by F. K. Beller, et al. GEBURTSHILFE UND FRAUENHEILKUNDE 40(2):142-144, February, 1980.

Social and individual responsibility in premature termination of pregnancy, by J. Rothe. MEDIZIN UND GESELLSCHAFT (3):90-96, 1978.

Special reasons for abortion, by L. Sundström-Feigenberg. LEKARTIDNINGEN 77(7):558-559, February 13, 1980.

The trend and pattern in attitudes toward abortion in the United States, 1965-1977, by M. Evers, et al. SOCIAL INDICATORS RESEARCH 7:251-267, January, 1980.

Who should decide? A survey of attitudes about bioethical decision-making, by C. Holmes, et al. ETHICS IN SCIENCE AND MEDICINE 6(3):137-144, 1979.

ABORTION: BIBLIOGRAPHY
Books on abortion, by N. Caynar. NEW COVENANT 10: 30, July, 1980.

ABORTION: COMPLICATIONS
Abortion associated with intrauterine infection by candida albicans. Case report, by R. Buchanan, et al. BRITISH JOURNAL OF OBSTETRICS AND GYNAECOLOGY 86(9):741-744, September, 1979.

Abortion for fetal abnormalities [letter]. NEW ZEALAND MEDICAL JOURNAL 90(639):31, July 11, 1979.

—, by P. S. Brooke. NEW ZEALAND MEDICAL JOURNAL 90(640):75-76, July 25, 1979.

Abortive T5 bacteriophage infections of *Escherichia coli* containing the colicinogenic factor, colib, by J. Glenn. DISSERTATION ABSTRACTS INTERNATIONAL 40(08): 3587-B, 1979.

Amniotic-fluid embolism and abortion [letter], by R. J. Guidotti, et al. LANCET 2(8148):911-912, October 27, 1979.

Analysis of harmful factors in abortion and premature labor, by J. Kuczynski, et al. GINEKOLOGIA POLSKA Suppl: 95-97, 1979.

Anovulation after pregnancy termination: ovarian versus hypothalamic-pituitary factors, by G. S. DiZerega, et al. JOURNAL OF CLINICAL ENDOCRINOLOGY AND METABOLISM 49(4):594-599, October, 1979.

Avoidance of late abortion [editorial] . LANCET 2(8152): 1113-1114, November 24, 1979.

Changes in the fibrinogen level and the risk of defibrination after the intra-amniotic instillation of a saline solution used for abortion purposes, by A. Atanasov. AKU-SHERSTVO I GINEKOLOGIIA 19(3):206-209, 1980.

Circadian changes of rheobase in patients with imminent a-bortion and premature labor, by H. Fendel, et al. ARCHIVES OF GYNECOLOGY 228(104):175-176, July 20, 1979.

Contact with the hospital service caused helplessness, shame and guilt, by B. Rennerstedt. LEKARTIDNINGEN 77 (7):533-536, February 13, 1980.

The cost of the termination of pregnancy. Delayed medical complications. A Lausanne study, by H. E. Stamm, et al. REVUE MEDICALE DE LA SUISSE ROMANDE 99 (12):885-888, December, 1979.

—. Medical aspects, by C. Revas, et al. REVUE MEDICALE DE LA SUISSE ROMANDE 99(12):873-883, December, 1979.

—. Psycho-social aspects, by M. Hurni. REVUE MEDICALE DE LA SUISSE ROMANDE 99(12):889-899, December, 1979.

Cultures from thymus and liver cells and blood lymphocytes for chromosome analysis in human abortions, by F. Dagna Bricarelli, et al. BOLLETTINO DELL ISTITUTO SIEROTERAPICO MILANESE 57(5):650-653, November 30, 1978.

Determination of HCG activity in the urine of women: possibilities of prognosis in abortion cases, by J. Peterek, et al. WIADOMOSCI LEKARSKIE 32(23):1681-1683, December 1, 1979.

Diagnostic value of serum HCG determination in disturbed early pregnancies (amminent abortion and extrauterine pregnancy), by V. G. Pahnke, et al. ARCHIVES OF GYNECOLOGY 228(1-4):224-226, July 20, 1979.

Disappearance of human chorionic gonadotropin and resumption of ovulation following abortion, by R. P. Marrs, et al. AMERICAN JOURNAL OF OBSTETRICS AND GYNECOLOGY 135(6):731-736, November 15, 1979.

Discussion on sterilization and abortion in middle age. JOURNAL OF BIOSOCIAL SCIENCE Suppl(6):157-162, 1979.

Do severe complications still occur in induced abortion? [letter], by D. Hleinknecht, et al. NOUVELLE PRESSE MEDICALE 9(3):187, January 12, 1980.

Early and late complications following surgical abortion, by F. K. Beller. ARCHIVES OF GYNECOLOGY 228(1-4): 349-364, July 20, 1979.

Effect of interrupting the first pregnancy on the course of the next pregnancy, labor, puerperium and the newborn infant's condition, by S. Lembrych, et al. WIADOMOSCI LEKARSKIE 33(5):345-350, March 1, 1980.

Effectiveness of partusysten in the therapy of interrupted pregnancy, by H. G. Stepankivs'ka, et al. PEDIATRIYA, AKUSHERSTVO I GINEKOLOHIYA (4):38-40, July-August, 1979.

Effects of antenatal diagnosis and selective abortion on frequencies of genetic disorders, by A. G. Motulsky, et al. CLINICAL OBSTETRICS AND GYNAECOLOGY 7(1): 121-133, April, 1980.

Evaluation of abortion deaths, by S. Basak. JOURNAL OF OBSTETRICS AND GYNECOLOGY OF INDIA 29(4): 790-794, 1979.

An extra week in case of the smallest doubt. SYGEPLE-JERSKEN 80(12):20, March 19, 1980.

Functional state of the sympathetic-adrenal system in interrupted pregnancy, by I. P. Gryzhak, et al. VOPROSY OKHRANY MATERINSTVA I DETSTVA 25(4):48-51, April, 1980.

Fatal myocarditis associated with abortion in early pregnancy, by D. A. Grimes, et al. SOUTHERN MEDICAL JOURNAL 73(2):236-238, February, 1980.

Fetal-maternal transfusion following early abortion, by M. Leong, et al. OBSTETRICS AND GYNECOLOGY 54 (4):424-426, October, 1979.

Gestational trophoblastic disease within an elective abortion population, by B. A. Cohen, et al. AMERICAN JOURNAL OF OBSTETRICS AND GYNECOLOGY 135(4): 452-454, October 15, 1979.

Haemophilus influenzae septicemia and midtrimester abortion, by E. Ogden, et al. JOURNAL OF REPRODUCTIVE MEDICINE 22(2):106-108, 1979.

Histological examination of abortion tissue, by B. Sikjaer. UGESKRIFT FOR LAEGER 141(30):2049-2051, July 23, 1979.

The incidence of abdominal surgical procedures in a popula-

tion undergoing abortion, by T. M. King, et al. AMERI-
CAN JOURNAL OF OBSTETRICS AND GYNECOL-
OGY 137(5):530-533, July 1, 1980.

Infectious complications following abortion, by U. Hoyme,
et al. ARCHIVES OF GYNECOLOGY 228(1-4):379,
July 20, 1979.

Interruption of pregnancy in the I. and II. trimester and its
relationship to the woman's health, by M. Chalupa.
SBORNIK VEDECKYCH PRACI LEKARSKE FAKUL-
TY KARLEVY UNIVERZITY V HRADCI KRALOVE
23(1):1-73, 1980.

Kinemometric study of the Achilles reflex during normal
pregnancy, abortions and early and late toxicoses, by N.
Nedev, et al. AKUSHERSTVO I GINEKOLOGIIA 18
(4):246-253, 1979.

Malignant group B streptococcal endocarditis associated with
saline-induced abortion, by J. G. Jemsek, et al. CHEST
76(6):695-697, December, 1979.

Management of first trimester pregnancy termination failures,
by R. F. Valle, et al. OBSTETRICS AND GYNECOLO-
GY 55(5):625-629, May, 1980.

Medical risks of abortion, by C. Berman. GOOD HOUSE-
KEEPING 191:230, October, 1980.

Miscarriages and DES daughters [research of L. Cousins].
SCIENCE NEWS 117:69, February 2, 1980.

Missed tubal abortion, by S. Burrows, et al. AMERICAN
JOURNAL OF OBSTETRICS AND GYNECOLOGY 136
(5):691-692, March 1, 1980.

Morphological changes of the Shwartzman type in endotoxic
shock after abortion, by D. Alessandrescu, et al. MOR-

PHOLOGIE ET EMBRYOLOGIE 26(1):41-45, January-March, 1980.

Mycoplasmas and ureaplasmas in infertility and abortion, by J. Friberg. FERTILITY AND STERILITY 33(4):351-359, April, 1980.

Organization of specialized care in miscarriage, by L. G. Kovtunova, et al. AKUSHERSTVO I GINEKOLOGIIA (5):13-16, May, 1980.

Problems arising from the interruption of pregnancy, by F. Zimmer. HAUTARZT 31 Suppl 4:31-35, 1980.

Re-acutized latent toxoplasmosis as a demonstrated cause of current abortion and probable cause of preceding abortive pregnancies and fetal death. Study of a case, by S. Deragna, et al. MINERVA GINECOLOGIA 32(102):43-47, January-February, 1980.

Reduction of maternal mortality due to post-abortion septic shock, by medical and surgical treatment, by S. Iturriaga Ruiz, et al. REVISTA CHILENA DE OBSTETRICIA Y GINECOLOGIA 43(6):330-343, 1978.

Risk of spontaneous abortion following legally induced abortion, by E. B. Obel. ACTA OBSTETRICIA ET GYNECOLOGICA SCANDINAVICA 59(2):131-135, 1980.

The role of a long-acting vaginal suppository of 15-ME-PGF2 alpha in first and second trimester abortion, by N. H. Lauersen, et al. ADVANCES IN PROSTAGLANDIN AND THROMBOXANE RESEARCH 8:1435-1441, 1980.

Rubella vaccination and unnecessary abortions [letter], by J. W. Peters, et al. BRITISH MEDICAL JOURNAL 2 (6204):1588-1589, December 15, 1979.

Rupture of the uterus during prostaglandin-induced abortion [letter], by G. J. Jarvis, et al. BRITISH MEDICAL JOURNAL 2(6191):671, September 15, 1979.

Seropositivity to toxoplasma in 3,455 women. Its role in abortion and evaluation of some probable risk factors, by C. Amici, et al. ANNALI SCLAVO 21(3):264-271, May-June, 1979.

Statistical studies on complications following abortion in the Federal Republic of Germany, by H. H. Bräutigam, et al. ARCHIVES OF GYNECOLOGY 228(1-4):344-348, July 20, 1979.

Strategies of despair: abortion in America and in American medicine, by J. B. Imber. DISSERTATION ABSTRACTS INTERNATIONAL 40(10):5617-A, 1979.

Thrombocyte aggregation in pregnancy termination in first trimester, by E. Kidess, et al. ARCHIVES OF GYNECOLOGY 228(1-4):629-630, July 20, 1979.

Uterine perforation in a legal abortion, by A. Beck, et al. JUGOSLAVENSKA GINEKOLOGIJA I OPSTETRICIJA 19(1-2):87-93, 1979.

Uterine rupture as a complication of second trimester abortion using intraamniotic prostaglandin E2 and augmentation with other oxytocic agents, by T. McCarthy, et al. PROSTAGLANDINS 19(6):849-854, June, 1980.

Uterine rupture caused by midtrimester saline abortion, by T. K. Bryson, et al. ACTA OBSTEYRICIA ET GYNECOLOGICA SCANDINAVICA 58(5):497-498, 1979.

Uterus perforation as complication of legal abortion, by A. Beck, et al. ARCHIVES OF GYNECOLOGY 228(1-4): 395, July 20, 1979.

Vegetative reaction during pregnancy interruption under general anesthesia, by S. Rajic, et al. SRPSKI ARHIV ZA DELOKUPNO LEKARSTVO 107(4):387-390, April, 1979.

Von Willebrand's disease complicating second-trimester abortion, by J. Sorosky, et al. OBSTETRICS AND GYNECOLOGY 55(2):253-254, February, 1980.

ABORTIONS: COMPLICATIONS: PSYCHOLOGICAL
Emotional distress patterns among women having first or repeat abortions, by E. W. Freeman, et al. OBSTETRICS AND GYNECOLOGY 55(5):630-636, May, 1980.

ABORTION: ETIOLOGY
Etiologies and subsequent reproductive performance of 100 couples with recurrent abortion, by T. T. Phung, et al. FERTILITY AND STERILITY 32(4):389-395, October, 1979.

ABORTION: HABITUAL
Catecholamine metabolic characteristics of women with habitual abortion, by I. P. Hryzhak. PEDIATRIIA AKUSHERSTVO I GINEKOLOGIIA (4):55-56, July-August, 1979.

Chromosome studies and alpha1-antitrypsin phenotypes in recurrent abortions, by J. P. M. Geraedts, et al. CLINICAL GENETICS 17(1):68, 1980.

Cytogenetic results in 96 couples with repeated abortions, by W. Schmid. CLINICAL GENETICS 17(1):85, 1980.

Crytogenetic studies in patients with a history of multiple abortions, by M. J. W. Faed, et al. CLINICAL GENETICS 17(1):64, 1980.

Etiologies and subsequent reproductive performance of 100 couples with recurrent abortion, by T. T. Phung, et al.

Full-term pregnancies following habitual abortions, by R. Berendes, et al. ARCHIVES OF GYNECOLOGY 228(1-4):553-554, July 20, 1979.

Genetic studies in habitual abortion, by N. A. Karetnikova, et al. AKUSHERSTVO I GINEKOLOGIIA (4):42-46, April, 1980.

NOR activity in two families with balanced D;D translocations and numerous consecutive miscarriages, by N. Gahmberg, et al. HEREDITAS 92(2):217-221, 1980.

Placental lactogen content in women with habitual abortion, by L. I. Tereshchenko. VOPROSY OKHRANY MATERINSTVA I DETSTVA February, 1980.

Possible relationship between lupus inhibitor and recurrent abortion in young women [letter], by B. G. Firkin, et al. LANCET 2(8190):366, August 16, 1980.

Recurrent abortions associated with Robertsonian translocation (22/22) in a male carrier, by P. Temperani, et al. CLINICAL GENETICS 17(1):90, 1980.

Recurrent miscarriage in a patient with chromosomal translocation—karyotype 46,XX,t(10;11) (q21;q23), by K. Boczkowski, et al. GINEKOLOGIA POLSKA 50(7):627-630, July, 1979.

Repeat abortions; blaming the victims, by B. Howe, et al. AMERICAN JOURNAL OF PUBLIC HEALTH 69:1242-1246, December, 1979.

Repeated abortions and histocompatibility antigens. Can HLA antigen restricted gene dose effects influence the feto-maternal relationship?, by L. Komlos, et al. MEDICAL HYPOTHESES 5(8):901-908, August, 1979.

Successful pregnancy in an abortion-prone woman: prostaglandin and hormone levels during implantation, gestation and lactation, by M. Korteweg, et al. PROSTA-GLANDINS AND MEDICINE 4(3):185-192, March, 1980.

Sugar tolerance test in the clinical investigation of the etiology of spontaneous and habitual abortions, by D. Popovic, et al. SRPSKI ARHIV ZA CELOKUPNO LEKARSTVO 107(9):469-475, September, 1979.

ABORTION: HISTORY

Abortion and the handicapped: present practice in the light of history, by G. Hogan. SOCIAL THOUGHT 6:37-46, Summer, 1980.

Abortion attitudes, 1965-1980: trends and determinants, by D. Granberg, et al. FAMILY PLANNING PERSPEC-TIVES 12:250-261, September-October, 1980.

Abortion deaths in Singapore (1968-1976), by L. S. Lim, et al. SINGAPORE MEDICAL JOURNAL 20(3):391-394, September, 1979.

Abortion in the United States, 1976-1977, by J. D. Forrest, et al. FAMILY PLANNING PERSPECTIVES 10(5):271-279, September-October, 1978.

Abortion in the United States: past, present and future trends, by R. S. Krannich. FAMILY RELATIONS 29: 365-374, July, 1980.

Comparative studies of abortions before and after the reform of Abortion Law 218, by S. Granitzka, et al. ARCHIVES OF GYNECOLOGY 228(1-4):384-385, July 20, 1979.

Decisions concerning applications for termination of pregnancy during the period from 1 April 1970 to 31 March 1979, by V. Sele. UGESKRIFT FOR LAEGER 142(12): 788-791, March 17, 1980.

Deliveries and abortions 1976-1979, by L. B. Knudsen, et al. UGESKRIFT FOR LAEGER 142(31):2003-2004, July 28, 1980.

ABORTION: ILLEGAL
Acute bacterial endocarditis following criminal abortion [letter], by R. L. Bhoola, et al. SOUTH AFRICAN MEDICAL JOURNAL 56(3):85, July 21, 1979.

Estimates of the rate of illegal abortion and the effects of eliminating therapeutic abortion, Alberta 1973-1974, by S. A. McDaniel, et al. CANADIAN JOURNAL OF PUBLIC HEALTH 70(6):393-398, November-December, 1979.

ABORTION: ILLEGAL: COMPLICATIONS
Acute renal insufficiency after criminal and septic abortion, by T. Szepietowski, et al. GINEKOLOGIA POLSKA 50 (11):927-934, November, 1979.

Intra-abdominal foreign bodies sequelae from attempted abortion, by E. Maggiore, et al. ANNALI ITALIANI DI CHIRURGIA 49(1-6):219-225, 1975-1976.

ABORTION: INDUCED
Abortion, deformed fetus, and the Omega pill, by L. M. Fleck. PHILOSOPHICAL STUDIES 36:271-283, October, 1979.

Abortion of fetuses with spina bifada? [letter], by P. F. Hall. CANADIAN MEDICAL ASSOCIATION JOURNAL 121 (7):846, October 6, 1979.

Analysis of patients and indications for induced abortion, by A. von Trotha, et al. ARCHIVES OF GYNECOLOGY 228(1-4):382, July 20, 1979.

A comparative study of spontaneous and self-induced abortion cases in married women, by C. Bose. JOURNAL OF

THE INDIAN MEDICAL ASSOCIATION 73(3-4):56-59, August, 1979.

Contraceptive practice and repeat induced abortion: an epidemiological investigation, by M. J. Shepard, et al. JOURNAL OF BIOSOCIAL SCIENCE 11(3):289-302, July, 1979.

Decision for induced abortion. A study on possible influences, by R. Rauskolb, et al. ARCHIVES OF GYNECOLOGY 228(1-4):392-393, July 20, 1979.

Dilatation and evacuation for induced abortion in developing countries: advantages and disadvantages, by W. Cutes, et al. STUDIES IN FAMILY PLANNING 11:128-133, April, 1980.

The effect of induced abortion on the incidence of Downs Syndrome in Hawaii, by R. G. Smith, et al. FAMILY PLANNING PERSPECTIVES 12:201-205, July-August, 1980.

From criminal offense to social service. An analysis of the social significance of induced abortion in The Netherlands, by E. Ketting. SAMSOM UITGEVERIJ 1978.

Induced abortion after feeling fetal movements: its causes and emotional consequences, by C. Brewer. JOURNAL OF BIOSOCIAL SCIENCE 10(2):203-208, April, 1978.

Induced abortion: free abortion freedom for whom? We meet the patients once the decision for abortion has been made, by K. Hindberg. SYGEPLEJERSKEN 80(12):17, March 19, 1980.

Induced abortion: free freedom to abort for whom? SYGEPLEJERSKEN 80(4):4-6, January 23, 1980.

Induced abortion from a social point of view, by Y. Kadman.

SOCIETY AND WELFARE 2(3):320-329, 1979.

Induced abortion in 1-day patients, by M. Anderer. AR-CHIVES OF GYNECOLOGY 228(1-4):385-386, July 20, 1979.

Induced abortion in primigravidae and subsequent pregnancy, with particular consideration of underweight, by B. Grindel, et al. ZENTRALBLATT FUR GYNAEKOLO-GIE 101(16):1009-1014, 1979.

Induced abortion in rural villages of Cavite, the Philippines: knowledge, attitudes, and practice, by J. M. Flavier, et al. STUDIES IN FAMILY PLANNING 11(2):65-71, February, 1980.

Induced abortion in the Wessex Health Region, England, UK, by J. R. Ashton. EPIDEMIOLOGY AND COMMUNITY HEALTH 33(2):168, 1979.

Induced abortion, 1979, by C. Tietze. POPULATION COUNCIL 1979.

Induced abortion—psychological implications, by M. Golomb. SOCIETY AND WELFARE 2(3):311-319, 1979.

The influence of sulprostone upon platelet function: in vitro and in vivo studies, by R. C. Briel, et al. AD-VANCES IN PROSTAGLANDIN AND THROMBOX-ANE RESEARCH 6:351-353, 1980.

Insertion of a coil (Gravigard) in induced abortion, by S. Olsen, et al. UGESKRIFT FOR LAEGER 142(13):820-822, March 24, 1980.

Late effects of induced abortion: hypothesis or knowledge, by W. Cates, Jr. JOURNAL OF REPRODUCTIVE MEDICINE 22(4):207-212, 1979.

The Marquis de Sade and induced abortion, by A. D. Farr. JOURNAL OF MEDICAL ETHICS 6(1):7-10, March, 1980.

Menstrual cycle after artificial abortion, by Z. Pavlic, et al. JUGOSLAVENSKA GINEKOLOGIJA I OPSTETRICI-JA 19(1-2):59-66, 1979.

Methodical aspects and results of studies into motivations for induced termination of pregnancy and the wish to have a child, by G. Henning, et al. ZENTRALBLATT FUR GYNAEKOLOGIE 101(10):666-672, 1979.

Outcome of the delivery following an induced or spontaneous abortion, by S. C. Schoenbaum, et al. AMERICAN JOURNAL OF OBSTETRICS AND GYNECOLOGY 136(1):19-24, January 1, 1980.

The outcome of pregnancies subsequent to induced and spontaneous abortion, by A. U. Oronsaye. INTERNATIONAL JOURNAL OF GYNAECOLOGY AND OBSTETRICS 17(3):274-277, November-December, 1979.

Pregnancy outcome after previous induced abortion, by M. Mandelin, et al. ANNALES CHIRURGIAE ET GYNAECOLOGIAE 68(5-6):147-154, 1979.

Prospective study of the Social Medical Service of the University Gynecological Hospital Basel on induced abortion, by M. Mall-Haefeli, et al. ARCHIVES OF GYNECOLOGY 228(1-4):389-391, July 20, 1979.

Repeat induced abortion: single, married and divorced women, by B. E. Aguirre. JOURNAL OF BIOSOCIAL SCIENCE 12:275-286, July, 1980.

Significance of preoperative diagnosis in induced abortion, by H. Wilken, et al. ARCHIVES OF GYNECOLOGY 228(1-4):379-381, July 20, 1979.

220

Skin and genital diseases of the mother as indications for induced abortion, by G. W. Korting. HAUTARZT 31 Suppl 4:9-12, 1980.

Sterilization performed in connection with induced abortion, by F. Hald, et al. UGESKRIFT FOR LAEGER 142 (5):321, January 28, 1980.

Study on induced abortion in married women in an urban area, by C. Bose. JOURNAL OF FAMILY WELFARE 26:40-49, June, 1980.

Vaginal tubal ligation concurrent with medical termination of pregnancy, by I. Gupta, et al. INDIAN JOURNAL OF MEDICAL RESEARCH 70:960-964, December, 1979.

ABORTION: INDUCED: COMPLICATIONS
Are the severe complications of induced abortion being abolished? Statistics from the emergency unit of the Claude Bernard Hospital 1970-1977, by F. Vachon, et al. NOUVELLE PRESSE MEDICALE 8(27):2247-2249, June 16, 1979.

Are there still severe complications in induced abortion? [letter], by D. Kleinknecht, et al. NOUVELLE PRESSE MEDICALE 9(7):460, February 9, 1980.

Association of induced abortion with subsequent pregnancy loss, by A. A. Levin, et al. JAMA 243(24):2495-2499, June 27, 1980.

Cervix rupture after prostaglandin-induced late abortion, by A. Ingvardsen, et al. UGESKRIFT FOR LAEGER 141 (51):3531-3532, December 17, 1979.

Complications and sequelae of induced abortion in the 2d trimester by hypertonic saline solution and PGF2alpha, by J. Vujic, et al. ARCHIVES OF GYNECOLOGY 228 (1-4):410-411, July 20, 1979.

Complications in induced abortions. Two-years material from Aker hospital, by O. H. Jensen, et al. TIDSSKRIFT FOR DEN NORSKE LAEGEFORENING 100(8-9):484-486, March 20, 1980.

Delayed reproductive complications after induced abortion, by K. Dalaker, et al. ACTA OBSTETRICIA ET GYNE-COLOGICA SCANDINAVICA 58(5):491-494, 1979.

Ectopic trophoblast as a complication of first-trimester induced abortion, by D. A. Dessouky. AMERICAN JOURNAL OF OBSTETRICS AND GYNECOLOGY 136(3): 407-408, February 1, 1980.

Induced abortion followed by pelvic osteomyelitis, by S. Yadav, et al. JOURNAL OF THE INDIAN MEDICAL ASSOCIATION 73(9-10):168-169, November, 1979.

Induced abortions and their complications, by S. Yarkoni, et al. HAREFUAH 96(11):603-607, June 1, 1979.

Pregnancy complications following legally induced abortion, by E. B. Obel. ACTA OBSTETRICIA ET GYNECOLO-GICA SCANDINAVICA 58(5):485-490, 1979.

Pregnancy complications following legally induced abortion: an analysis of the population with special reference to prematurity, by E. B. Obel. DANISH MEDICAL BULLETIN 26(4):192-199, July, 1979.

Preoperative prostaglandin administration, for avoidance of dilatation-caused damages in induced abortion, by S. Heinzl, et al. ARCHIVES OF GYNECOLOGY 228 (1-4):422-423, July 20, 1979.

Problems of fertility in women with a history of induced abortion in the first pregnancy, by S. Lembrych, et al. GINEKOLOGIA POLSKA 50(8):669-673, August, 1979.

A prospective study of spontaneous fetal losses after induced abortions, by S. Harlap, et al. NEW ENGLAND JOURNAL OF MEDICINE 301(13):677-681, September 27, 1979.

Rate of Rh immunization after induced abortions, by I. Simonovits, et al. VOX SANGUINIS 38(3):161-164, 1980.

Ultero-abdominal fistula following an induced abortion, by B. Ghosh. JOURNAL OF OBSTETRICS AND GYNECOLOGY OF INDIA 29(4):927-929, 1979.

Urinary estrogen excretion and concentration of serum human placental lactogen in pregnancies following legally induced abortion, by E. B. Obel, et al. ACTA OBSTETRICIA ET GYNOCOLOGICA SCANDINAVICA 59 (1):37-41, 1980.

ABORTION: INDUCED: TECHNIQUES
Choice of method and complication prevention in induced abortion, by K. A. Walz, et al. ARCHIVES OF GYNECOLOGY 228(1-4):393-395, July 20, 1979.

Comparison of intra- and paracervical anesthesia in induced abortion, by F. D. Peters, et al. ARCHIVES OF GYNECOLOGY 228(1-4):381-382, July 20, 1979.

Maturation of the cervix by prostaglandins before inducing termination of pregnancy, in the first trimester, by B. Bourrit, et al. JOURNAL DE GYNECOLOGIE OBSTETRIQUE ET BIOLOGIE DE LA REPRODUCTION 8 (6):567-570, 1979.

Plasma hormone concentrations in abortion induction using sulprostone, a prostaglandin E2 derivative, by H. O. Hoppen, et al. ARCHIVES OF GYNECOLOGY 228(1-4):399-400, July 20, 1979.

Plasma levels of 15 (S) 15-methyl-PGF 2 alpha-methyl ester following vaginal administration for induction of abortion in women, by A. Bhaskar, et al. CONTRACEPTION 20(5):519-531, November, 1979.

Techniques of induced abortion, their health implications and service aspects: a review of the literature, by K. Edström. WHO BULLETIN 57(3):481-497, 1979.

Various prostaglandins and various administration forms for induced abortion, by H. Steiner, et al. ARCHIVES OF GYNECOLOGY 228(1-4):404-405, July 20, 1979.

ABORTION: LAWS AND LEGISLATION
Abortion debate continues: a look at laws, regulations, restrictions and funding, by J. A. Smith. CALIFORNIA NURSE 76(1):8, June, 1980.

Abortion: issues of access, policy, rights continue to be tested, by A. H. Bernstein. HOSPITALS 54(3):28-30, February 1, 1980.

Abortion. Legal basis, methods, complications, by D. Wagner. ZFA ZEITSCHRIFT FUR ALLGEMEINMEDIZIN 55(26):1413-1418, September 20, 1979.

Abortion: legal medical and social perspectives, by J. Widdicombe, et al. FAMILY COMMUNITY HEALTH 2(3):17-28, November, 1979.

Abortion: perversion of 'help'. Legal claims to killing free of charge? 'Final solutions' of perverse emancipation, by J. Bokmann. CONCEPTE 15(4):27-32, 1979.

Abortion rights [with reply by E. Morgan], by C. Poster. HUMANIST 40:42-44, September-October, 1980.

Abortion rights: overruling neo-fascists, by E. Willis. VILLAGE VOICE 25:1+, February 4, 1980.

Abortion ruling [unconstitutionality of Hyde amendment; ruling by Judge J. F. Dooling, Jr.]. TIME 115:30, January 28, 1980.

Abortion—zoning. FAMILY LAW REPORTER: COURT OPINIONS 6(11):2173-2174, January 22, 1980.

Avortement: quelle legislation pour demain?, by P. Verspieren. ETUDES 351:319-338, October, 1979.

Birthrights at the barricades [bill designed to toughen abortion law], by C. Kennedy. MACLEANS 93:32-33, February 18, 1980.

The Catholic Church and reform of abortion legislation, by A. Lorenzer. KRITISCHE JUSTIZ 13(1):28-38, 1980.

Coercive and noncoercive abortion deterrence policies: a comparative state analysis, by C. A. Johnson, et al. LAW AND POLICY QUARTERLY 2:106-108, January, 1980.

Comparative studies of abortions before and after the reform of Abortion Law 218, by S. Granitzka, et al. ARCHIVES OF GYNECOLOGY 228(1-4):384-385, July 20, 1979.

Congress and the Hyde amendment: how the House moved to stop abortions, by P. O'Hara. CONGRESSIONAL QUARTERLY WEEKLY REPORT 38:1038-1039, April 19, 1980.

Congressman Hyde cautiously optimistic about court. OUR SUNDAY VISITOR 69:7, May 11, 1980.

Constitutional law—abortion—statutory interpretation—void for vagueness. DUQUESNE LAW REVIEW 18:161-172, Fall, 1979.

Constitutional law—due process—a state abortion statute that imposes a blanket parental consultation requirement on minors, and fails to distinguish between mature and immature minors constitutes a denial of due process. UNIVERSITY OF DETROIT JOURNAL OF URBAN LAW 57:337-363, Winter, 1980.

Constitutional law—minor's right of privacy-state may require third-party consent for a minor's abortion. TULANE LAW REVIEW 54:233-243, December, 1979.

Constitutional law—parental and judicial consent restrictions on a minor's decision to have an abortion. SUFFOLK UNIVERSITY LAW REVIEW 14:48-59, Winter, 1980.

Constitutional law: permissible requirements of parental consent for abortion. WASHBURN LAW JOURNAL 19: 601-608, Spring, 1980.

Constitutional law—Supreme Court is undecided on parental notification requirement for minor's abortion. SANTA CLARA LAW REVIEW 31:604-616, February, 1980.

Court upholds right to privacy in abortion matters, by F. Speaker. PENNSYLVANIA MEDICINE 83(6):38, June, 1980.

Court's abortion decision likely to affect all Medicaid patients. AMERICAN MEDICAL NEWS 23(27):1+, July 11, 1980.

The courts and elective abortions under Medicaid, by J. E. Menselson, et al. SOCIAL SERVICE REVIEW 54(1): 124-134, 1980.

Development of commonwealth abortion laws, by B. M. Dickens, et al. INTERNATIONAL AND COMPARATIVE LAW QUARTERLY 28:424-457, July, 1979.

Dissent of four just men [Hyde Amendment]. MS MAGA-

ZINE 9:24, September, 1980.

Ethics: what would you do? Abortion—moral or legal question. Part II, by C. Gilbert. NEW JERSEY NURSE 10 (1):6, January-February, 1980.

A fraudulent means to circumvent the abortion law [letter], by E. D. Seegers. SOUTH AFRICAN MEDICAL JOURNAL 56(14):545, September 29, 1979.

Funded adoption: a "viable" alternative to abortion. BRIGHAM UNIVERSITY LAW REVIEW 1979:363-393, 1979.

House protects funding for child health program, adds anti-abortion rider, by E. Wehr. CONGRESSIONAL QUARTERLY WEEKLY REPORT 37:2764, December 8, 1979.

House takes hard line on abortion funding. AIR FORCE TIMES 41:4, October 6, 1980.

Is a fetus a person?, by C. Donovan. SCIENCE FOR THE PEOPLE 12:9-11, November-December, 1980.

The juridical status of the fetus: a proposal for legal protection of the unborn, by P. A. King. MICHIGAN LAW REVIEW 77(7):1647-1687, August, 1979.

Law requiring doctor to notify parents in minor's abortion valid. FAMILY LAW REPORTER: COURT OPINIONS 6(10):2153-2154, January 15, 1980.

Legal abortion: questions of law from practice, by E. W. Hanack, et al. ARCHIVES OF GYNECOLOGY 228(1-4):331-343, July 20, 1979.

Legislation on abortion in the countries of the world (a review of the literature), by V. K. Kuznetsov, et al.

ZDRAVOOKHRANENIYE ROSSIISKOL FEDERATZII (5):37-40, 1980.

Legislation, public opinion, and the press: an interrelationship reflected in the New York Times' reporting of the abortion issue, by N. Buutap. DISSERTATION ABSTRACTS INTERNATIONAL 40(10):5599-A, 1979.

Medicolegal aspects of abortion, by W. Spann. HAUTARZT 31 Suppl 4:3-7, 1980.

Minnesota abortion statute held unconstitutional. FAMILY LAW REPORTER: COURT OPINIONS 6(13):2194-2195, February 5, 1980.

North Dakota law barring funds to abortion referral agency is unconstitutional. FAMILY LAW REPORTER: COURT OPINIONS 6(32):2562, June 17, 1980.

New abortion bill for old, by J. Turner. NEW SOCIETY p62, January 10, 1980.

New poll shows most want abortion law left alone, by P. Kellner, et al. SUNDAY TIMES p3, February 3, 1980.

Parent, child, and the decision to abort: a critique of the Supreme Court's statutory proposal in Bellotti v. Baird (99 Sup Ct 3035). SOUTHERN CALIFORNIA LAW REVIEW 52:1869-1915, September, 1979.

Poor have rights. ECONOMIST 274:38, January 26, 1980.

Possible landmark abortion case faces Supreme Court, by F. Franzonia. OUR SUNDAY VISITOR 69:3, November 2, 1980.

Pro-life PAC eyes 1980 races (National Pro-Life Political Action Committee). CONSERVATIVE DIGEST 6:12+, January, 1980.

Public support for pro-choice abortion policies in the nation and states: changes and stability after the Roe and Doe decisions, by E. M. Uslaner, et al. MICHIGAN LAW REVIEW 77(7):1772-1789, August, 1979.

A recent experiment the author conducted on US Senators revealed a wide variety of strategies used to answer constituent letters from single-issue voters; in the case of the experiment, the Senators were asked to state their position on abortions, by M. Feldstein. WASHINGTON MONTHLY 11(8):41-48, 1979.

Right to abortion: the courts versus the legislatures, by A. H. Bernstein. HOSPITALS 54(1):30-34, January 1, 1980.

Safety of legal abortion [letter], by W. Cates, Jr., et al. LANCET 1(8161):198-199, January 26, 1980.

State implementation of Supreme court decisions: abortion rates since Roe v. Wade, by S. B. Hanse. JOURNAL OF POLITICS 42:372-395, May, 1980.

State regulation of late abortion and the physician's duty of care to the viable fetus, by M. A. Wood, et al. MISSOURI LAW REVIEW 45:394-422, Summer, 1980.

That the fetus should be considered a legal person, by J. Boyle. AMERICAN JOURNAL OF JURISPRUDENCE 24:59-71, 1979.

Two Princeton scholars cast a cold eye on the Supreme Court's abortion ruling: nobody wins [Hyde Amendment ruling; interview by R. K. Rein], by J. Trussell, et al. PEOPLE 14:77+, July 21, 1980.

Voluntary interruption of pregnancy: admission in the facilities concerned under the application of the legislation. SOINS 25(8):30-32, April 20, 1980.

Wardship and abortion prevention, by J. Phillips. LAW
QUARTERLY REVIEW 95:332-335, July, 1979.

Worldwide laws and policies on contraception, abortion and
sterilization affect service provision. FAMILY PLAN-
NING PERSPECTIVES 12:210-211, July-August, 1980.

AUSTRALIA
Premier in storm over tough new abortion law, by D.
Reinhardt. SUNDAY TIMES p8, May 4, 1980.

THE COMMONWEALTH
Abortion laws in Commonwealth countries, by R. J.
Cook, et al. INTERNATIONAL DIGEST OF
HEALTH LEGISLATION 30(3):395-502, 1979.

EUROPE
Abortion law reform in Europe: the European commission on human rights upholds German restrictions
on abortion. TEXAS INTERNATIONAL LAW
JOURNAL 15:162-186, Winter, 1980.

FRANCE
Most French back 1975 abortion law; birthrate decline
worries many [news]. FAMILY PLANNING PER-
SPECTIVES 12(3):158-159, May-June, 1980.

GREAT BRITAIN
Abortion (Amendment) Bill (letter). BRITISH MEDI-
CAL JOURNAL 280(6212):477-479, February 16,
1980.

—, by J. Ashton. LANCET 1(8163):315-316, February 9, 1980.

—, by M. A. Church. LANCET 1(8165):430, February
23, 1980.

—, by A. K. Clarke. LANCET 1(8160):156, January 19,

GREAT BRITAIN
1980.

—, by A. D. Clift. LANCET 1(8165):429-430, February 23, 1980.

—, by S. Dundon. LANCET 1(8165):429, February 23, 1980.

—, by E. Fottrell. LANCET 1(8163):315, February 9, 1980.

—, by R. Graham-Brown. LANCET 1(8162):260, February 2, 1980.

—, by M. Simms. LANCET 1(8162):260, February 2, 1980.

Abortion law in the UK [editorial]. SOUTH AFRICAN MEDICAL JOURNAL 57(20):803-804, May 17, 1980.

Abortion: mercy or murder?, by J. Bellini. LISTENER 103:162-163, February 7, 1980.

No case for an abortion bill [editorial]. BRITISH MEDICAL JOURNAL 2(6184):230, July 28, 1979.

Parliament overrules churches on abortion, by T. Beeson. CHRISTIAN CENTURY 97:461-462, April 23, 1980.

Prenatal diagnosis, selective abortion, and the Abortion (Amendment) Bill, by K. M. Laurence. LANCET 1(8162):249-250, February 2, 1980.

NIGERIA
Abortion and the law in Nigeria: a psychiatrist's view, by J. Niger. NIGERIAN MEDICAL JOURNAL 9(5-6): 631-634, May-June, 1979.

UNITED STATES
Abortion. FAMILY LAW REPORTER: COURT OPIN-
IONS 6(30):2536, June 3, 1980.

Abortion and the Constitution. AMERICA 143:24,
July 19-26, 1980.

Abortion and the law in 1980 [effects of U.S. supreme
court decisions since 1972], by E. W. Paul, et al.
NEW YORK STATE LAW SCHOOL LAW REVIEW
25(3):497-525, 1980.

Abortion and the poor [ruling by Judge John F. Dooling,
Jr. on the unconstitutionality of the Hyde amend-
ment]. AMERICA 142:73, February 2, 1980.

Abortion as a local option; views of J. T. Noonan.
AMERICA 141:426-427, December 29, 1979.

Abortion clinic zoning: the right to procreative freedom
and the zoning power, by L. Robinson. WOMEN'S
RIGHTS LAW REPORTER 5:283-299, Summer,
1979.

Abortion for the poor [ruling by U.S. Judge J. F. Dooling, Jr. declaring Hyde amendment unconstitutional],
by A. Press, et al. NEWSWEEK 95:81, January 28,
1980.

The abortion-funding cases and population control: an
imaginary lawsuit (and some reflections on the uncertain limits of reproductive privacy), by S. Frelich
Appleton. MICHIGAN LAW REVIEW 77(7):1723,
1979.

The abortion-funding cases: a response to Professor
Perry, by C. Fahy. GEORGETOWN LAW JOURNAL
67(5):1205-1208, 1979.

UNITED STATES
Abortion issue sparks denials. OKLAHOMA OBSERVER
12:12, March 10, 1980.

Abortion law's husband-notification requirement held
unconstitutional. CRIMINAL LAW REPORTER:
COURT DECISIONS AND PROCEEDINGS 26(17):
2373-2375, January 30, 1980.

Abortion laws, religious beliefs and the First Amendment, by S. L. Skahn. VALPARAISO UNIVERSITY
LAW REVIEW 14:487-526, Spring, 1980.

Abortion—parental notification—constitutionality of a
statute—U.S. District Court (D. Maine). JUVENILE
LAW DIGEST 12(4):113-114, April, 1980.

Abortion—parental notification—constitutionality of a
statute—Utah. JUVENILE LAW DIGEST 12(4):
109-112, April, 1980.

Abortion—parental notification—judicial consent—con-
stitutionality of a statute—U.S. District Court (S.D.
Florida). JUVENILE LAW DIGEST 12(1):17-19,
January, 1980.

Abortion—parental notification—judicial consent—constitutionality of a statute—U.S. Supreme Court.
JUVENILE LAW DIGEST 11(10):299-303, October, 1979.

Abortion: problems of legal logic, by J. M. B. Crawford.
MONTH 13:122-127, April, 1980.

Abortion rights: Hyde and seek? UNION W.A.G.E.
(61):10-11, September-October, 1980.

Abortion—welfare. FAMILY LAW REPORTER:
COURT OPINIONS 6(11):2173, January 22, 1980.

UNITED STATES
After Hyde. NATIONAL CATHOLIC REPORTER 16: 14, July 18, 1980.

After the Hyde Amendment: public funding for abortion in February 1978, by R. B. Gold. FAMILY PLANNING PERSPECTIVES 12(3):131-134, May-June, 1980.

Arkansas criminal abortion laws suffer constitutional flaws. CRIMINAL LAW REPORTER: COURT DECISIONS AND PROCEEDINGS 27(17):2365-2366, July 30, 1980.

Artificial gestation: new meaning for the right to terminate pregnancy, by R. J. Favole. ARIZONA LAW REVIEW 21(3):755-776, 1979.

Brooklyn judge rules against Hyde Amendments: federal funding of abortion. ORIGINS 9:525+, January 31, 1980.

Committee to Defend Reproductive Rights v. Myers (156 Cal Rptr 73): medi-Cal funding of abortion. GOLDEN GATE UNIVERSITY LAW REVIEW 9: 361-419, 1978-1979.

Congressmen challenge abortion funding order. OUR SUNDAY VISITOR 68:2, April 6, 1980.

The court continues its bamboozlement. ECONOMIST 276:21-22, July 5, 1980.

Court dismisses NCCB abortion provisions suit. NATIONAL CATHOLIC REPORTER 16:6, February 1, 1980.

Court hears Hyde views. NATIONAL CATHOLIC REPORTER 16:3, May 2, 1980.

234

UNITED STATES
Court to rule on "Hyde Amendment." CONGRESSION-
AL QUARTERLY WEEKLY REPORT 38:683,
March 8, 1980.

Court's opinion in Hyde amendment case [partial text of
the Supreme court's majority opinion in Harris v.
McRae, which upheld, 5-4, congressional restrictions
on federal funding of abortions]. CONGRESSION-
AL QUARTERLY WEEKLY REPORT 38:1864-
1866, July 5, 1980.

Department of Health, Education, and Welfare—abortions: final regulation. FEDERAL REGISTER 44
(109):61597-61598, October 26, 1979.

Does the Hyde amendment violate religious freedom?
Harris v. McRae (100 S Ct 2671) and the first amend-
ment, by J. A. Gold. AMERICAN JOURNAL OF
LAW AND MEDICINE 6:361-372, Fall, 1980.

Edges of life. 1. COMMUNITIES 107:420-421, August 1, 1980.

—. 2. COMMUNITIES 107:421, August 1, 1980.

—. [Supreme Court's ruling on the Hyde Amendment].
COMMONWEAL 107:421, August 1, 1980.

Florida law governing abortions held unconstitutional.
FAMILY LAW REPORTER: COURT OPINIONS
6(10):2154-2156, January 15, 1980.

Federal statutes—constitutional law—medicaid act requires states to fund all medically necessary abortions
subject to Hyde amendment. NOTRE DAME LAW-
YER 55:412-423, February, 1980.

High court may resolve Hyde Amendment controversy.

UNITED STATES
   OUR SUNDAY VISITOR 68:6, December 9, 1979.

High court overturns Dooling decision ruling Hyde constitutional; HHS discontinues Medicaid financing for
   abortions, by K. Kaunitz. HEALTH LAW VIGIL
   3(15):3-5, July 25, 1980.

The Hyde amendment. AMERICA 142:181, March 8,
   1980.

Hyde amendment. SCIENCE NEWS 118:20-21, July 12,
   1980.

The Hyde amendment and the future, by J. I. Rosoff, ed.
   FAMILY PLANNING PERSPECTIVES 12:172-173,
   July-August, 1980.

Hyde amendment ban on Medicaid abortions ruled unconstitutional. NATIONAL CATHOLIC REPORT-
   ER 16:20, January 25, 1980.

Hyde amendment declared unconstitutional by U. S.
   District Court. FAMILY LAW REPORTER:
   COURT OPINIONS 6(12):2181-2182, January 29,
   1980.

Hyde amendment goes beforeU. S. Supreme Court. OUR
   SUNDAY VISITOR 69:7, May 4, 1980.

Hyde amendment [Supreme Court's refusal to suspend
   Judge John Dooling's order for Federal funding of
   abortions]. AMERICA 142:181, March 8, 1980.

Hyde and hysteria: the liberal banner has been planted
   on the wrong side of the abortion debate, by R. J.
   Neuhaus. CHRISTIAN CENTURY 97:849-852,
   September 10-17, 1980.

UNITED STATES

Hyde ruling: abortion forces intensify fight: pro-choice 'will win in long run,' by S. Russell. NATIONAL CATHOLIC REPORTER 16:1+, July 18, 1980.

Hyde ruling opinions: from an opponent and a supporter, by E. McCormack. NATIONAL CATHOLIC REPORTER 16:22, July 13, 1980.

Injustices of the court rule Hyde constitutional [McRae v. Harris], by M. Rylance. OFF OUR BACKS 8:2, August-September, 1980.

Inmate abortion—the right to government funding behind the prison gates, by A. T. Vitale. FORDHAM LAW REVIEW 48(4):550-567, 1980.

Legal abortions and trends in fetal and infant mortality rates in the United States, by K. E. Bauman, et al. AMERICAN JOURNAL OF OBSTETRICS AND GYNECOLOGY 136(2):194-202, January 15, 1980.

Legal blow to abortion [Supreme Court decision in favor of the Hyde amendment], by C. Fox. MACLEANS 93:33-34, July 14, 1980.

Missouri abortion statute struck down on equal protection grounds. FAMILY LAW REPORTER: COURT OPINIONS 6(13):2193-2194, February 5, 1980.

Let them eat cake, says the Supreme Court [Harris vs McRae decision; Hyde Amendment and Medicaid], by D. M. Kelley. CHRISTIAN CENTURY 97:820-824, August 27-September 3, 1980.

McRae decision on abortion: seizing the moral imperative [ruling on constitutionality of Hyde amendment by Judge J. F. Dooling]. MS MAGAZINE 8:22-24, April, 1980.

UNITED STATES
Missouri abortion statute unconstitutional in part. CRIMINAL LAW REPORTER: COURT DECISIONS AND PROCEEDINGS 26(23):2503-2505, March 12, 1980.

Missouri law regulating abortions declared unconstitutional. FAMILY LAW REPORTER: COURT OPINIONS 6(16):2262-2264, February 26, 1980.

Mr. Hyde; Medicaid funds, by R. Becker. NEW REPUBLIC 181:10-11, Novemver 17, 1979.

Not free to choose [Harris vs McRae decision; Hyde Amendment and Medicaid]. NATION 231:33, July 12, 1980.

Right-to-lifers fear being pushed to wall by courts, by R. Shaw. OUR SUNDAY VISITOR 68:7, February 17, 1980.

Right-to-lifers waging tough battle for Senate seats, by F. Franzonia. OUR SUNDAY VISITOR 69:6, October 19, 1980.

Special project: survey of abortion law. Introduction. History of abortion law. Perspectives of viability. Federal funding of abortion. Appendix: the impact of changes in Arizona's abortion funding—a statistical analysis. Epilogue. ARIZONA STATE LAW JOURNAL 1980:70-216, 1980.

The Supreme Court and abortion: the irrelevance of medical judgment, by G. J. Annas. HASTINGS CENTER REPORT 10:23-24, October, 1980.

Supreme Court and a minor's abortion decision, by N. Dembitz. COLUMBIA LAW REVIEW 80:1251-1263, October, 1980.

UNITED STATES
Supreme Court report: abortion . . . minors, by R. L.
Young. AMERICAN BAR ASSOCIATION JOUR-
NAL 65:1388-1389, September, 1979.

Supreme Court ruling a victory for unborn life, by F.
Franzonia. OUR SUNDAY VISITOR 69:3, July 13,
1980.

Supreme Court upholds Hyde amendment [prohibiting
federal funding of most abortions], by K. A. Weiss.
CONGRESSIONAL QUARTERLY WEEKLY RE-
PORT 38:1860-1862, July 5, 1980.

The Supreme Court's Hyde amendment ruling: Medicaid
abortion restrictions, by P. Stewart. ORIGINS 10:
113+, July 17, 1980.

Survey of abortion law [United States]. ARIZONA
STATE LAW JOURNAL 1980:67-216, 1980.

Symposium on the law and politics of abortion, by M. A.
Vinovskis, ed. MICHIGAN LAW REVIEW 77:1569-
1827, August, 1979.

U.S.A.: a legal blow to abortion, by C. Fox. MAC-
LEAN'S 93:33-34, July 14, 1980.

Where abortion fight goes from here: the high court's
new ruling cheered foes of abortion, distressed supporters; now both camps plan to battle even harder.
US NEWS AND WORLD REPORT 89:42, July 14,
1980.

Will High Court usurp Congressional authority? (by overturning the Hyde amendment which forbids federal
money for abortions). HUMAN EVENTS 40:6+,
April 26, 1980.

Classification and treatment of missed abortion, by S. Levin, et al. GEBURTSCHILFE UND FRAUENHEILKUNDE 39(8):727-733, August, 1979.

Contribution to the etiology and prevention of missed abortion, by P. Drac. BRATISLAVSKE LEKARSKE LISTY 73(2):217-223, February, 1980.

Maternal plasma alpha-feto-protein in missed abortion, by Z. Habib. BIOLOGY OF THE NEONATE 35(5-6):264-267, 1979.

Platelet function, coagulation and fibrinolysis during termination of missed abortion and missed labor by PGF2 alpha and oxytocin, by R. C. Briel, et al. ACTA OBSTETRICIA ET GYNECOLOGICA SCANDINAVICA 58(4): 361-364, 1979.

ABORTION: MORTALITY AND MORTALITY STATISTICS
Abortion deaths in Singapore (1968-1976), by L. S. Lim, et al. SINGAPORE MEDICAL JOURNAL 20(3):391-394, September, 1979.

Deaths from legal and illegal abortion drop after 1973 decisions [news]. FAMILY PLANNING PERSPECTIVES 11 (5):318, October, 1979.

Legal abortion in England and Wales 1968-1978, by T. L. T. Lewis. BRITISH MEDICAL JOURNAL 6210:295-296, February 2, 1980.

Second-trimester abortion deaths—a clarification [letter], by J. M. Benditt. FAMILY PLANNING PERSPECTIVES 12(1):5+, January-February, 1980.

ABORTION: OUTPATIENT TREATMENT
Day-care abortion [letter], by M. Simms. LANCET 1(8180): 1253, June 7, 1980.

Economic benefits of day care abortion, by J. C. Catford, et al. COMMUNITY MEDICINE 1(2):115-122, May, 1979.

Electrocardiography and outpatient termination of pregnancy [letter], by E. Major. ANAESTHESIA 34(9):919, October, 1979.

Induced abortion in 1-day patients, by M. Anderer. ARCHIVES OF GYNECOLOGY 228(1-4):285-286, July 20, 1979.

Outpatient termination of early pregnancies using syringe and plastic cannula, by B. R. Marshall, et al. WESTERN JOURNAL OF MEDICINE 132(3):186-188, March, 1980.

ABORTION: PSYCHOLOGY AND PSYCHIATRY
Abortion: the effects of contraception and motivations. An enquiry in Bordeaus; social and medical aspects of abortion. Two enquiries in Brittany and Creteil (1975-1977), by M. Fresel-Losey. POPULATION 35:545-580, May-June, 1980.

Abortion and the law in Nigeria: a psychiatrist's view, by J. Edeh. NIGERIAN MEDICAL JOURNAL 9(5-6):631-634, May-June, 1979.

Adolescent pregnancy decision-making: are parents important?, by R. H. Rosen. ADOLESCENCE 15:43-54, Spring, 1980.

Are there psychiatric grounds for terminating a pregnancy?, by W. Murdoch. CENTRAL AFRICAN JOURNAL OF MEDICINE 25(7):158-160, July, 1979.

A comparison of the effects of anxiety on self-concept between pregnant women seeking an abortion and pregnant women not seeking an abortion, by E. Proud. DISSERTATION ABSTRACTS INTERNATIONAL 40(12):

5827-B, 1979.

Factor analysis of the decision process for acceptance of medical termination of pregnancy, by S. A. R. Chaurasia, et al. JOURNAL OF FAMILY WELFARE 26:58-52, March, 1980.

Factors influencing the decision to seek abortion, by G. Geijerstam. LEKARTIDNINGEN 77(7):560-564, February 13, 1980.

Health professionals' perceptions of the psychological consequences of abortion, by U. Baluk, et al. AMERICAN JOURNAL OF COMMUNITY PSYCHOLOGY 8(1):67-75, February, 1980.

The impact of abortion, by T. Cooke. ORIGINS 10:283-285, October 16, 1980.

Induced abortion after feeling fetal movements: its causes and emotional consequences, by C. Brewer. JOURNAL OF BIOSOCIAL SCIENCE 10(2):203-208, April, 1978.

Induced abortion—psychological implications, by M. Golomb. SOCIETY AND WELFARE 2(3):311-319, 1979.

Mental health consequences of abortion and refused abortion, by W. W. Watter. CANADIAN JOURNAL OF PSYCHIATRY 25(1):68-73, February, 1980.

Postabortion depressive reactions in college women, by N. B. Gould. JOURNAL OF THE AMERICAN COLLEGE HEALTH ASSOCIATION 28(6):316-320, June, 1980.

Predicting the psychological consequences of abortion, by L. R. Shusterman. SOCIAL SCIENCE AND MEDICINE 13A(6):683-689, November, 1979.

Previous induced abortion and antenatal depression in primiparae: preliminary report of a survey of mental health in pregnancy, by R. Kumer, et al. PSYCHOLOGICAL MEDICINE 8(4):711-715, November, 1978.

Psychiatric problems presented at abortion, by C. Protheroe. CONFRONTATION PSYCHIATRIQUES (16):125-148, 1978.

Psychological factors involved in request for elective abortion, by M. Blumenfield. JOURNAL OF CLINICAL PSYCHIATRY 39(1):17-25, January, 1978.

Psychological sequelae of the termination of pregnancy and their prevention, by P. A. Gloor. REVUE MEDICALE DE LA SUISSE ROMANDE 99(12):901-904, December, 1979.

Psychosocial aspects of abortion, by J. A. Nunez-Lopez. BOLETIN-ASOCIACION MEDICA DE PUERTO RICO 71(5):178-181, May, 1979.

The short term effects of psychological preparation for surgery, by A. E. Reading. SOCIAL SCIENCE AND MEDICINE 13A(6):641-654, November, 1979.

ABORTION: RESEARCH
Experimental study of the permeability of the fallopian tubes in the rabbit after division of the isthmus and microsurgical anastomosis, by J. Barbot, et al. JOURNAL DE CHIRURGIE (PARIS) 116(4):307-310, April, 1979.

ABORTION: SEPTIC
Hemosorption in hepatic insufficiency after septic abortion, by A. D. Kozhanov, et al. AKUSHERSTVO I GINEKOLOGIIA (7):42-43, July, 1979.

Intrauterine microbial flora in septic abortion, with special reference to anaerobic germs, by R. Valle Ponce, et al. REVISTA CHILENA DE OBSTETRICIA Y GINECOLO-

GIA 43(3):137-139, 1978.

Septic abortion. Complications and therapeutic considerations, by E. Canas, et al. MEDICINA CLINICA 74(2): 43-47, January 25, 1980.

ABORTION: SEPTIC: COMPLICATIONS
Acute renal failure with hemolytic crisis as a complication of septic abortion, by N. Rojansky, et al. HAREFUAH 96 (5):241-243, March 1, 1979.

Acute renal insufficiency after criminal and septic abortion, by T. Szepietowski, et al. GINEKOLOGIA POLSKA 50 (11):927-934, November, 1979.

Bowel injury in septic abortion: the need for more aggresive management, by U. Megafu. INTERNATIONAL JOURNAL OF GYNAECOLOGY AND OBSTETRICS 17(5): 450-453, March-April, 1980.

Case of complicated septic abortion in the 16th week of pregnancy, by J. Lysakowski, et al. WIADOMOSCI LE-KARSKIE 32(17):1249-1251, September 1, 1979.

Microbiological aspects of the clinical features of puerperal infections and post-septic abortion with special reference to anaerobic bacteria, by C. M. Ulson, et al. REVISTA DO INSTITUTO DE MEDICINA TROPICAL DE SAO PAULO 21(4 Suppl 3):24-66, July-August, 1979.

Therapeutic procedure in acute renal insufficiency developing after septic abortion, by V. L. Cherniakov, et al. AKUSHERSTVO I GINEKOLOGIIA (7):32-34, July, 1979.

ABORTION: SEPTIC: TECHNIQUES
Use of vaginal prostaglandin-E2 suppositories in septic abortion, by C. T. Milano, et al. PROSTAGLANDINS 19(3): 455-456, March, 1980.

Abortion: legal, medical and social perspectives, by J. Widdicombe, et al. FAMILY COMMUNITY HEALTH 2(3):
17-28, November, 1979.

Biological paternity, social maternity: on abortion and infanticide as unrecognized indicators of the cultural
character of maternity, by N. C. Mathieu. SOCIOLOGI-
CAL REVIEW MONOGRAPH 28:232-240, 1979.

Social and individual responsibility in premature termination
of pregnancy, by J. Rothe. MEDIZIN UND GESELL-
SCHAFT (3):90-96, 1978.

Social and psychological correlates of pregnancy resolution
among adolescent women: a review, by L. Olson.
AMERICAN JOURNAL OF ORTHOPSYCHIATRY 50
(3):432-445, July, 1980.

ABORTION: SPONTANEOUS
Agent Orange and spontaneous abortions [letter], by R. R.
Cook. JAMA 243(14):1423, April 11, 1980.

Alcohol and spontaneous abortion [editorial]. LANCET 2
(8187):188, July 26, 1980.

Alcohol, smoking, and incidence of spontaneous abortions in
the first and second trimester, by S. Harlap, et al. LAN-
CET 2(8187):173-176, July 26, 1980.

Analysis of the geographical variations of twinning rate in
France. An indirect approach to study spontaneous abortions, by D. Hemon, et al. REVUE D EPIDEMIOLOGIE
ET DE SANTE PUBLIQUE 27(2):91-99, September 18,
1979.

Attempt to establish a relationship between ultraviolet irradiation and early spontaneous abortions, by V. Donchev.
AKUSHERSTVO I GINEKOLOGIIA 19(2):99-103,
1980.

Chromosomal polymorphic variants in couples with recurrent spontaneous abortions, by I. Tejada, et al. CLINICAL GENETICS 17(1):90, 1980.

Chromosome variants and abnormalities detected in 51 married couples with repeated spontaneous abortions, by P. Genest. CLINICAL GENETICS 16(6):387-389, December, 1979.

A comparative study of spontaneous and self-induced abortion cases in married women, by C. Bose. JOURNAL OF THE INDIAN MEDICAL ASSOCIATION 73(3-4):56-59, August, 1979.

Cytogenetic studies in 100 couples with recurrent spontaneous abortions, by B. E. Ward, et al. AMERICAN JOURNAL OF HUMAN GENETICS 32(4):549-554, July, 1980.

Drinking during pregnancy and spontaneous abortion, by J. Kline, et al. LANCET 2(8187):176-180, July 26, 1980.

Factors affecting the incidence of miscarriage among the female employees, by H. Kashiwazaki, et al. SANGYO IGAKU 21(3):250-256, May, 1979.

Hormone therapy of spontaneous abortion. Our experience with treatment with Graviginan, by A. Drazancic, et al. JUGOSLAVENSKA GINEKOLOGIJA I OPSTETRICIJA 18(3-4):325-333, May-August, 1978.

Immunobiological examination of women with spontaneous abortions, by B. Mejsnarova, et al. SBORNIK LEKARSKY 81(11-12):337-340, November-December, 1979.

Karyotype, toxoplasma investigation, and the LAI test in women with spontaneous abortions, by B. Mejsnarova, et al. CESKOSLOVENSKA GYNEKOLOGIE 44(10):741-742, December, 1979.

Menarcheal age and spontaneous abortion: a casual connection?, by K. Liestol. AMERICAN JOURNAL OF EPIDEMIOLOGY 111(6):753-758, June, 1980.

Origin of triploidy in spontaneous abortuses, by J. G. Lauritsen, et al. ANNALS OF HUMAN GENETICS 43(1): 1-6, July, 1979.

Outcome of the delivery following an induced or spontaneous abortion, by S. C. Schoenbaum, et al. AMERICAN JOURNAL OF OBSTETRICS AND GYNECOLOGY 136 (1):19-24, January 1, 1980.

The outcome of pregnancies subsequent to induced and spontaneous abortion, by A. U. Oronsaye. INTERNATIONAL JOURNAL OF GYNAECOLOGY AND OBSTETRICS 17(3):274-277, November-December, 1979.

Outcome of pregnancy after spontaneous abortion, by T. J. David, et al. BRITISH MEDICAL JOURNAL 280 (6212):447-448, February 16, 1980.

Ovulation following spontaneous abortion (a histological and cytological study), by E. I. Efiong. NIGER MEDICAL JOURNAL 9(3):357-359, March, 1979.

Parental origin of triploidy and D and G trisomy in spontaneous abortions, by B. G. Grennan, et al. JOURNAL OF MEDICAL GENETICS 16(4):285-287, August, 1979.

Pathogenesis of late spontaneous abortions of phenotypically normal fetuses, by T. V. Zhukova, et al. VOPROSY OKHRANY MATERINSTVA I DETSTVA 24(12):48-50, December, 1979.

Ring-like chromosome 18 and osteogenesis imperfecta in a family in which spontaneous abortions appear, by S. Markovic, et al. SRPSKI ARHIV ZA CELOKUPNO LEKARSTVO 107(3):245-252, March, 1979.

Risk of spontaneous abortion following legally induced abortion, by E. B. Obel. ACTA OBSTETRICIA ET GYNECOLOGICA SCANDINAVICA 59(2):131-135, 1980.

Role of the prenatal consultation in controlling spontaneous abortions and the results of the measures taken, by I. Vasileva. AKUSHERSTVO I GINEKOLOGIIA 19(3): 209-214, 1980.

Sequential analysis of spontaneous abortion [letter], by W. H. James. FERTILITY AND STERILITY 32(3):350-351, September, 1979.

Some pathologic findings in spontaneous abortions, by J. Byrne, et al. BIRTH DEFECTS 15(5A):137-147, 1979.

Spontaneous abortion, by F. Willgeroth. ZFA. ZEITSCHRIFT FUR ALLGEMEINMEDIZIN 55(29):1625-1627, October 20, 1979.

Spontaneous abortion rates, gravidity and neural tube defectes, by W. James. EARLY HUMAN DEVELOPMENT 2(3):291-296, 1978.

Spontaneous abortions among female chemical workers in Finland, by K. Hemminki, et al. INTERNATIONAL ARCHIVES OF OCCUPATIONAL AND ENVIRONMENTAL HEALTH 45(2):123-126, February, 1980.

Spontaneous abortions and chromosomal anomalies: current questions, by A. Boue, et al. CLINICAL GENETICS 17 (1):57, 1980.

Spontaneous abortions and terminations of pregnancy: histological differences, by A. S. Bodey. MEDICAL JOURNAL OF AUSTRALIA 2(13):709-710, December 29, 1979.

Structural chromosomal aberrations in parents with spon-

taneous abortions, by S. Adzic, et al. JUGOSLAVENS-
KA GINEKOLOGIJA I OPSTETRICIJA 18(3-4):295-
302, May-August, 1978.

Studies on phenotype, development, and viability of human
spontaneous abortuses with acrocentric trisomies and
polyploidies: with reference to the relationship of the
viability to the origin of extrachromosomes, by N. Niikawa. HOKKAIDO IGAKU ZASSHI 54(3):235-244,
May, 1979.

A study of the spontaneous abortions in rural community, by
K. N. Yadava, et al. INDIAN JOURNAL OF PUBLIC
HEALTH 23(2):100-102, April-June, 1979.

A study of spontaneously aborted twins, by J. E. Livingston,
et al. TERATOLOGY 21(2):139-148, April, 1980.

Thyroid gland activity and the state of the thiol compounds
in early spontaneous abortions, by V. I. Kachala, et al.
VOPROSY OKHRANY MATERINSTVA I DETSTVA
24(7):52-54, July, 1979.

Toxic hepatitis and spontaneous abortions in female anesthesiologists: 2 cases, by S. Popova, et al. KHIRURGIIA
33(2):118-120, 1980.

Transferrin C subtypes and spontaneous abortion, by G.
Beckman, et al. HUMAN HEREDITY 30(5):316-319,
1980.

Treatment of spontaneous abortions with the preparation,
Provera, by D. Despodova, et al. AKUSHERSTVO I
GINEKOLOGIIA 18(6):457-461, 1979.

Twinning in postpill spontaneous abortions [letter] , by L. H.
Honore. AMERICAN JOURNAL OF OBSTETRICS
AND GYNECOLOGY 135(5):700-701, November 1,
1979.

Variant chromosome 9 (9qh+) in families with spontaneous abortion, by K. Mijin, et al. SRPSKI ARHIV ZA CELO-KUPNO LEKARSTVO 107(10):547-553, October, 1979.

ABORTION: SPONTANEOUS: COMPLICATIONS
The effect of missed abortion and spontaneous abortion on the fate of subsequent pregnancies, by S. Levin, et al. ACTA OBSTETRICIA ET GYNECOLOGICA SCANDI-NAVICA 58(4):371-373, 1979.

Heterochromatic polymorphism in spontaneous abortions, by L. Hemming, et al. JOURNAL OF MEDICAL GE-NETICS 16(5):358-362, October, 1979.

A high incidence of unbalanced translocations and triploidy in an unselected sample of human spontaneous abortion, by C. C. Lin, et al. GENETICS 91(4 pt 2 Suppl):s68-s69, 1979.

The increased incidence of renal stones in women with spon-taneous abortion: a retrospective study, by L. H. Hon-ore. AMERICAN JOURNAL OF OBSTETRICS AND GYNECOLOGY 137(1):145-146, May 1, 1980.

A significant association between spontaneous abortion and tubal ectopic pregnancy, by L. H. Honore. FERTILITY AND STERILITY 32(4):401-402, October, 1979.

Spontaneous abortion and grieving, by J. M. Stack. AMERI-CAN FAMILY PHYSICIAN 21(5):99-102, May, 1980.

ABORTION: STATISTICS
Abortion reporting, by M. R. Stark. ARIZONA MEDICINE 36(11):834, November, 1979.

Abortion surveillance shows slower increase. AORN JOUR-NAL 30(6):1108, December, 1979.

Abortions—statistics and reality, by E. J. Hickl. DEUTSCHE

MEDIZINISCHE WOCHENSCHRIFT 105(13):423-426, March 28, 1980.

Evaluation of abortion deaths, by S. Basak. JOURNAL OF OBSTETRICS AND GYNECOLOGY OF INDIA 29(4): 790-794, 1979.

Induced abortion: 1979, 3rd edition, by C. Tietze. 108pp, 1979.

Maternal age, stillbirths, abortions and factors related to maternal blood groups: a hospital survey from Lahore (Punjab, Pakistan), by S. A. Shami, et al. JPMA: JOURNAL OF THE PAKISTAN MEDICAL ASSOCIATION 30(2):27-34, February, 1980.

Public health need for abortion statistics, by J. Smith. PUBLIC HEALTH REPORTS 43(2):194-197, March-April, 1978.

What can we learn from the present abortion statistics?, by U. Takman. LAKARTIDNINGEN 77(7):526-530, February 13, 1980.

ABORTION: TECHNIQUES
Abdominal hysterectomy for abortion-sterilization. A report of 500 consecutive cases, by P. G. Stumpf, et al. AMERICAN JOURNAL OF OBSTETRICS AND GYNECOLOGY 136(6):714-720, March 15, 1980.

Abortion by extraamnial and intravenous administration of a new prostaglandin E2 derivative, by J. Kunz, et al. ARCHIVES OF GYNECOLOGY 228(1-4):423-424, July 20, 1979.

Abortion by means of suction curettage compared to the conventional metal curettage, by K. W. Schweppe, et al. MEDIZINISCHE WELT 31(13):479-483, March 28, 1980.

Abortion induction with the PGE2 derivative sulprostone, by N. Dennemark. ARCHIVES OF GYNECOLOGY 228(1-4):425-426, July 20, 1979.

Abortion induction with prostaglandin, by W. Lichtenegger. ARCHIVES OF GYNECOLOGY 228(1-4):405-406, July 20, 1979.

Abortion induction with 3 mg PF2alpha gel, by H. Knabe, et al. ARCHIVES OF GYNECOLOGY 228(1-4):415-416, July 20, 1979.

Abortion technics, by S. Trotnow, et al. ZFA. ZEIT-SCHRIFT FUR ALLGEMEINMEDIZIN 55(29):1628-1631, October 20, 1979.

Adjuvants in tubal surgery, by W. H. Pfeffer. FERTILITY AND STERILITY 33(3):245-256, March, 1980.

Anti-D immunoglobulin and abortion [letter], by D. Tovey. BRITISH MEDICAL JOURNAL 2(6193):793, September 29, 1979.

A casual model of psychosomatic reactions to vacuum aspiration abortion, by M. B. Bracken. SOCIAL PSYCHIATRY 13(3):135-145, 1978.

Cervical priming prior to first-trimester suction abortion with a single 15-methyl-prostaglandin F2 alpha vaginal suppository, by N. H. Lauersen, et al. AMERICAN JOURNAL OF OBSTETRICS AND GYNECOLOGY 135(8):1116-1118, December 15, 1979.

Change of factor XIII activity in pregnancy termination using suction curettage, by E. Kidess, et al. ARCHIVES OF GYNECOLOGY 228(1-4):627, July 20, 1979.

Chemical methods of abortion, by H. Schmidt-Matthiesen. ARCHIVES OF GYNECOLOGY 228(1-4):365-378,

July 20, 1979.

Comparison between intraamniotic PGF2 alpha and vaginal PGE2 for second-trimester abortion, by J. P. Lebed, et al. OBSTETRICS AND GYNECOLOGY 56(1):90-96, July, 1980.

Comparison of the effectiveness of metal and flexible plastic cannulas in abortion by vacuum aspiration, by L. Randic, et al. JUGOSLAVENSKA GINEKOLOGIJA I OPSTE-TRICIJA 18(3-4):229-237, May-August, 1978.

Comparison of the results of interruption of advanced pregnancy using prostaglandin F2-alpha and a NaC1 solution, by D. Dragovic, et al. SRPSKI ARHIV ZA CELOKUPNO LAKARSTVO 107(1):43-51, January, 1979.

Comparison of 2% and 5% lidocaine solution for local anesthesia of both fallopian tubes in laparoscopic sterilization, by E. Neeser, et al. ARCHIVES OF GYNECOLO-GY 228(1-4):279, July 20, 1979.

Differences in hormonal patterns during the first postabortion menstrual cycle after two techniques of termination of pregnancy, by A. S. Blazar, et al. FERTILITY AND STERILITY 33(5):493-500, May, 1980.

Experience from direct injection of low prostaglandin F2-alpha doses into protio for low-complication dilatation of cervix for abruptio, by R. Voigt, et al. ZENTRAL-BLATT FUR GYNAEKOLOGIE 101(24):1592-1594, 1979.

Experience with the induction of second-trimester abortion by extra-amniotic physiological saline infusion. Report of 127 cases, by M. Blum. EUROPEAN JOURNAL OF OBSTETRICS, GYNECOLOGY AND REPRODUCTIVE BIOLOGY 10(3):183-185, March, 1980.

Experiences with vacuum aspiration and uterotomy for induced abortion, by J. Kunz, et al. ARCHIVES OF GYNECOLOGY 228(1-4):388, July 20, 1979.

Extraamnial and intraamnial abortion induction using PGF2-alpha, by G. Göretzlehner, et al. ARCHIVES OF GYNECOLOGY 228(1-4):408-409, July 20, 1979.

Extraamniotic intermittent administration of prostaglandin F2 alpha during the first and second trimesters of pregnancy, by G. Goeretzlehner, et al. ANNALES CHIRURGIAE ET GYNAECOLOGIAE 68(3):100-103, 1979.

First clinical experiences with prostaglandin E derivative sulprostone in extraamnial abortion induction, by R. C. Briel, et al. ARCHIVES OF GYNECOLOGY 228(1-4): 425, July 20, 1979.

First experiences with abortion induction using sulprostone, a prostaglandin E2 derivative, by U. Gethmann, et al. ARCHIVES OF GYNECOLOGY 228(1-4):400-401, July 20, 1979.

Further studies on the trichosanthin-induced termination of pregnancy, by I. F. Lau, et al. CONTRACEPTION 21 (1):77-86, January, 1980.

Facilitation of suction termination using extra-amniotic prostaglandins in gel, by I. L. Craft, et al. PROSTAGLANDINS 18(1):143-152, July, 1979.

Histological appearances of the human placenta observed by electron microscopy after hypertonic saline abortion, by J. H. Stegeman, et al. ACTA OBSTETRICIA ET GYNECOLOGICA SCANDINAVICA 59(1):45-53, 1980.

Improvement in artificial second-trimester abortion with a new tissue-selective prostaglandin E2 derivative, by R. Schmidt-Gollwitzer, et al. AMERICAN JOURNAL OF

OBSTETRICS AND GYNECOLOGY 137(7):867-868,
August 1, 1980.

Induced abortion with prostaglandin gel in the 1st pregnancy
trimester, by H. Kühnle, et al. ARCHIVES OF GYNE-
COLOGY 228(1-4):414, July 20, 1979.

Induction of abortion by intramuscular administration of
(15S)-15-methyl PGF2 alpha. An overview of 815 cases,
by P. C. Schwallie, et al. JOURNAL OF REPRODUC-
TIVE MEDICINE 23(6):289-293, December, 1979.

Induction of first and second-trimester abortion by the
extra-amniotic administration of a prostaglandin E2-
derivate, by J. Kunz, et al. GEBURTSCHILFE UND
FRAUENHEILKUNDE 39(9):798-808, September,
1979.

Induction of therapeutic abortion with intravenous administration of prostaglandin F 2-alpha, by A. Nasi, et al.
MINERVA GINECOLOGIA 31(12):927-931, December,
1979.

Interruptio—conventional or drug induced? A report on
58 abortions using intramuscular injections of sulproston,
by K. Schlüter, et al. MEDIZINISCHE WELT 31(10):
370-373, March 7, 1980.

Interruption of early pregnancy with Enzaprost-F, by P.
Mocsary. THERAPIE HUNGARICA 27(2):84-86, 1979.

Interruption of early stages of pregnancy (menstrual regulation, mini-interruption), by F. Havranek, et al. CESKO-
SLOVENSKA GYNEKOLOGIE 44(8):561-566, September, 1979.

Interruption of pregnancy. Use of prostaglandins in the
gynecology-obstetrics service of CHUV, Lausanne, by P.
De Grandi. REVUE MEDICALE DE LA SUISSE RO-

MANDE 99(9):665-670, September, 1979.

Interruption of pregnancy with vaginal suppositories containing 16,16-dimethyl-trans-delta 2-prostaglandin E1 methyl ester, by T. Wagatsuma, et al. CONTRACEPTION 19(6):591-597, June, 1979.

Intramural-intrauterine administration of prostaglandin E2 derivative for abortion induction in semi-hospitalized care in the operating room, by H. Wiechell. ARCHIVES OF GYNECOLOGY 228(1-4):409-410, July 20, 1979.

Local versus general anesthesia: which is safer for performing suction curettage abortions?, by D. A. Grimes, et al. AMERICAN JOURNAL OF OBSTETRICS AND GYNECOLOGY 135(8):1030-1035, December 15, 1979.

Management of intrauterine fetal death with prostaglandin E2 vaginal suppositories, by N. H. Lauersen, et al. AMERICAN JOURNAL OF OBSTETRICS AND GYNECOLOGY 137(7):753-757, August 1, 1980.

Menstrual induction in preference to abortion [letter], by A. I. Csapo, et al. LANCET 1(8159):90-91, January 12, 1980.

Midtrimester abortion by dilatation and evacuation versus intra-amniotic instillation of prostaglandin F2 alpha: a randomized clinical trial, by D. A. Grimes, et al. AMERICAN JOURNAL OF OBSTETRICS AND GYNECOLOGY 137(7):785-790, August, 1, 1980.

Midtrimester dilatation and evacuation abortion, by D. A. Grimes, et al. SOUTHERN MEDICAL JOURNAL 73 (4):448-451, April, 1980.

Operation methods in early and late abortions, by M. Bygdeman. LAKARTIDNINGEN 77(7):546+, February 13, 1980.

Our experience with the early termination of unwanted pregnancy by Karman's method, by A. Khubenov. AKU-SHERSTVO I GINEKOLOGIIA 18(5):385-388, 1979.

Outpatient termination of early pregnancies using syringe and plastic cannula, by B. R. Marshall, et al. WESTERN JOURNAL OF MEDICINE 132(3):186-188, March, 1980.

Plasmatic coagulation and thrombocyte function in abortion induction with prostaglandin E2 derivative sulprostone, by K. Schander, et al. ARCHIVES OF GYNECOLOGY 228(1-4):635-637, July 20, 1979.

Prostaglandin as an abortifacient agent, by M. Bygdeman. LAKARTIDNINGEN 77(7):549-551, February 13, 1980.

Prostaglandin biosynthesis and catabolism in fetal and neonatal tissues, by R. Skidgel. DISSERTATION ABSTRACTS INTERNATIONAL 40(07):3117-B, 1979.

Prostaglandin E2 for abortion and labor induction in pregnancies with fetal death, by J. H. Duenhoelter. ARCHIVES OF GYNECOLOGY 228(1-4):407-408, July 20, 1979.

Prostaglandin E2 vaginal suppositories in pregnancy with an anencephalic fetus, by F. H. Boehm, et al. OBSTETRICS AND GYNECOLOGY 55(6):758-760, June, 1980.

Prostaglandin F2 alpha for interrupting pregnancy, managing intrauterine death and molar pregnancy and inducing labor, by H. de Gezelle, et al. INTERNATIONAL JOURNAL OF GYNAECOLOGY AND OBSTETRICS 17(4): 362-327, January-February, 1980.

Prostaglandin F2 alpha for oestrus synchronisation or abortion in Polwarth ewes, by R. N. Reid, et al. AUSTRALIAN VETERINARY JOURNAL 56(1):22-24, January,

1980.

Prostaglandins in gynecology and obstetrics. Prostaglandins offer new methods for abortion, anticonception and regulating fertility, by M. Bygdeman. NORDIC MEDICINE 94(8-9):217-219, September, 1979.

The relative value of two concentrations of hypertonic saline for midtrimester abortion, by A. K. Ghosh, et al. INTERNATIONAL JOURNAL OF GYNAECOLOGY AND OBSTETRICS 17(4):368-371, January-February, 1980.

Saline-instillation abortion with laminaria and megadose oxytocin, by M. Hachamovitch, et al. AMERICAN JOURNAL OF OBSTETRICS AND GYNECOLOGY 135(3): 327-330, October 1, 1979.

Scraping out the pregnant uterus using suction curette compared to treatment with stump curette, by K. W. Schweppe, et al. ARCHIVES OF GYNECOLOGY 228 (1-4):386-387, July 20, 1979.

Second trimester abortion with prostaglandin F2 alpha, by T. K. Chatterjee, et al. INTERNATIONAL JOURNAL OF GYNAECOLOGY AND OBSTETRICS 17(4):357-361, January-February, 1980.

Second-trimester D & E [letter], by L. Iffy, et al. OBSTETRICS AND GYNECOLOGY 55(6):766-767, June, 1980.

Sequence of fibrinogen proteolysis and platelet release after intrauterine infusion of hypertonic saline, by H. L. Nossel, et al. JOURNAL OF CLINICAL INVESTIGATION 64(5):1371-1378, November, 1979.

Sonography in 74 abortions using prostaglandin F2alpha gel, by R. Ulbrich, et al. ARCHIVES OF GYNECOLOGY 228(1-4):421-422, July 20, 1979.

Surgical abortion, by W. Lichtenegger, et al. ARCHIVES OF GYNECOLOGY 228(1-4):397, July 20, 1979.

Termination of pregnancy by medical induction: new DHSS guidelines. MIDWIVES CHRONICLE 93(1107):112-113, March, 1980.

Termination of pregnancy by vaginal administration of prostaglandin F2 alpha, by L. Matadial, et al. WEST INDIAN MEDICAL JOURNAL 29(1):57-59, March, 1980.

Termination of pregnancy complicated by anencephaly with intra-amniotic prostaglandin F2 alpha, by M. L. Schwartz, et al. AMERICAN JOURNAL OF OBSTETRICS AND GYNECOLOGY 136(2):203-204, January 15, 1980.

Termination of pregnancy in adolescents in Vaud, by P. A. Michaud, et al. REVUE MEDICALE DE LA SUISSE ROMANDE 99(12):921-929, December, 1979.

Tonometric studies on the pregnant cervix uteri in abortion before and after intracervical administration of prostaglandin F2 gel, by W. Rath, et al. ARCHIVES OF GYNECOLOGY 228(1-4):416-417, July 20, 1979.

Use of differentiated PGE2, PGF2alpha and prostaglandin-derivative administration for avoidance of complications in abortion induction, by M. Cornely. ARCHIVES OF GYNECOLOGY 228(1-4):413-414, July 20, 1979.

Use of 15-methyl PGF2-alpha for termination of early pregnancy, by I. A. Manuilova, et al. SOVETSKAIA MEDITSINA (3):49-53, 1980.

Use of intra-amniotic urea as a second trimester abortifacient, by A. Khare, et al. JOURNAL OF POSTGRADUATE MEDICINE 25(3):158-161, July, 1979.

Voluntary interruption of pregnancy, by B. Achard. SOINS 25(8):19-23, April 20, 1980.

ABORTION: THERAPEUTIC

Case of coexistent intra- and extrauterine pregnancy, by M. Semczuk, et al. WIADOMOSCI LEKARSKIE 33(2): 137-139, January 15, 1980.

Effect of althesin anesthesia on blood loss during therapeutic abortion. A comparison with local and thiopental anesthesia, by B. R. Moller, et al. ACTA OBSTETRICIA ET GYNECOLOGICA SCANDINAVICA 58(5):481-483, 1979.

Estimates of the rate of illegal abortion and the effects of eliminating therapeutic abortion, Alberta 1973-1974, by S. A. McDaniel, et al. CANADIAN JOURNAL OF PUBLIC HEALTH 70(6):393-398, November-December, 1979.

An evaluation of the counselling given to patients having a therapeutic abortion, by R. B. Hunton, et al. AUSTRALIAN AND NEW ZEALAND JOURNAL OF OBSTETRICS AND GYNAECOLOGY 19(3):169-173, August, 1979.

Induction of therapeutic abortion with intravenous administration of prostaglandin F 2-alpha, by A. Nasi, et al. MINERVA GINECOLOGIA 31(12):927-931, December, 1979.

Interruption of pregnancy based on prenatal diagnosis, by J. D. Murken, et al. HAUTARZT 31(Suppl 4):25-30, 1980.

Long-term outcome of sterilization as a function of the indication, marital status, age, number of children and concurrently performed therapeutic abortions, by U. Bänninger, et al. GEBURTSHILFE UND FRAUENHEILKUNDE 39(6):492-496, June, 1979.

Miscarriages and DES daughters [research of L. Cousins] .
SCIENCE NEWS 117:69, February 2, 1980.

Recent changes in the emotional reactions of therapeutic
abortion applicants, by S. Meikle, et al. CANADIAN
PSYCHIATRIC ASSOCIATION JOURNAL 22(2):67-70,
March, 1977.

Social security and public welfare—federal assistance and
state cooperation, statutes, and regulations in general—
statute disallowing apyment of Medicaid funds for therapeutic abortions held invalid. NORTH DAKOTA LAW
REVIEW 56:289-299, 1980.

Therapeutic abortion data from the Wergelandsveiens Clinic
in Oslo, by K. K. Klem. TIDSSKRIFT FOR DEN
NORSKE LAEGEFORENING 99(28):1418-1421, October 10, 1979.

ABORTION: THERAPEUTIC: COMPLICATIONS
Pregnancy in a non-communicating, rudimentary uterine
horn. A reason for failed therapeutic second trimester
abortion, by R. Kirschner, et al. ACTA OBSTETRICIA
ET GYNECOLOGICA SCANDINAVICA 58(5):499-501,
1979.

Vacuum aspiration at therapeutic abortion: blood loss at
operation in multigravid women, by B. Sandström, et al.
GYNECOLOGY AND OBSTETRICS INVESTIGATION
9(6):292-298, 1978.

—: influence of two different negative pressures on blood
loss during and after operation, by B. Sandström, et al.
GYNECOLOGY AND OBSTETRIS INVESTIGATION
9(6):299-303, 1978.

ABORTION: THERAPEUTIC: TECHNIQUE
New considerations in therapeutic abortions using a second
generation prostaglandins, by H. Steiner, et al. GEBURT-

SHILFE UND FRAUENHEILKUNDE 39(6):464-469, June, 1979.

A new therapeutic approach for terminating intact and disturbed pregnancies: three years of experience with the prostaglandin E2-derivative sulprostone (SHB 286), by K. Schmidt-Gollwitzer, et al. GEBURTSHILFE UND FRAUENHEILKUNDE 39(8):667-675, August, 1979.

A new therapeutic possibility of abortion in 2d trimester using intravenous administration of sulprostone, by K. Schmidt-Gollwitzer, et al. ARCHIVES OF GYNECOLOGY 228(1-4):402-403, July 20, 1979.

ABORTION: THREATENED
Activity of various enzymes of venous blood serum in advanced normal pregnancy and in pregnancy complicated by threatened abortion and premature labor, by T. Laudanski, et al. WIADOMOSCI LEKARSKIE 32(12):833-836, June 15, 1979.

Comments and the diagnosis of vitality of early pregnancy in threatening abortion, by H. Jung, et al. GEBURT-SHILFE UND FRAUENHEILKUNDE 39(6):437-446, June, 1979.

Condition of fetuses and newborn infants in pregnancies complicated by threatened abortion, by J. Kuczynski, et al. GINEKOLOGIA POLSKA Suppl:75-76, 1979.

Corpus luteum dysfunction: serum progesterone levels in diagnosis and assessment of therapy for recurrent and threatened abortion, by P. A. Hensleigh, et al. FERTILITY AND STERILITY 32(4):396-400, October, 1979.

Enzymatic activity in the blood of pregnant women undergoing acupuncture treatment in threatened abortion, by G. M. Vorontsova, et al. AKUSHERSTVO I GINEKOLOGIIA (4):38-40, April, 1980.

Enzymatic activity in the erythrocytes in threatened abortion and in acupuncture treatment, by S. A. Brilliantova, et al. AKUSHERSTVO I GINEKOLOGIIA (4):40-42, April, 1980.

Estradiol, estriol and human placental lactogen in serum in threatened abortion, by J. B. Hertz, et al. ACTA OB-STETRICIA ET GYNECOLOGICA SCANDIVICA 58 (4):365-370, 1979.

The evaluation of prognosis in threatened early pregnancy, by P. Jouppila. JOURNAL OF PERINATAL MEDICINE 8(1):3-12, 1980.

Evaluation of threatened abortion by ultrasound, by M. J. Bennett, et al. INTERNATIONAL JOURNAL OF GY-NAECOLOGY AND OBSTETRICS 17(4):38-44, January-February, 1980.

Hysterographic studies of uterine contractile activity during partusysten treatment of threatened late abortion and premature labor, by O. I. Vinnyts'kyi. PEDIATRIIA AKUSHERSTVO I GINEKOLOGIIA (4):40-41, July-August, 1979.

Immunological tolerance of women during imminent abortion and during EPH-gestosis, by V. Knobloch, et al. CESKOSLOVENSKA GYNEKOLOGIE 44(9):639-643, November, 1979.

Management of threatened abortion with real-time sonography, by S. G. Anderson. OBSTETRICS AND GYNE-COLOGY 55(2):259-262, February, 1980.

Progesterone and human chorionic gonadotrophin in serum and pregnandiol in urine in threatened abortion, by J. B. Hertz, et al. ACTA OBSTETRICIA ET GYNECOLO-GICA SCANDINAVICA 59(1):23-27, 1980.

Prognosis in threatened abortion evaluated by hormone assays and ultrasound scanning, by P. S. Eriksen, et al. OBSTETRICS AND GYNECOLOGY 55(4):435-438, April, 1980.

Prognostic significance of maternal serum beta1-glycoprotein determination using LC partigen plates in threatened abortion in early pregnancy, by W. Eiermann, et al. ARCHIVES OF GYNECOLOGY 228(1-4):231-232, July 20, 1979.

Prognostic value of pregnancy-specific serum beta glycoprotein in threatened abortion, by N. Karg, et al. ORVOSI HETILAP 121(16):939-941, April 20, 1980.

Proposition of a method to evaluate the prognosis of threatening premature labor and the possibility of success in the treatment. Tocolytic index, by M. Pommier, et al. GINECOLOGIA Y OBSTETRICIA DE MEXICO 46 (275):173-181, September, 1979.

Results of treatment of threatened abortion with synthetic ACTH, by R. Klimek, et al. GINEKOLOGIA POLSKA Suppl:254-256, 1979.

Status of humoral immunity in threatened abortion, by K. N. Prozorovskaia, et al. AKUSHERSTVO I GINEKOLOGIIA (11):57, November, 1979.

A study of investigations used to predict outcome of pregnancy after threatened abortion, by G. B. Duff, et al. BRITISH JOURNAL OF OBSTETRICS AND GYNAECOLOGY 87(3):194-198, March, 1980.

Therapeutic value of indomethacin in threatened abortion, by A. R. Souka, et al. PROSTAGLANDINS 19(3):457-460, March, 1980.

Threatened abortion, hormone therapy and malformed

embryos [letter], by G. P. Oakley. TERATOLOGY 20
(3):481-482, December, 1979.

Threatened abortion studies by estradiol-17 beta in serum
and ultrasound, by J. B. Hertz, et al. OBSTETRICS AND
GYNECOLOGY 55(3):324-328, March, 1980.

Ultrasonographic idfferential diagnosis of imminent abortion,
by S. Zanke, et al. ZENTRALBLATT FUR GYNAE-
KOLOGIE 101(23):1523-1527, 1979.

Use of central electroanalgesia for treating threatened abortions, by N. V. Bashmakova. VOPROSY OKHRANY
MATERINSTVA I DETSTVA 25(2):54-56, February,
1980.

ABORTION: THREATENED: COMPLICATIONS
Effect of threatened abortion on the development of speech
and motor functions in children, by N. I. Sokolova.
VOPROSY OKHRANY MATERINSTVA I DETSTVA
24(11):69, November, 1979.

Effect of tocolysis on the clinical state of the fetus and
newborn infant from pregnancy complicated by threat-
need abortion, by J. Bajorek, et al. GINEKOLOGIA
POLSKA Suppl:91-93, 1979.

ABORTION AND ACUPUNCTURE
Enzymatic activity in the blood of pregnant women undergoing acupuncture treatment in threatened abortion,
by G. M. Vorontsova, et al. AKUSHERSTVO I GINE-
KOLOGIIA (4):38-40, April, 1980.

Enzymatic activity in the erythrocytes in threatened abortion and in acupuncture treatment, by S. A. Brilliantova,
et al. AKUSHERSTVO I GINEKOLOGIIA (4):40-42,
April, 1980.

ABORTION AND ANAESTHESIA

Abortion and the use of anaesthesia. Observations after two
years' experience, by M. Palot, et al. ANESTHESIA
AND ANALGESIA 36(3-4):151-154, March-April, 1979.

ABORTION AND CHILD ABUSE
Abortion and child abuse, by S. M. Smith. CANADIAN
JOURNAL OF PSYCHIATRY 24(7):589-591, Novem-
ber, 1979.

Relationship between abortion and child abuse, by P. Ney.
CANADIAN JOURNAL OF PSYCHIATRY 24(7):610-
620, November, 1979.

ABORTION AND CHROMOSOMES
Contribution of chromosome abnormalities to stillbirths,
neonatal deaths and abortions over 20 weeks of gestation, by R. Evans, et al. CLINICAL GENETICS 17(1):
64, 1980.

ABORTION AND COLLEGE STUDENTS
Abortion: only nice girls need apply [study of college stu-
dents by Elizabeth Allgeier and others]. PSYCHOLOGY
TODAY 13:95, January, 1980.

Abortion support waning in college, says young pro-lifer, by
C. Anthony. OUR SUNDAY VISITOR 69:6, July 6,
1980.

Postabortion depressive reactions in college women, by N. B.
Gould. JOURNAL OF THE AMERICAN COLLEGE
HEALTH ASSOCIATION 28(6):316-320, June, 1980.

The relationship of knowledge to perceived benefits and
risks of oral contraceptives among college women, by B.
T. Lively. DISSERTATION ABSTRACTS INTERNA-
TIONAL 40(12):6159-A, 1979.

Seth Low Junior College of Columbia University: a case
study on an abortive experiment, by B. Carron. DIS-

SERTATION ABSTRACTS INTERNATIONAL 40(09): 4072-B, 1979.

ABORTION AND ERA
ERA supporters deny pro-abortion link. OUR SUNDAY VISITOR 68:2, April 27, 1980.

Equal Rights Amendment and abortion: separate and distinct, by E. Alexander, et al. AMERICA 142:314-318, April 12, 1980.

ABORTION AND FERTILITY
Abortion and fertility, by H. M. Hafmann. REVUE MEDICALE DE LA SUISSE ROMANDE 99(12):905-912, December, 1979.

ABORTION AND GENETICS
Effects of antenatal diagnosis and selective abortion on frequencies of genetic disorders, by A. G. Motulsky, et al. CLINICAL OBSTETRICS AND GYNAECOLOGY 7 (1):121-133, April, 1980.

Genes, chromosomes, and reproductive failure, by J. L. Simpson. FERTILITY AND STERILITY 33(2):107-116, February, 1980.

Genetic and epidemiologic investigation of spontaneous abortion: relevance to clinical practice, by D. Warburton, et al. BIRTH DEFECTS 15(5A):127-136, 1979.

Genetic studies in habitual abortion, by N. A. Karetnikova, et al. AKUSHERSTVO I GINEKOLOGIIA (4):42-46, April, 1980.

Genodermatoses as an indication for the interruption of pregnancy: hereditary epidermolysis, by U. W. Schnyder. HAUTARZT 31(Suppl 4):23-24, 1980.

Incidence of chromosomal rearrangements in couples with

reproductive loss, by N. B. Kardon, et al. HUMAN GE-
NETICS 53(2):161-164, February, 1980.

Recurrent miscarriage in a patient with chromosomal translocation—karyotype 46,XX,t(10;11) (q21;q23), by K.
Boczkowski, et al. GINEKOLOGIA POLSKA 50(7):627-
630, July, 1979.

Ring-like chromosome 18 and osteogenesis imperfecta in a
family in which sponteneous abortions appear, by S.
Markovic, et al. SRPSKI ARHIV ZA CELOKUPNO LE-
KARSTVO 107(3):245-252, March, 1979.

Spontaneous abortions and chromosomal anomalies: current
questions, by A. Boue, et al. CLINICAL GENETICS 17
(1):57, 1980.

Structural chromosomal aberrations in parents with spontan-
eous abortions, by S. Adzic, et al. JUGOSLAVENSKA
GINEKOLOGIJA I OPSTETRICIJA 18(3-4):295-302,
May-August, 1978.

Studies on phenotype, development, and viability of human
spontaneous abortuses with acrocentric trisomies and
polyploidies: with reference to the relationship of the
viability to the origin of extrachromosomes, by N. Niikawa. HOKKAIDO IGAKU ZASSHI 54(3):235-244, May,
1979.

Variant chromosome 9 (9qh+) in families with spontaneous
abortion, by K. Mijin, et al. SRPSKI ARHIV ZA CELO-
KUPNO LEKARSTVO 107(10):547-553, October, 1979.

ABORTION AND THE HANDICAPPED
Abortion and the handicapped: present practice in the light
of history. SOCIAL THOUGHT 6:37-46, Summer, 1980.

ABORTION AND HORMONES
Abortion by extraamnial and intravenous administration of a

new prostaglandin E2 derivative, by J. Kunz, et al. AR-
CHIVES OF GYNECOLOGY 228(1-4):423-424, July 20,
1979.

Abortion induction with prostaglandin, by W. Lichtenegger.
ARCHIVES OF GYNECOLOGY 228(1-4):405-406,
July 20, 1979.

Alpha fetoprotein and HbF cells in maternal blood in prostaglandin abortion, by D. H. Maas, et al. ARCHIVES OF
GYNECOLOGY 228(1-4):298-299, July 20, 1979.

Differences in hormonal patterns during the first postabortion menstrual cycle after two techniques of termination
of pregnancy, by A. S. Blazar, et al. FERTILITY AND
STERILITY 33(5):493-500, May, 1980.

Role of prostaglandins in endotoxic abortion and intrauterine
fetal death, by R. C. Skarnes, et al. TOXICON 17
(Suppl 1):173, 1979.

ABORTION AND HOSPITALS
Hospital response to the legalization of abortion in New York
State: ana analysis of program innovation, by J. Miller.
JOURNAL OF HEALTH AND SOCIAL BEHAVIOR 20:
363-375, December, 1979.

Hospital support of legal abortion can overcome MD's negative attitudes. FAMILY PLANNING PERSPECTIVES
12:264-265, September-October, 1980.

ABORTION AND MALES
Abortion law's husband-notification requirement held uncon-
stitutional. CRIMINAL LAW REPORTER: COURT DE-
CISIONS AND PROCEEDINGS 26(17):2373-2375,
January 30, 1980.

Helping men cope with abortions, by J. Bosveld. MS MAGA-
ZINE 8:21, May, 1980.

How men who accompany women to an abortion service perceive the impact of abortion upon their relationship and themselves, by M. R. Smith. DISSERTATION ABSTRACTS INTERNATIONAL 40(07):3792-A, 1979.

Husbands' attitudes towards abortion and Canadian abortion law, by R. W. Osborn, et al. JOURNAL OF BIOSOCIAL SCIENCE 12(1):21-30, January, 1980.

A husband's consent to his wife's abortion, by L. E. Rozovsky. DIMENSIONS IN HEALTH SERVICE 57(1):34-36, January, 1980.

ABORTION AND THE MILITARY
Abortion restrictions will have little impact. AIR FORCE TIMES 41:15, December 8, 1980.

ABORTION AND NURSES
Abortion counselling by nurse specialists, by J. R. Newton, et al. CONTRACEPTION 20(5):429-439, November, 1979.

American nurse-tourist: lesson from the Philippines, by M. Clymer. TEXAS NURSING 54(5):6-7, May, 1980.

Meeting special needs. NURSING ADMINISTRATION QUARTERLY 4(4):61-74, Summer, 1980.

Nurse's role in voluntary pregnancy interruption and contraception, by A. Vagogne. SOINS 25(8):25-29, April 20, 1980.

ABORTION AND PARENTAL CONSENT
Abortion and dissenting parents: a dialogue, by S. R. Levy. ETHICS 90:162-163, Spring, 1980.

Abortion—parental notification—constitutionality of a statute—U.S. District Court (D. Maine). JUVENILE LAW DIGEST 12(4):113-114, April, 1980.

Abortion—parental notification—constituionality of a statute—Utah. JUVENILE LAW DIGEST 12(4):109-112, April, 1980.

Abortion—parental notification—judicial consent—constitutionality of a statute—U.S. District Court (S.D. Florida). JUVENILE LAW DIGEST 12(1):17-19, January, 1980.

Abortion—parental notification—judicial consent—constitutionality of a statute—U.S. Supreme Court. JUVENILE LAW DIGEST 11(10):299-303, October, 1979.

Adolescent pregnancy decision-making: are parents important?, by R. H. Rosen. ADOLESCENCE 15:43-54, Spring, 1980.

Constitutional law: permissible requirements of parental consent for abortion. WASHBURN LAW JOURNAL 19: 601-608, Spring, 1980.

Governor signs parental consultation bill. OUR SUNDAY VISITOR 69:2, June 22, 1980.

How many girls do parents drive to abortion, by M. Finley. OUR SUNDAY VISITOR 68:5, November 4, 1979.

Law requiring doctor to notify parents in minor's abortion valid. FAMILY LAW REPORTER: COURT OPINIONS 6(10):2153-2154, January 15, 1980.

Parental notice statutes: permissible state regulation of a minor's abortion decision. FORDHAM LAW REVIEW 49:81-111, October, 1980.

Parental notification as a prerequisite for minors' access to contraceptives: a behavioral and legal analysis, by M. N. Finger. UNIVERSITY OF MICHIGAN JOURNAL OF LAW REFORM 13:196-223, Fall, 1979.

Abortion referral and MD emigration: areas of concern and study for CMA, by D. A. Geekie. CANADIAN MEDI-CAL ASSOCIATION JOURNAL 118(2):175+, January 21, 1978.

American Association of Gynecologic Laparoscopists' 1977 membership survey, by J. M. Phillips, et al. JOURNAL OF REPRODUCTIVE MEDICINE 23(2):61-64, August, 1979.

Constitutional law—United States Supreme Court abortion decision clarifies concept of fetal viability and scope of physician's discretion in determining when viability is reached. TEMPLE LAW QUARTERLY 52:1240-1259, 1979.

Doctors and torture [letter], by R. C. Short. MEDICAL JOURNAL OF AUSTRALIA 2(2):89-90, July 28, 1979.

Hippocratic Oath as anachronistic [letter], by R. R. Winton. MEDICAL JOURNAL OF AUSTRALIA 2(7):365-366, October 6, 1979.

Hospital support of legal abortion can overcome MD's negative attitudes. FAMILY PLANNING PERSPECTIVES 12:264-265, September-October, 1980.

Obstetricians' attitudes and hospital abortion services, by C. A. Nathanson, et al. FAMILY PLANNING PERSPEC-TIVES 12(1):26-32, January-February, 1980.

A physician's lament, by R. White. JOURNAL OF THE AMERICAN COLLEGE HEALTH ASSOCIATION 28 (3):191-192, December, 1979.

Questions of bio-ethics in the termination of pregnancy in the second and third trimester of pregnancy for eugenic indications, by F. K. Beller, et al. GEBURTSHILFE UND FRAUENHEILKUNDE 40(2):142-144, February,

1980.

Values relating to abortion as expressed by the inner city
adolescent girl: report of a physician's experience, by
T. J. Silber. ADOLESCENCE 15:171-182, Spring, 1980.

ABORTION AND POLITICS
Abortion and the elections: Cardinal Medeiros, by H. Medeiros. ORIGINS 10:239, September 25, 1980.

Abortion and the 1978 Congressional elections, by M. W.
Traugott, et al. FAMILY PLANNING PERSPECTIVES
12:238-245, September-October, 1980.

Abortion and the presidential election of 1976: a multivariate analysis of voting behavior, by M. A. Vinovskis.
MICHIGAN LAW REVIEW 77(7):1750-1771, August,
1979.

Abortion: the liberals have abandoned the poor, by D. Baldwin. PROGRESSIVE 44:28-31, September, 1980.

Abortion politics and policy: is there a middle ground?, by
M. C. Segers. CHRISTIANITY AND CRISIS 40:21-27,
February 18, 1980.

Abortion politics in the United States, by C. Francome.
POLITICAL STUDIES 28:613-621, December, 1980.

Anti-abortion groups oppose Baker. (Senator Baker's pro-
abortion record). HUMAN EVENTS 40:3+, May, 1980.

"Anti-family" charge and a popular foe endanger McGovern;
abortion is emotional issue in race against Radnor [sena-
torial race in South Dakota], by J. M. Perry. WALL
STREET JOURNAL 196:1+, September 23, 1980.

Chrysalis reviews abortion as politics and experience, by E.
Willis, et al. CHRYSALIS 9:51-54, Fall, 1979.

273

Citizens United For Life: Status politics, symbolic reform and the anti-abortion movement, by S. L. Markson. DISSERTATION ABSTRACTS INTERNATIONAL 40(08): 4770-A, 1979.

Fetal-politics, by J. E. Lalonde. WEEKLY 3(3):14, April 12, 1978.

Nineteen-eighty presidential campaign: abortion question poses constant concern, by L. B. Weiss. CONGRESSIONAL QUARTERLY WEEKLY REPORT 38:733-734, March 15, 1980.

On impoverished spirits [judicial appointment plank of Republican Party platform], by W. F. Buckley, Jr. NATIONAL REVIEW 32:1041, August 22, 1980.

Political developments in the abortion area, by J. L. Robinson. CATHOLIC LAWYER 25:319-326, Autumn, 1980.

The political parties on abortion; Democrats ambivalent, by T. Blackburn. NATIONAL CATHOLIC REPORTER 16: 11, October 17, 1980.

—; Republicans consistent, by S. Valentine. NATIONAL CATHOLIC REPORTER 16:11, October 17, 1980.

Politics of abortion, by S. Flynn, et al. WORKING WOMEN 5:47-49, August, 1980.

The politics of abortion in the House of Representatives in 1976, by M. A. Vinovskis. MICHIGAN LAW REVIEW 77(7):1790-1827, August, 1979.

Politics of abortion stalls exemptions from OSHA visits. BUSINESS INSURANCE 13:28, November 12, 1979.

Pressure politics revisited: the anti-abortion campaign [emphasis on Pennsylvania], by M. Margolis, et al. POLICY

STUDIES JOURNAL 8:698-716, Spring, 1980.

Public support for pro-choice abortion policies in the nation and states: changes and stability after the Rod and Doe decisions, by E. M. Uslaner, et al. MICHIGAN LAW REVIEW 77(7):1772-1789, August, 1979.

A recent experiment the author conducted on US Senators revealed a wide variety of strategies used to answer constituent letters from single-issue voters; in the case of the experiment, the Senators were asked to state their position on abortions, by M. Feldstein. WASHINGTON MONTHLY 11(8):41-48, 1979.

The Supreme Court and abortion: the irrelevance of medical judgment, by G. J. Annas. HASTINGS CENTER REPORT 10:23-24, October, 1980.

ABORTION AND THE POOR
Abortion and the poor. AMERICA 142:73, February 2, 1980.

Abortion: the liberals have abandoned the poor, by D. Baldwin. PROGRESSIVE 44:28-31, September, 1980.

Abortion: the poor have rights. ECONOMIST 274:38, January 26, 1980.

Abortion: U.S. case bodes ill for poor, by L. Duncan. BRANCHING OUT 7(2):54, 1980.

Abortion—welfare. FAMILY LAW REPORTER: COURT OPINIONS 6(11):2173, January 22, 1980.

Abortions for the poor [ruling by U.S. Judge J. F. Dooling, Jr. declaring Hyde amendment unconstitutional], by A. Press, et al. NEWSWEEK 95:81, January 28, 1980.

Birth among strangers: pregnancy, delivery and perinatal

care of poor women in an American city, by S. S. Hopper. DISSERTATION ABSTRACTS INTERNATIONAL 1979.

Department of Health, Education, and Welfare—abortions: final regulation. FEDERAL REGISTER 44(109):61597-61598, October 26, 1979.

The poor have rights. ECONOMIST 274:38, January 26, 1980.

ABORTION AND RELIGION
Abortion and Christian morality, by J. Gaffney. CATHOLIC CHARISMATIC 5:31-33, June-July, 1980.

Abortion and the elections: Cardinal Medeiros, by H. Medeiros. ORIGINS 10:239, September 25, 1980.

Abortion—and moral qualms, by M. M. Malinovich. MADEMOISELLE 86:82+, September, 1980.

Abortion and the right to life, by A. H. Goldman. PERSONALIST 60:402-406, October, 1979.

Abortion and the right to life: a statement by the archbishops of Great Britain. TABLET 234:91-92, January 26, 1980.

Abortion—a Christian feminist perspective, by L. Campbell. NEW BLACKFRIARS 61:370-377, September, 1980.

Abortion: courting severe judgment: while all sins are equal, some sins are more equal than others, by J. W. Montgomery. CHRISTIANITY TODAY 24:54+, January 25, 1980.

Abortion discussed at Notre Dame [October, 1979], by T. P. Wojcik. ST. VLADIMIR'S THEOLOGICAL QUARTERLY 24(1):52-58, 1980.

Abortion, distant peoples, and future generations, by J. P. Sterba. JOURNAL OF PHILOSOPHY 77:424-440, July, 1980.

Abortion entitlement: absolute or qualified, by J. Crawford. LINACRE 47:77-87, February, 1980.

Abortion funding: out of the courtroom, into the legislature, by J. Duerr. OUR SUNDAY VISITOR 69:4-5, October 5, 1980.

Abortion insignificant in caucuses. NATIONAL CATHOLIC REPORTER 16:3+, February 1, 1980.

Abortion is no answer. TABLET 234:75, January 26, 1980.

The abortion issue: exercising religion freely on both sides, by J. Maust. CHRISTIANITY TODAY 24:72+, September 5, 1980.

Abortion: a Jewish view, by T. J. Silber. JOURNAL OF RELIGION AND HEALTH 19:231-239, Fall, 1980.

Abortion laws, religious beliefs and the First Amendment, by S. L. Skahn. VALPARAISO UNIVERSITY LAW REVIEW 14:487-526, Spring, 1980.

Abortion: the left has betrayed the sanctity of life, by M. Meehan. PROGRESSIVE 44:32-34, September, 1980.

The abortion movement: retreat from reality, by D. DeMarco. HOMILETIC AND PASTORAL REVIEW 80:10-20, January, 1980.

Abortion party has ruled too long, professor charges. OUR SUNDAY VISITOR 69:7, June 22, 1980.

Abortion politics and policy: is there a middle ground?, by M. C. Segers. CHRISTIANITY AND CRISIS 40:70-80,

March 31, 1980.

The abortion problem from the moral point of view (Hebrew), by A. Azmon. SOCIETY AND WELFARE 2(3): 302-310, 1979.

Abortion support waning in college, says young pro-lifer, by C. Anthony. OUR SUNDAY VISITOR 69:6, July 6, 1980.

Abortion: an unhappy stand-off [Harris vs McCrae], by R. L. Shinn. CHRISTIANITY AND CRISIS 40:219+, August 18, 1980.

The agony of abortion, by J. F. Alexander, et al. OTHER SIDE (105):5-59, June, 1980.

Anti-abortion group fights church bans on soliciting, by B. Kenkelen. NATIONAL CATHOLIC REPORTER 16(1): 3, September 12, 1980.

Aspectos medicos del aborto, by S. Cobos. CHRISTUS 45: 6-11, March, 1980.

Avant le debat parlementaire sur l'avortement: substituer a une loi de mort une loi de vie, by G. Duchene. LA DOCUMENTATION CATHOLIQUE 76:893-895, October 21, 1979.

Between abortion and infanticide, by P. Langham. SOUTHERN JOURNAL OF PHILOSOPHY 17:465-471, Winter, 1979.

Beyond personal piety. CHRISTIANITY TODAY 23:13, November 16, 1979.

Bishops appeal pregnancy discrimination act ruling. OUR SUNDAY VISITOR 69:7, June 29, 1980.

Bishops soft on abortion, say critics, by J. Michaels, Jr. NA-
TIONAL CATHOLIC REPORTER 16:9, January 18,
1980.

The Catholic Church and reform of abortion legislation, by
A. Lorenzer. KRITISCHE JUSTIZ 13(1):28-38, 1980.

Catholics agree with Protestants that abortion and contraception should be widely available [news] . FAMILY PLAN-
NING PERSPECTIVES 12(1):51, January-February,
1980.

Center for Life provides accessible maternity care, by B.
Myerson. HOSPITAL PROGRESS 60(10):30+, October,
1979.

Children: the blessed burden, by W. Willimon. RELIGION
IN LIFE 49;24-34, Spring, 1980.

Competing ethical claims in abortion, by A. J. Davis. AMER-
ICAN JOURNAL OF NURSING 80:1359, July, 1980.

Congressman Hyde cautiously optimistic about court. OUR
SUNDAY VISITOR 69:7, May 11, 1980.

Could right-wing alliance backfire for pro-lifers?, by L. Pumphrey. NATIONAL CATHOLIC REPORTER 16:9+,
January 18, 1980.

Decoding the election games plan of the new right, by L. C.
Wohl. MS MAGAZINE 8:57-59+, August, 1979.

Denial of medi-Cal funds for abortion: an establishment of
religion. GOLDEN GATE UNIVERSITY LAW REVIEW
9:421-449, 1978-1979.

Dispute about abortion ad policy erupts. NATIONAL
CATHOLIC REPORTER 16:43, February 15, 1980.

Does life begin before birth: we cannot fix criteria of humanness and then conclude that, lacking these, the fetus is not human, by J. R. W. Stott. CHRISTIANITY TODAY 24:50-51, September 5, 1980.

ERA supporters deny pro-abortion link. OUR SUNDAY VISITOR 68:2, April 27, 1980.

Ecumenical war over abortion. TIME 113:62-63, January 29, 1979.

Edges of life. 1. COMMUNITIES 107:420-421, August 1, 1980.

—. 2. COMMUNITIES 107:421, August 1, 1980.

— [Supreme Court's ruling on the Hyde Amendment]. COMMONWEAL 107:421, August 1, 1980.

Ethical aspects of abortion—some European views (Hebrew), by J. Tsafrir. SOCIETY AND WELFARE 2(3):341-347, 1979.

Ethics and nature, by A. Edwards. NEW BLACKFRIARS 60:117-125, March, 1979.

The ethics of abortion, by R. F. Gardner. PRACTITIONER 223(1334):244-248, August, 1979.

Ethics: what would you do? Abortion—moral or legal question. Part II, by C. Gilbert. NEW JERSEY NURSE 10 (1):6, January-February, 1980.

—. Part III, by C. Gilbert. NEW JERSEY NURSE 10(2):9, March-April, 1980.

Even an atheist can have a change of heart on abortion, by L. Pumphrey. OUR SUNDAY VISITOR 69:8, October 5, 1980.

Evolution demographique et conscience morale, by C. Mertens. NOUVELLE REVUE THEOLOGIQUE 102:519-538, July-August, 1980.

Fetal adoption: a technological solution to the problem of abortion ethics, by R. A. Freitas, Jr. HUMANIST 40:22-23, May-June, 1980.

Governor signs parental consultation bill. OUR SUNDAY VISITOR 69:2, June 22, 1980.

If a ship is a person, what is a pre-born child, by D. Mothersill. OUR SUNDAY VISITOR 69:5, June 29, 1980.

In defense of life, by C. Anthony, et al. OUR SUNDAY VISITOR 68:3-4+, January 20, 1980.

The jargon of hypocrisy, by J. Noonan, Jr. NEW COVENANT 10:12-16, October, 1980.

A life, a life style, and the way of life; cond from the Florida Catholic, February 2, 1980, by T. Grady. CATHOLIC DIGEST 44:34-36, June, 1980.

Lobbyist quits: abortion issue cited, by M. Papa. NATIONAL CATHOLIC REPORTER 17:7, November 7, 1980.

Media treatment of life march 'terrible.', by F. Franzonia. OUR SUNDAY VISITOR 68:3, February 10, 1980.

Medicine and killing: the Catholic view, by R. R. Roach. JOURNAL OF MEDICAL PHILOSOPHY 4(4):383-397, 1979.

A middle ground on abortion [replies to M. C. Segers, "Abortion politics and policy", Christianity and Crisis February 18, 1980; rejoinder], by J. W. Dellapenna, et al. CHRISTIANITY AND CRISIS 40:70-80, March 31, 1980.

Miscarriage, by C. Rankovic. SAINT ANTHONY MESSEN-
GER 87:28-33, February, 1980.

Mother Teresa: abortion greatest misery of our time. OUR
SUNDAY VISITOR 69:7, August 17, 1980.

Mother Teresa: abortion makes rich nations poor. OUR
SUNDAY VISITOR 69:7, December 23, 1979.

A new breed of right-to-lifers. NATIONAL CATHOLIC RE-
PORTER 16:23, July 18, 1980.

Norwegian Christians and abortion [in Norway], by F. Hale.
DIAL 19:45-50, Winter, 1980.

On the protection of the life of the child, by B. Arthadeva.
CHRIST TO THE WORLD 24:401-405, November-
December, 1979.

One thousand march against Right-to-Life [Anaheim, California, June 28, 1980], by R. Katz. OFF OUR BACKS
8:3, August-September, 1980.

Open letter to participants in the 1980 Sunod of Bishops, by
A. Zimmerman. LINACRE 47:171-181, May, 1980.

Other right-to-lifers, by M. Meehan. COMMONWEAL 107:
13-16, January 18, 1980; Discussion 107:158-159,
March 14, 1980.

Ought we to try to save aborted fetuses?, by D. I. Wikler.
ETHICS 90:58-65, October, 1979.

Our purpose is to fight for life. OUR SUNDAY VISITOR
68:3, February 3, 1980.

Parliament overrules churches on abortion, by T. Beeson.
CHRISTIAN CENTURY 97:461-462, April 23, 1980.

The political parties on abortion; Democrats ambivalent, by T. Blackburn. NATIONAL CATHOLIC REPORTER 16:11, October 17, 1980.

—; Republicans consistent, by S. Valentine. NATIONAL CATHOLIC REPORTER 16:11, October 17, 1980.

Pope, critics debate Italy's abortion law, by P. Hebble-thwaite. NATIONAL CATHOLIC REPORTER 16:4, October 3, 1980.

Population dip dangerous, economist warns. OUR SUNDAY VISITOR 69:2, July 6, 1980.

The population problem and the Synod on the family, by A. McCormack. CLERGY REVIEW 65:328-338, September, 1980.

Pro-life means more than anti-abortion, by J. Garvey. US CATHOLIC 45:35-37, March, 1980.

The prolife movement and the new right, by G. Higgins. AMERICA 143:107-110, September 13, 1980.

Pro-life: not a Catholic monopoly, by T. O'Reilly. LI-GUORIAN 68:11-13, January, 1980.

Pro-life ready to reap seeds sown since 1973, by F. Franzonia. OUR SUNDAY VISITOR 68:3, January 20, 1970.

Pro-life squabble follows Marx's leave of absence. NATION-AL CATHOLIC REPORTER 17:3+, December 5, 1980.

Pro-life violence. OUR SUNDAY VISITOR 67:2, January 14, 1979.

Pro-lifer's cross-country march may end in jail, by P. Cullen. OUR SUNDAY VISITOR 68:8, January 20, 1980.

Pro-lifers look to final victory, by B. Kenkelen. NATIONAL CATHOLIC REPORTER 16:1+, July 18, 1980.

Quality of life: from Roe to Quinlan and beyond, by J. Cincotta. CATHOLIC LAWYER 25:13-31, Winter, 1979.

Rebirth of the abortion furore [right to life groups in Canada], by A. Grescoe. MACLEANS 93:46-47, June 2, 1980.

The right takes aim. ECONOMIST 277:27+, October 4, 1980.

Right-to-life head finds facts of life hard to live with, by R. McClory. NATIONAL CATHOLIC REPORTER 16:1+, June 20, 1980.

Right to life homily, by H. Ratner. LINACRE 47:110-113, May, 1980.

Right to life/women's death, by R. Katz, et al. OFF OUR BACKS 10:11+, June, 1980.

Right-to-lifers fear being pushed to wall by courts, by R. Shaw. OUR SUNDAY VISITOR 68:7, February 17, 1980.

Right-to-lifers waging tough battle for Senate seats, by F. Franzonia. OUR SUNDAY VISITOR 69:6, October 19, 1980.

The right to private and public dissent from specific pronouncements of the ordinary magisterium, by R. M. Gula. EGLISE ET THEOLOGIE 9:319-343, May, 1978.

Rights of religion. COMMONWEAL 107:100, February 29, 1980.

Scarlet letter [pastoral letter published by H. Medeiros] , by E. J. Dionne, Jr. COMMONWEAL 107:554-555, October 10, 1980.

Self-ownership, abortion and infanticide, by E. F. Paul, et al. JOURNAL OF MEDICAL ETHICS 5(3):133-138, September, 1979.

Single-issue voting: interview of C. Anthony, by D. O'Brien. OUR SUNDAY VISITOR 69:4-5, September 7, 1980.

A small but significant pro-life victory, by R. McMunn. OUR SUNDAY VISITOR 68:4, December 9, 1979.

St. Louis pro-lifers sued for $1 million. OUR SUNDAY VISITOR 69:2, May 4, 1980.

Statement on abortion: Australian Episcopal Conference. L'OSSERVATORE ROMANO 27(640):19-20, July 7, 1980.

Strategy for human life amendment announced. OUR SUNDAY VISITOR 69:2, July 13, 1980.

Supreme Court ruling a victory for unborn life, by F. Franzonia. OUR SUNDAY VISITOR 69:3, July 13, 1980.

That the fetus should be considered a legal person, by J. M. Boyle. AMERICAN JOURNAL OF JURISPRUDENCE 24:59-71, 1979.

The tiniest humans, by D. Dooley. TABLET 233:1116-1117, November 17, 1979.

U.S. Supreme Court affirms society's interest in 'potential life,' by P. Geary. HOSPITAL PROGRESS 61(8):22-24, August, 1980.

Washington Catholics rap single issue abortion vote, by B.

Kenkelen. NATIONAL CATHOLIC REPORTER 16:3+, August 1, 1980.

We need to free our hearts, by C. Gallagher. OUR SUNDAY VISITOR 69:11, May 18, 1980.

What did the cardinal really say in controversial letter?, by H. Medeiros. OUR SUNDAY VISITOR 69:8, October 5, 1980.

When does human life begin?, by J. F. Crosby. AMERICAN JOURNAL OF ORTHOPSYCHIATRY 50(2):356-364, April, 1980.

When I was being made in secret, by E. Elliot. CHRISTIAN HERALD 102:29-30, November, 1979.

ABORTION AND YOUTH
Abortion in adolescence: the ethical dimension, by T. Silber. ADOLESCENCE 15(58):461-474, Summer, 1980.

Abortion rights of minors, by M. Griffin. WOMEN'S RIGHTS LAW REPORTER 6:13-14, Fall-Winter, 1979-1980.

Clinic staffing patterns and the pregnant adolescent, by M. J. Kieffer, et al. JOGN 8(6):333-335, November-December, 1979.

Competence to consent of minors in a termination of pregnancy, by K. Albrecht, et al. BEITRAEGE ZUR GERICHTLICHEN MEDIZIN 37:249-251, 1979.

How many girls do parents drive to abortion, by M. Finley. OUR SUNDAY VISITOR 68:4, November 4, 1979.

Minor consent in birth control and abortion; Part 1, by D. Trandel-Korenchuk, et al. NURSE PRACTITIONER 5 (2):47+, March-April, 1980.

—; Part 2, by D. Trandel-Korenchuk, et al. NURSE PRAC-
TITIONER 5(3):48+, May-June, 1980.

Minor's right to abortion and contraception: prospects for
invalidating less than absolute restrictions, by D. Klassel,
et al. WOMEN'S RIGHTS LAW REPORTER 4(3):165-
183, Spring, 1978.

Pregnant low-income teenagers: a social structural model of
the determinants of abortion-seeking behavior, by R.
Dworkin. YOUTH AND SOCIETY 11(3):295-309,
March, 1980.

Problem pregnancy and abortion counseling with teenagers,
by J. S. Chesler, et al. SOCIAL CASEQORK 61:173-
179, March, 1980.

Social and psychological correlates of pregnancy resolution
among adolescent women: a review, by L. Olson. A-
MERICAN JOURNAL OF ORTHOPSYCHIATRY 50
(3):432-445, July, 1980.

Supreme Court and a minor's abortion decision, by N. Dembitz. COLUMBIA LAW REVIEW 80:1251-1263, October, 1980.

Supreme Court report: abortion . . . minors, by R. L. Young.
AMERICAN BAR ASSOCIATION JOURNAL 65:1388-
1389, September, 1979.

Termination of pregnancy in adolescents in Vaud, by P. A.
Michaud, et al. REVUE MEDICALE DE LA SUISSE
ROMANDE 99(12):921-929, December, 1979.

Values relating to abortion as expressed by the inner city
adolescent girl—report of a physician's experience, by T.
J. Silber. ADOLESCENCE 15(57):183-189, Spring,
1980.

ABORTION CLINICS

Abortion clinic zoning: the right to procreative freedom and the zoning power, by L. Robinson. WOMEN'S RIGHTS LAW REPORTER 5:283-299, Summer, 1979.

Abortion clinics rush to diversify. BUSINESS WEEK p68+, December 10, 1979.

Abortion services lacking in local areas, study says. UNITED STATES MEDICINE 16(5):3-4, March 1, 1980.

Obstructionist activities at abortion clinics: a framework for remedial litigation. NEW YORK UNIVESITY REVIEW OF LAW AND SOCIAL CHANGE 8:325-360, 1978-1979.

Regulating abortion services [letter], by M. B. Kapp. NEW ENGLAND JOURNAL OF MEDICINE 302(6):350, February 7, 1980.

—, by V. P Riggs. NEW ENGLAND JOURNAL OF MEDICINE 302(6):350, February 7, 1980.

Regulation of abortion services—for better or worse?, by W. Cates, Jr., et al. NEW ENGLAND JOURNAL OF MEDICINE 301(13):720-723, September 27, 1979.

Zoning control of abortion clinics. CLEVELAND STATE LAW REVIEW 28:507-527, 1979.

ABORTION COMMISSIONS
Activities of abortion commissions, by D. Fukalova. CESKOSLOVENSKA GYNEKOLOGIE 44(10):752-754, December, 1979.

ABORTION COUNSELING
Abortion counselling by nurse specialists, by J. R. Newton, et al. CONTRACEPTION 20(5):429-439, November, 1979.

288

Alternative pathways for abortion services [editorial] . LAN-CET 1(8178):1121, May 24, 1980.

Counseling the abortion patient: a pastoral perspective, by J. R. Rzepka. PASTORAL PSYCHOLOGY 28:168-180, Spring, 1980.

The determinants of mothers. knowledge of the Down syndrome before genetic counseling: part II, by M. J. Seidenfeld, et al. AMERICAN JOURNAL OF MEDICAL GENETICS 6(1):9-23, 1980.

Effectiveness of contraception counseling and decision before legal abortion, by S. Kunz, et al. ARCHIVES OF GYNECOLOGY 228(1-4):391-392, July 19, 1979.

An evaluation of the counselling given to patients having a therapeutic abortion, by R. B. Hunton, et al. AUSTRALIAN AND NEW ZEALAND JOURNAL OF OBSTETRICS AND GYNAECOLOGY 19(3):169-173, August, 1979.

Experience of a model counseling center after amendment 218 to the abortion law, by D. Hobich, et al. ARCHIVES OF GYNECOLOGY 228(1-4):383-384, July 20, 1979.

On being a certifying abortion consultant: an ethical dilemma [editorial] , by S. E. Clarkson. NEW ZEALAND MEDICAL JOURNAL 91(659):346-347, May 14, 1980.

Sex education and contraceptive practice amongst abortion patients, by J. R. Ashton. JOURNAL OF BIOSOCIAL SCIENCE 12(2):211-217, April, 1980.

ABORTION DIRECTORIES
Abortion [directory of organizations] . MS MAGAZINE 9: 76, August, 1980.

Abortion and the constitution [Supreme Court decision holding the Hyde amendment constitutional]. AMERICA 143:24, July 19-26, 1980.

Abortion and the poor [ruling by Judge John F. Dooling, Jr. on the unconstitutionality of the Hyde amendment]. AMERICA 142:73, February 2, 1980.

Abortion debate continues: a look at laws, regulations, restrictions and funding, by J. A. Smith. CALIFORNIA NURSE 76(1):8, June, 1980.

The abortion funding cases: a response to Professor Perry, by C. Fahy. GEORGETOWN LAW JOURNAL 67(5): 1205-1208, 1979.

The abortion-funding cases and population control: an imaginary lawsuit (and some reflections on the uncertain limits of reproductive privacy), by S. F. Appleton. MICHIGAN LAW REVIEW 77(7):1688-1723, August, 1979.

Abortion funding: out of the courtroom, into the legislature, by J. Duerr. OUR SUNDAY VISITOR 69:4-5, October 5, 1980.

Abortion inequities [editorial]. BUSINESS INSURANCE 14:8, January 21, 1980.

Abortion—medicaid funding—equal protection. FAMILY LAW REPORTER: COURT OPINIONS 6(14):2221, February 12, 1980.

Abortion: perfersion of 'help'. Legal claims to killing free of charge? 'Final solutions' of perverse emancipation, by J. Bökmann. CONCEPTE 15(4):27-32, 1979.

Abortions—funding. FAMILY LAW REPORTER: COURT OPINIONS 6(17):2283, March 4, 1980.

Committee to defend reproductive rights v. Myers (156 Cal Rptr 73): medi-Cal funding of abortion. GOLDEN GATE UNIVERSITY LAW REVIEW 9:361-419, 1978-1979.

Congressmen challenge abortion funding order. OUR SUNDAY VISITOR 68:2, April 6, 1980.

Controversy over abortion funding increases. HOSPITAL PROGRESS 61(3):32, March, 1980.

Court frees tax dollars for abortions, for now at least. OUR SUNDAY VISITOR 68:7, March 2, 1980.

Court's abortion decision likely to affect all Medicaid patients. AMERICAN MEDICAL NEWS 23(27):1+, July, 11, 1980.

The courts and elective abortions under Medicaid, by J. E. Mendelson, et al. SOCIAL SERVICE REVIEW 54(1): 124-134, March, 1980.

Denial of medi-Cal funds for abortion: an establishment of religion. GOLDEN GATE UNIVERSITY LAW REVIEW 9:421-449, 1978-1979.

Eighty percent of Americans believe abortion should be legal; 70 percent approve Medicaid Funding [news]. FAMILY PLANNING PERSPECTIVES 11(3):189-190, May-June, 1979.

Employee benefits: no abortion benefits, no contracts, by J. Geisel. MODERN HEALTHCARE 10(2):30, February, 1980.

Employee must complain to EEOC before feds force abortion payment, by J. Geisel. MODERN HEALTHCARE 10(3):34, March, 1980.

Experiences of women refused National Health Service abortion, by J. R. Ashton. JOURNAL OF BIOSOCIAL SCIENCE 12(2):201-210, April, 1980.

Federal dollars for obstetrical care in Nebraska, by B. Cooper, et al. NEBRASKA MEDICAL JOURNAL 64 (8):251-253, August, 1979.

Federal judge strikes down abortion funding restriction. OUR SUNDAY VISITOR 68:8, January 27, 1980.

Feds may force contractors to pay abortion benefits, by J. Geisel. BUSINESS INSURANCE 14:9, January 14, 1980.

For a graduated scale of fees for legal abortion; against a graduated scale, by W. Cates, et al. FAMILY PLANNING PERSPECTIVES 12:219-221, July-August, 1980.

Foreign aid for abortion, by D. P. Warwick. HASTINGS CENTER REPORT 10(2):30-37, April, 1980.

Free abortion and voluntary parenthood, by K. Sundström-Feigenberg. LAKARTIDNINGEN 77(7):522-525, February 13, 1980.

Funded adoption: a "viable" alternative to abortion. BRIGHAM YOUNG UNIVERSITY LAW REVIEW 1979:363-393, 1979.

High Court reinstates full abortion funding: suspends Hyde Amendment. HUMAN EVENTS 40:3+, March 1, 1980.

House takes hard line on abortion funding. AIR FORCE TIMES 41:4, October 6, 1980.

Hyde Amendment ban on Medicaid abortions ruled unconstitutional. NATIONAL CATHOLIC REPORTER 16: 20, January 25, 1980.

The impact of restricting Medicaid financing for abortion [based on conference paper] , by J. Trussell, et al. FAM-ILY PLANNING PERSPECTIVES 12:120-123+, May-June, 1980.

Inmate abortions—the right to government funding behind the prison gates. FORDHAM LAW REVIEW 48:550-567, March, 1980.

Label game: views of D. Callahan on Medicaid funding. COMMONWEAL 106:614-615, November 9, 1979.

"Let them eat cake", says the Supreme Court [decisions on the Hyde Amendment] , by D. M. Kelley. CHRISTIAN CENTURY 97:820-824, August 27-September 3, 1980.

Limiting public funds for abortions: state response to Congressional action. SUFFOLK UNIVERSITY LAW REVIEW 13:923-959, Summer, 1979.

Mr. Hyde: Medicaid funds, by R. Becker. NEW REPUBLIC 181:10-11, November 17, 1979.

Office of Human Development Services—service programs for families and children, individuals and families, and aged, blind, or disabled persons; federal financial participation in state claims for abortions. FEDERAL REGISTER 44 (109):61599-61600, October 26, 1979.

Restrictive regulations for Medicaid, by C. D. Davis. TEXAS HOSPITALS 36(2):57, July, 1980.

Social security and public welfare—federal assistance and state cooperation, statutes, and regulations in general—statute disallowing payment of Medicaid funds for therapeutic abortions held invalid. NORTH DAKOTA LAW REVIEW 56:289-299, 1980.

State-funded abortions: judicial acquiescence in the sanctity

of a physician's medical judgment, by T. D. Harper.
JOURNAL OF THE MEDICAL ASSOCIATION OF
GEORGIA 69(4):313-315, April, 1980.

Utah law restricting abortion funding declared unconstitutional. FAMILY LAW REPORTER: COURT OPIN-
IONS 6(22):2370-2371.

ABORTION IN LITERATURE
Defeated sexuality in the plays and novels of Samuel Beckett,
by K. Morrison. COMPARATIVE DRAMA 14:18-34,
Spring, 1980.

Hemingway hills: symbolism in Hills like white elephants,
by L. E. Weeks, Jr. STUDIES IN SHORT FICTION 17:
75-77, Winter, 1980.

BIRTH CONTROL
Birth control, by G. G. Panter. PARENTS 55:72+, July,
1980.

—: cases [Doe v. Irwin 615 F 2d 116Z]. AMERICAN
JOURNAL OF TRIAL ADVOCACY 4:470-473, Fall,
1980.

Birth-control etiquette, by B. Snider. OUI 9:92-95, September, 1980.

Birth control: the new breakthroughs, by M. Abrams.
HARPERS BAZAAR 113:154-155+, April, 1980.

Birth control: not for women only?, by T. Schultz. FAMI-
LY HEALTH 12:44, June, 1980.

Birth control practices and conservatism, by V. C. Joe, et al.
JOURNAL OF PERSONALITY ASSESSMENT 43(5):
536-540, October, 1979.

The couple as a unit: sexual, social and behavioral considerations to reproductive barriers, by E. Mudd. JOURNAL OF MARITAL AND FAMILY THERAPY 6(1):23-28, January, 1980.

Current concepts in prevention, by P. Holma. KATILOLEH-TI 84(12):482, December, 1979.

Dealing with the unfit to breed, by E. S. Royce. INQUIRY 3(3):9-11, May 26, 1980.

Destroying myths about birth control, by B. Branley. SOLDIERS 35:44-46, November, 1980.

Has legal abortion replaced other methods of birth control?, by O. Meirik. LAKARTIDNINGEN 77(7):531-532+, February 13, 1980.

Keep the official flag flying over birth control services, by A. Leathard. HEALTH AND SOCIAL SERVICE JOURNAL 90(4695):704-707, May 30, 1980.

Of feminism and birth control propaganda (1790-1840), by N. Weiner. INTERNATIONAL JOURNAL OF WOMEN'S STUDIES 3:411-430, September-October, 1980.

Perspectives on fertility control, by M. Potts. INTERNATIONAL JOURNAL OF GYNAECOLOGY AND OBSTETRICS 16(6):449-455, 1978-1979.

Six score and then . . . , by J. Robertson. OBSERVER p46, February 10, 1980.

BANGLADESH
Another five-year plan for family planning, by R. Wigg. TIMES (LONDON) pIII, June 16, 1980.

BELGIUM
Regulation of fecundity. Knowledge, attitude and opinions of French-speaking female Belgian university

BELGIUM
    students, by G. Rucquoy, et al. ACTA PSYCHIA-
    TRICA BELGICA 78(6):869-1166, November-
    December, 1978.

BRAZIL
    Brazil: community-based distribution in Rio Grande do
    Norte [of oral contraceptives], by M. E. Gorosh, et
    al. INTERNATIONAL FAMILY PLANNING PER-
    SPECTIVES 5:150-159, December, 1979.

CHINA
    Birth planning in China [nine articles], by S. L. Camp,
    ed. DRAPER FUND REPORT p1-28, March, 1980.

    Chinese cotton on, by L. De Silva. GUARDIAN p15,
    March 3, 1980.

    The single child family—China's prospects for the 1980's:
    sexual restraint, birth control or both, by S. E.
    Fraser. JOURNAL OF FAMILY WELFARE 26:3-
    12, March, 1980.

    Taking the pledge for just one child, by T. Munford.
    DAILY TELEGRAPH p15, October 21, 1980.

COLOMBIA
    The management of early pregnancy: Colombian folk
    concepts of fertility control, by C. Browner. SO-
    CIAL SCIENCE AND MEDICINE 14B(1):25-32,
    February, 1980.

DEVELOPING COUNTRIES
    On allocating resources for fertility reduction in develop-
    ing countries, by B. Berelson, et al. POPULATION
    STUDIES 34:227-237, July, 1980.

GREAT BRITAIN
    More than just a packet of pills, by K. Margolis.

GREAT BRITAIN
GUARDIAN p10, November 17, 1980.

Tell tale signs, by H. Franks. GUARDIAN p8, February 25, 1980.

INDIA
Infant mortality, birth order and contraception in India, by S. K. B. Pathak. JOURNAL OF FAMILY WELFARE 25:12-21, June, 1979.

IRAN
Causes of clinic drop-out among Iranian pill users, by C. Lee, et al. JOURNAL OF BIOSOCIAL SCIENCE 10(1):7-15, January, 1978.

IRELAND
Legalised, or just localised? ECONOMIST 276:41, August 9, 1980.

ROMANIA
Romania raises birthrate by restricting abortion, birth control access [news]. FAMILY PLANNING PERSPECTIVES 11(5):317-318, October, 1979.

BIRTH CONTROL: ATTITUDES
Birth control: different conceptions, by R. V. Wells. JOURNAL OF INTERDISCIPLINARY HISTORY 10:511-516, Winter, 1980.

Changes in acceptors' and users' ages: a test of an explanatory mechanism, by J. A. Ross, et al. POPULATION STUDIES 34:367-380, July, 1980.

Development of a scale to measure attitudes toward using birth control pills, by E. S. Herold, et al. JOURNAL OF SOCIAL PSYCHOLOGY 110(First Half):115-122, February, 1980.

Fear barrier to teenage birth control [high school and college women's attitudes: study by Lucy Olson], by L. Asher. PSYCHOLOGY TODAY 13:109, September, 1979.

Post-abortion attitudes and patterns of birth control, by M. Abrams, et al. JOURNAL OF FAMILY PRACTICE 9 (4):593-599, October, 1979.

BIRTH CONTROL: HISTORY
Margaret Sanger: birth control's successful revolutionary, by D. Wardell. AMERICAN JOURNAL OF PUBLIC HEALTH 70(7):736-742, July, 1980.

BIRTH CONTROL: LAWS AND LEGISLATION
Recovery for wrongful conception: who gets the benefit— the parents or the public? NEW ENGLAND LAW RE-VIEW 14:784-811, Spring, 1979.

Roles for non-physicians in fertility regulation: an international overview of legal obstacles and solutions, by J. M. Paxman. AMERICAN JOURNAL OF PUBLIC HEALTH 70(1):31-39, January, 1980.

Wrongful conception. WILLIAM MITCHELL LAW REVIEW 5:464-508, 1979.

Wrongful life: birth control spawns a tort. JOHN MAR-SHALL LAW REVIEW 13:401-420, Winter, 1980.

BIRTH CONTROL: NATURAL
Two methods of natural family planning [letter], by T. W. Hilgers. AMERICAN JOURNAL OF OBSTETRICS AND GYNECOLOGY 136(5):696-697, March 1, 1980.

Why natural family planning is different, by H. Klaus. MAR-RIAGE 62:14-15, April, 1980.

BIRTH CONTROL: PSYCHOLOGY OF
Sociodemographic and psychological aspects of contracep-

tive practice. SOINS 25(8):15-18, April 20, 1980.

BIRTH CONTROL: SOCIOLOGY OF
Socio-personal variables associated with attitudes of Tharus toward birth control, by M. Seth, et al. JOURNAL OF FAMILY WELFARE 25:34-39, June, 1979.

BIRTH CONTROL: TECHNIQUES
Birth-control chart: what works, what's safe now, by M. L. Schildkraut. GOOD HOUSEKEEPING 190:274-275, May, 1980.

IFRP supports search for safer methods in 30 developing lands [news]. FAMILY PLANNING PERSPECTIVES 11 (5):315-316, October, 1979.

Regulation of epididymal function and sperm maturation— endocrine approach to fertility control in male, by B. S. Setty. ENDOKRINOLOGIE 74(1):100-117, April, 1979.

Research on birth control technology, by A. Kessler. IN- TERDISCIPLINARY SCIENCE REVIEWS 3(3):196-201, 1978.

BIRTH CONTROL AND COLLEGE STUDENTS
Regulation of fecundity. Knowledge, attitude and opinions of French-speaking female Belgian university students, by G. Rucquoy, et al. ACTA PSYCHIATRICA BEL- GICA 78(6):869-1166, November-December, 1978.

BIRTH CONTROL AND DIABETIES
Family planning and the diabetic mother, by W. N. Spellacy. SEMINARS IN PERINATOLOGY 2(4):395-399, Octo- ber, 1978.

BIRTH CONTROL AND JOURNALISM
The American press and birth control: preparing the ground for dissent, by I. Hitchcock. HOMILETIC AND PAS-

TORAL REVIEW 80:10-26, July, 1980.

BIRTH CONTROL AND PARENTAL CONSENT
Parents and teens agree: teenagers should get birth control information—from parents primarily [news]. FAMILY PLANNING PERSPECTIVES 11(3):200-201, May-June, 1979.

BIRTH CONTROL AND PHYSICIANS
Birth control: the minor and the physician. QUEENS LAW REVIEW 5:269-287, 1980.

Why adolescents go to birth-control clinics rather than to their family physicians, by E. S. Herold, et al. CANADIAN JOURNAL OF PUBLIC HEALTH 70(5):317-320, September-October, 1979.

BIRTH CONTROL AND RELIGION
Again, a rift over birth control [Synod of Bishops]. U. S. NEWS AND WORLD REPORT 89:69, October 13, 1980.

Artificial birth control backers bemoan lack of funds. OUR SUNDAY VISITOR 69:7, August 24, 1980.

Birth control grabs headlines but issue distorts synod, by D. O'Grady. OUR SUNDAY VISITOR 69:8, October 19, 1980.

Birth control a hot issue at bishop's synod on families, by D. O'Grady. OUR SUNDAY VISITOR 69:3, October 12, 1980.

Bishop hits 'teen crisis' booklet sent to public schools, by F. Franzonia. OUR SUNDAY VISITOR 68:6, March 23, 1980.

Bishops 100 percent behind Humanae Vitae but . . . , by J. Delany. OUR SUNDAY VISITOR 69:8, November 30, 1980.

Bishops' statement reaffirms Church's reverence for spousal love, by D. McCarthy. HOSPITAL PROGRESS 61:41-42, September, 1980.

Cardinal beards the political lion with abortion, by F. Franzonia. OUR SUNDAY VISITOR 69:3, September 28, 1980.

Childfree marriage—a theological view, by D. Doherty. CHICAGO STUDIES 18:137-145, Summer, 1979.

Church and state in Boston [pastoral letter published by H. Medeiros]. AMERICAN 143:180, October 4, 1980.

Council of the Italian Episcopal Conference. L'OSSERVATORE ROMANO 11(572):6-9, March 11, 1979.

Ecological values, the state, and the individual's right to liberty, by H. J. McCloskey. PACIFIC PHILOSOPHICAL QUARTERLY 61:212-232, July, 1980.

Ecology and conservation of the human species [letter], by D. Vann. MEDICAL JOURNAL OF AUSTRALIA 2(4): 203, August 25, 1979.

Low birthrate a problem in France. OUR SUNDAY VISITOR 69:2, July 20, 1980.

Notes on moral theology, 1978: *Humanae vitae* and the Magisterium, by R. A. McCormick. THEOLOGICAL STUDIES 40:80-97, March, 1979.

Pope and the pill [Synod of Bishops meeting], by K. L. Woodward, et al. NEWSWEEK 96:85, October 13, 1980.

Pope asks 'self-mastery' in marital sex, by P. Hebblethwaite. NATIONAL CATHOLIC REPORTER 16:20, November 16, 1979.

The ten years of Humanae vitae: tr and cond from Moralia: revista de ciencas morales 1:2, 1979, by F. Elizari. THEOLOGICAL DIGEST 28:33-37, Spring, 1980.

BIRTH CONTROL AND SEX BEHAVIOR
Sexual experience and responses to a birth control film, by E. S. Herold, et al. JOURNAL OF SCHOOL HEALTH 50:66-68, February, 1980.

BIRTH CONTROL AND YOUTH
Adolescent pregnancy prevention services in high school clinics, by L. E. Edwards, et al. FAMILY PLANNING PERSPECTIVES 12(1):6-7+, January-February, 1980.

Adolescent pregnancy prevention: sexual learning and self-esteem, by C. H. Shapiro. HUMAN ECOLOGY FORUM 10:21-24, Spring, 1980.

Birth control: facing the facts of life [teenagers], by J. Marks. TEEN 24:18+, March, 1980.

Birth control: the minor and the physician. QUEENS LAW REVIEW 5:269-287, 1980.

Communication about sex and birth control between mothers and their adolescent children, by P. B. Rothenberg. POPULATION AND ENVIRONMENT 3(1):35-50, Spring, 1980.

Dyadic and social network influences on adolescent exposure to pregnancy risk, by S. R. Jorgensen, et al. JOURNAL OF MARRIAGE AND FAMILY 42:141-155, February, 1980.

Fear barrier to teenage birth control [high school and college women's attitudes: study by Lucy Olson], by L. Asher. PSYCHOLOGY TODAY 13:109, September, 1979.

Minor consent in birth control and abortion: Part 1, by D.

Trandel-Korenchuk, et al. NURSE PRACTITIONER
5(2):47+, March-April, 1980.

Outreach education: a possible preventer of teenage pregnancy, by R. W. Block, et al. ADOLESCENCE 15:657-
660, Fall, 1980.

Sexual experience and responses to a birth control film, by
E. S. Herold, et al. JOURNAL OF SCHOOL HEALTH
50(2):66-73, February, 1980.

Twenty-seven strategies for teaching contraception to adolescents, by J. Chesler. JOURNAL OF SCHOOL HEALTH
50(1):18-21, January, 1980.

Why adolescents go to birth-control clinics rather than to
their family physicians, by E. S. Herold, et al. CANA-
DIAN JOURNAL OF PUBLIC HEALTH 70(5):317-320,
September-October, 1979.

BIRTH CONTROL CLINICS
Contraceptive delivery systems: an evaluation of clinic vs.
village in Indonesia, by J. D. Teachman, et al. EVALU-
ATION REVIEW 4:75-92, February, 1980.

Peeling off the labels [Canada's youth], by J. Timson.
MACLEANS 93:40-41, March 31, 1980.

The user perspective: an evolutionary step in contraceptive
service programs: implementing the user perspective, by
G. Zeidenstein, et al. STUDIES IN FAMILY PLANNING
11(1):24, January, 1980.

BIRTH CONTROL COUNSELING
Contraceptive counselor's dilemma: safety or effectiveness?,
by C. Cooperman. JOURNAL OF SEX RESEARCH
14(3):145-150, August, 1978.

Effectiveness of contraception counseling and decision before

legal abortion, by S. Kunz, et al. ARCHIVES OF GYNE-
COLOGY 228(1-4):391-392, July 20, 1979.

BIRTH CONTROL FUNDING
Artificial birth control backers bemoan lack of funds. OUR
SUNDAY VISITOR 69:7, August 24, 1980.

CONTRACEPTION: ATTITUDES
Contraception, abortion and self concept, by R. H. Rosen,
et al. JOURNAL OF POPULATION 2(2):118-139, Summer, 1979.

CONTRACEPTION: PSYCHOLOGY
The psychoanalytic approach to contraception today, by M.
Bydlowski, et al. JOURNAL DE GYNECOLOGIE OB-
STETRIQUE ET BIOLOGIE DE LA REPRODUCTION
8(6):527-531, 1979.

Psychological and situation-specific coreelates of contraceptive behavior among university women, by W. A. Fisher,
et al. JOURNAL OF SEX RESEARCH 15(1):38-55,
February, 1979.

Psychological resistance of women to the principal feminine
contraception methods: toward a clinical classification,
by M. C. Wauty-Dancot, et al. ACTA PSYCHIATRICA
BELGICA 75(1):49-73, January, 1975.

CONTRACEPTION AND DIABETES
Contraception and diabetes [letter], by J. M. Steel, et al.
DIABETES CARE 2(1):60, January-February, 1979.

CONTRACEPTION AND POLITICS
The politics of contraception: the view from Beijing, by C.
Djerassi. NEW ENGLAND JOURNAL OF MEDICINE
303:334-336, August 7, 1980.

CONTRACEPTION AND CONTRACEPTIVES
Abortion or contraception, by A. Goldsmith, et al. REPRO-

DUCCION 4(1):55-68, January-March, 1980.

Contraception, by J. C. Guillat. SOINS 25(8):3-7, April 20, 1980.

Contretemps over contraception [views of Archbishop P. R. Quinn]. TIME 116:74, October 13, 1980.

Effectiveness and risks of contraception, by W. Droegemueller, et al. ANNUAL REVIEW OF MEDICINE 31:329-343, 1980.

Evaluation of modern contraception, by M. Mall-Haefeli. MEDIZINISCHE MONATSSCHRIFT FUR PHARMA-ZEUTEN 1(5):139-146, May, 1978.

Future methods of fertility regulation, by E. B. Connell. CLINICAL OBSTETRICS AND GYNAECOLOGY 6 (1):171-184, April, 1979.

Indications for ovulation inhibitors. Recommendations of the Swiss Society for Family Planning 119(3):297-299, March, 1980.

Information in matters of contraception: a role for the nurse [editorial], by C. Kurz. SOINS 25(8):2, April 20, 1980.

Intimacy and human sexuality: a challenge to the consensus on contraception, by L. B. Porter. COMMUNIO 7:269-277, Autumn, 1980.

Lactational amenorrhoea, prolactin and contraception [editorial], by P. W. Howie, et al. EUROPEAN JOURNAL OF CLINICAL INVESTIGATION 9(4):237-238, August, 1979.

Method, age, education, and race influence success in contraceptive use. FAMILY PLANNING PERSPECTIVES 12:266-267, September-October, 1980.

CONTRACEPTION AND CONTRACEPTIVES

Repeat abortion and self-reported contraceptive behavior
[letter], by R. D. Gillette. AMERICAN JOURNAL OF
PUBLIC HEALTH 70(6):637, June, 1980.

Sex education and contraceptive practice amongst abortion
patients, by J. R. Ashton. JOURNAL OF BIOSOCIAL
SCIENCE 12:211-218, April, 1980.

Some practical aspects of contraception, by R. J. Beard.
CLINICAL OBSTETRICS AND GYNAECOLOGY 6
(1):157-170, April, 1979.

Trends in medico-legal aspects of contraception, by J. Gardner. CLINICAL OBSTETRICS AND GYNAECOLOGY
6(1):185-195, April, 1979.

CONTRACEPTION AND CONTRACEPTIVES: BIBLIOGRAPHIES
Contraception in adolescence—a review of the literature, by
E. Ryde-Blomqvist. JOURNAL OF BIOSOCIAL SCI-
ENCE Suppl(5):129-158, 1978.

CONTRACEPTION AND CONTRACEPTIVES: EDUCATION
Contraceptive education favored by teenagers [news]. FAM-
ILY PLANNING PERSPECTIVES 11(4):255, July-
August, 1979.

Factors affecting adolescent contraception practices: implications for sex education, by M. H. Dembo, et al. ADO-
LESCENCE 14:658-664, Winter, 1979.

CONTRACEPTION AND CONTRACEPTIVES: RESEARCH
Active immunization of female rabbits with purified rabbit
acrosin and effect on fertility, by F. N. Syner, et al.
FERTILITY AND STERILITY 32(4):468-473, October,
1979.

Alterations in rheology of cervical mucus—a new approach to
contraception, by V. P. Kamboj, et al. INDIAN JOUR-
NAL OF EXPERIMENTAL BIOLOGY 17(12):1379-

1380, December, 1979.

Antifertility efficacy of twice daily oral administration of 6-chloro-6-deoxy-D-glucose (6 CDG) in male rats, by L. A. Warren, et al. CONTRACEPTION 20(3):275-289, September, 1979.

Antifertility effects of 6-chloro-6-deoxy-glucose in the male rat, by F. Heitfeld, et al. CONTRACEPTION 19(6):543-555, June, 1979.

Central action of prostaglandins in spawning behavior of female goldfish, by N. E. Stacey, et al. PHYSIOLOGY AND BEHAVIOR 22(6):1157-1162, June, 1979.

Contraceptive properties of luteinising hormone releasing hormone [letter], by R. F. Lambe, et al. LANCET 2 (8146):801, October 13, 1979.

Contraceptive research and development, by R. J. Aitken. BRITISH MEDICAL BULLETIN 35(2):199-204, May, 1979.

Current contraceptive research, by J. M. Benditt. FAMILY PLANNING PERSPECTIVES 12(3):149-155, May-June, 1980.

The development and evaluation of an ovulation inhibitor (DIAne) containing an antiandrogen, by U. Lachnit-Fixson. ACTA OBSTETRICIA ET GYNECOLOGICA SCANDINAVICA 88(Suppl):33-42, 1979.

Does pyridoxal phosphate have a non-co-enzymatic role in steroid hormone action? NUTRITION REVIEWS 38: 93-95, February, 1980.

In search of the perfect contraceptive, by C. Channing. THE SCIENCES 19(4):14+, December, 1979.

Peptide hormones tested as contraceptives. CHEMICAL AND ENGINEERING NEWS 58:18+, February 11, 1980.

Peptides could be contraceptives and fertility promoters. CHEMISTRY AND INDUSTRY p298, April 19, 1980.

Prolongation of normotest clotting times in rats on the pill, by M. C. Roncaglioni, et al. THROMBOSIS AND HAEMOSTASIS 43(1):73, February 29, 1980.

Prospects for improved contraception, by L. Atkinson, et al. FAMILY PLANNING PERSPECTIVES 12:173-175+, July-August, 1980.

CONTRACEPTION AND CONTRACEPTIVES: TECHNIQUES
Choice of a contraceptive method, by J. C. Guillat. SOINS 25(8):13-14, April 20, 1980.

New approaches to immunological contraception, by P. Matangkasombut. CLINICAL OBSTETRICS AND GY-NAECOLOGY 6(3):531-548, December, 1979.

Safety of modern contraceptive technology. Current status, by S. K. Khoo. AUSTRALIAN FAMILY PHYSICIAN Suppl:3-7, February, 1980.

CONTRACEPTION AND CONTRACEPTIVES AND EPILEPSY
Antiepileptic drugs and oral contraceptives. Preliminary note, by M. Meduri, et al. BOLLETTINO DELLA SOCI-ETA ITALIANA DI BIOLOGIA SPERIMENTALE 54 (23):2462-2467, December 15, 1978.

CONTRACEPTION AND CONTRACEPTIVES AND MEN
Male juvenile delinquints: birth control knowledge, practice and attitudes, by J. Bingham, et al. CLINICAL RE-SEARCH 27(1):134A, 1979.

Male responsibility in sexual activity and family planning: perspectives of a college mental health professional, by

A. Roach. JOURNAL OF THE AMERICAN COLLEGE
HEALTH ASSOCIATION 28(3):173-175, December,
1979.

CONTRACEPTION AND CONTRACEPTIVES COUNSELING
A comparison of three approaches to providing contraceptive
counseling, by Y. M. DeCuir. DISSERTATION AB-
STRACTS INTERNATIONAL 40(12):5806-B, 1980.

A guide to contraceptive advice, by J. Abrams. MEDICAL
TIMES 108(3):1s-3s+, March, 1980.

CONTRACEPTIVE AGENTS
Peptide hormones tested as contraceptives. CHEMICAL
AND ENGINEERING NEWS 58:18+, February 11, 1980.

Pharmacokinetics and pharmacodynamics of sustained release systems, by K. Fotherby. JOURNAL OF STEROID
BIOCHEMISTRY 11(1B):457-459, July, 1979.

Studies on a peerless contraceptive, by J. S. Greenstein.
CHEMICAL TECHNOLOGY 9:217-221, April, 1979.

Tomorrow's contraceptives—yesterday's problem [editorial].
BRITISH MEDICAL JOURNAL 2(6196):951, October
20, 1979.

CONTRACEPTIVE AGENTS: COMPLICATIONS
Improved long-acting fertility regulating agents: what are the
problems?, by E. Diczfalusy. JOURNAL OF STEROID
BIOCHEMISTRY 11(1B):443-448, July, 1979.

Interaction between anticoagulants and contraceptives: an
unsuspected finding, by E. de Teresa, et al. BRITISH
MEDICAL JOURNAL 2(6200):1260-1261, November
17, 1979.

Parasitism and contraceptives: a preliminary survey of the
effect on haemoglobin levels, by E. A. Imohiosen, et al.

NIGERIAN MEDICAL JOURNAL 9(4):487-491, April, 1979.

CONTRACEPTIVE AGENTS: FEMALE
Effects on sex hormone binding globulin of different oral contraceptives containing norethisterone and lynestrenol, by V. Odlind, et al. BRITISH JOURNAL OF OBSTE-TRICS AND GYNAECOLOGY 87(5):416-421, May, 1980.

Experimental models in the search for antigestagenic compounds with menses-inducing activity, by L. Schenkel-Hulliger, et al. JOURNAL OF STEROID BIOCHEMIS-TRY 11(1C):757-769, July, 1979.

Experimental pharmacologic studies on the male antifertility agent alpha-chlorohydrin and its analogues, by R. F. Lu, et al. YAO HSUEH HSUEH PAO; ACTA PHARMACEU-TICA SINICA 14(7):402-407, July, 1979.

The first three-stage preparation for hormonal contraception. Clinical results, by U. Lachnit-Fixson. MMW 121(43): 1421-1426, October 26, 1979.

First year clinical experience with six levonorgestrel rods as subdermal contraception, by A. Faundes, et al. CON-TRACEPTION 20(2):167-175, August, 1979.

Fertility regulation using 'triphasic' administration of ethinyl estradiol and levonorgestrel in comparison with the 30 plus 150 micorgrams fixed dose regime, by G. Zador. ACTA OBSTETRICIA ET GYNECOLOGICA SCANDI-NAVICA 88(Suppl):43-48, 1979.

Gregory Pincus and steroidal contraception: a new departure in the history of mankind, by E. Diczfalusy. JOURNAL OF STEROID BIOCHEMISTRY 11(1A):3-11, July, 1979.

Hormonal contraception, by G. Göretzlehner, et al. ZEN-

TRALBLATT FUR GYNAEKOLOGIE 101(21):1361-1380, 1979.

Hormonal factors in the regulation of myometrial activity. An in vivo study, by T. Laudanski. ACTA OBSTETRI-CIA ET GYNECOLOGICA SCANDINAVICA 91(Suppl): 1-32, 1979.

Importance of HDL-cholesterol as a negative risk factor and the relationship between HDL and oral contraceptives, by A. C. Arntzenius. NEDERLANDS TIJDSCHRIFT VOOR GENEESKUNDE 123(44):1910-1912, November 3, 1979.

Intensive control of pregnancy. Comparison of plasma and urine estriol, by R. Göser, et al. ARCHIVES OF GYNE-COLOGY 228(1-4):229, July 20, 1979.

Local antifertility effect of luteinizing hormone-releasing hormone (LRH), by R. C. Jones. CONTRACEPTION 20(6):569-578, December, 1979.

The long-term effect of various hormonal contraceptives on the excretion of sodium, potassium, calcium, magnesium, chloride, phosphorus, uric acid, oxalic acid, citric acid, sulfate and lysozyme in the 24 hour urine, by G. Klinger, et al. ZEITSCHRIFT FUR UROLOGIE UND NEPH-ROLOGIE 72(6):393-398, June, 1979.

Medroxyprogesterone acetate in depot form for contraception, by I. Mark. UGESKRIFT FOR LAEGER 141(29): 1965-1968, July 16, 1979.

Menstrual regulation and the law, by J. M. Paxman, et al. INTERNATIONAL JOURNAL OF GYNAECOLOGY AND OBSTETRICS 17(5):493-503, March-April, 1980.

Menstrual regulation clients in a village based family planning programme, by S. Bhatia, et al. JOURNAL OF BIOSO-

CIAL SCIENCE 12:31-40, January, 1980.

The metabolic effects of contraception with estrogen-progestogen products, by J. Heim. JOURNAL DE GYNECOLOGIE OBSTETRIQUE ET BIOLOGIE DE LA REPRODUCTION 8(8):745-749, 1979.

Metabolic effects of oral contraceptives containing 30 micrograms and 50 micrograms of oestrogen, by A. L. Nash, et al. MEDICAL JOURNAL OF AUSTRALIA 2(6):277-281, September 22, 1979.

Microanalysis of lipids in discrete brain areas of the rabbit following intramuscular administration of steroid contraceptive, by F. Islam, et al. CONTRACEPTION 21(4): 434-442, April, 1980.

New effects from old ginseng. MMW 122(13):50, March 28, 1980.

A new non-steroidal drug for long-acting contraception, by P. C. Das, et al. ACTA PHYSIOLOGICA POLONICA 30 (3):289-391, March-April, 1979.

Ovulation inhibition with a combined oral contraceptive containing 20 micrograms ethinyl estradiol and 250 micrograms levonorgestrel. Serum levels of the active ingredients and FSH, LH, estradiol 17-beta and progesterone, by N. O. Lunell, et al. ACTA OBSTETRICIA ET GYNECOLOGICA SCANDINAVICA 88(Suppl):17-21, 1979.

Phytoestrol in the hormone-free interval during administration of contraceptives, by M. Mettenleiter. FORTSCHRITTE DER MEDIZIN 98(13):498-500, April 3, 1980.

Plasma progesterone levels in normal and pregnant Chinese women and effects of contraceptives on the, by Z. P. Gu, et al. CHINESE MEDICAL JOURNAL 93(8):523-527,

August, 1980.

Plasma Xa inhibitory activities and plasma concentrations of norgestrel and ethinyloestradiol in women on oral contraceptive steroids, by D. J. Back, et al. BRITISH JOURNAL OF CLINICAL PHARMACOLOGY 8(5):505-506, November, 1979.

Preferences for sweet in relationship to use of oral contraceptives and pregnancy, by R. L. Dippel, et al. HORMONES AND BEHAVIOR 14(1):1-6, March, 1980.

The probability of side effects with ovral, norinyl 1/50 and norlestrin, by G. S. Berger, et al. CONTRACEPTION 20 (5):447-453, November, 1979.

The progestational activity of different gestagens used for human contraception in the beagle bitch, by S. Beier, et al. CONTRACEPTION 20(6):533-548, December, 1979.

Progestational potency of oral contraceptives: a polemic, by R. A. Edgren. INTERNATIONAL JOURNAL OF FERTILITY 23(3):162-169, 1978.

Prospective studies of the gonadotropin responses to graded injections of gonadotopin-releasing factor in women using a low-estrogen type oral contraceptive for three months, by W. N. Spellacy, et al. FERTILITY AND STERILITY 32(6):661-663, December, 1979.

A prospective study of the effects of the progestagen content of oral contraceptives on measures of affect, automatization, and perceptual restructuring ability, by A. Worsley. PSYCHOPHARMACOLOGY 67(3):289-296, 1980.

Prospective study of oral contraceptives effects on platelets and blood clotting: a preliminary report, by R. Abbate, et al. THROMBOSIS AND HAEMOSTASIS 42(1):393, 1979.

Significance for abortion with special reference to various administration forms, by M. Schmidt-Gollwitzer, et al. ARCHIVES OF GYNECOLOGY 228(1-4):403, July 20, 1979.

Thombocyte function in relation to the long term application of medroxyprogesterone acetate as a female contraceptive agent, by L. Mettler, et al. JOURNAL OF POST-GRADUATE MEDICINE 25(3):154-157, July, 1979.

Transcortin as an indicator of estrogenic potency in oral contraceptives, by W. Carol, et al. ENDOKRINOLOGIE 75 (2):167-172, 1980.

Values and risks of pregnancy-protecting progesterones, by I. Pazonyi. ORVOSI HETILAP 120(50):3078, December 16, 1979.

Varicosity, hormones and pregnancy, by L. Wenner. VASA 8(3):258-262, 1979.

CONTRACEPTIVE AGENTS: FEMALE: COMPLICATIONS
From arthritis pain to dysmenorrhea: a new indication for prostaglandin inhibitors, by L. N. Gever. NURSING 10 (4):81, April, 1980.

A further case of hepatocytic adenoma following oestrogen-progestogen treatment. Review of the literature, by J. P. Grandjean, et al. SEMAINES DES HOPITAUX DE PARIS 56(7-8):383-392, February 18-25, 1980. Also in: ANNALES DE CHIRURGIE 33(5):361-370, May, 1979.

Hemolytic syndrome and recurrent uremia. Irreversible cortical necrosis due to estro-progestational hormones (proceedings), by G. Rifle, et al. JOURNAL OF UROLOGY 85(4-5):331, April-May, 1979.

Hormonal contraceptives and high blood pressure, by J. M. Coderch Gimeno, et al. MEDICINA CLINICA 73(2):77-

82, June 25, 1979.

Problems posed by birth control in cardiac and hypertensive patients, by J. H. Soutoul, et al. ANNALES DE CARDI-OLOGIE ET D'ANGEIOLOGIE 28(6):419-422, November, 1979.

Progestogens and cardiovascular reactions associated with oral contraceptives and a comparison of the safety of 50- and 30-microgram oestrogen preparations, by T. W. Meade, et al. BRITISH MEDICAL JOURNAL 280 (6224):1157-1161, May 10, 1980.

Recurrent jaundice in the course of natural and iatrogenic estrogen metabolism disorders, by G. Mach, et al. POL-SKI TYGODNIK LEKARSKI 34(49):1923-1924, December 3, 1979.

Steroid contraception and cancer, by L. Andolsek. JUGO-SLAVENSKA GINEKOLOGIJA I OPSTETRICIJA 18 (2):193-199, March-April, 1978.

Wallenberg's syndrome in a young woman following long-term use of a contraceptive agent, by G. J. Petten, et al. NEDERLANDS TIJDSCHRIFT VOOR GENEESKUNDE 123(26):1058-1060, June 30, 1980.

CONTRACEPTIVE AGENTS: FEMALE: IMPLANTED
Subcutaneous steroid hormone capsules. The future contraceptive?, by M. Osler. UGESKRIFT FOR LAEGER 141 (45):3097-3099, November 5, 1979.

Subdermal norethindrone pellets—a method for contraception?, by V. Odlind, et al. CONTRACEPTION 19(6): 639-648, June, 1979.

Successful pregnancy in an abortion-prone woman: prostaglandin and hormone levels during implantation, gestation and lactation, by M' Korteweg, et al. PROSTA-

GLADINS AND MEDICINE 4(3):185-192, March, 1980.

CONTRACEPTIVE AGENTS: FEMALE: ORAL
Modification by oral contraceptives in rat of 14C acetate incorporation into platelet lipids, by M. Ciavatti, et al. HORMONE AND METABOLIC RESEARCH 11(7):441-444, July, 1979.

Oral contraceptive steroids: effects on iron and zinc levels and on tryptophan pyrrolase and alkaline phosphatase activities in tissues of iron-deficient anemic rats, by Y. Kanke, et al. AMERICAN JOURNAL OF CLINICAL NUTRITION 33(6):1244-1250, June, 1980.

Phenobarbitone interaction with oral contraceptive steroids in the rabbit and rat, by D. J. Back, et al. BRITISH JOURNAL OF PHARMACOLOGY 69(3):441-452, July, 1980.

Pregnancy attributable to interaction between tetracycline and oral contraceptives, by J. F. Bacon, et al. BRITISH MEDICAL JOURNAL 280(6210):293, February 2, 1980.

Prostaglandins in gynecology and obstetrics. Prostaglandins offer new methods for abortion, anticonception and regulating fertility, by M. Bygdeman. NORDISK MEDICIN 94(8-9):217-219, September, 1979.

A randomized double blind study of two oral contraceptives, by H. Sanhueza, et al. CONTRACEPTION 20(1):29-48, July, 1979.

Serum copper and zinc in hormonal contraceptive users, by K. Prema, et al. FERTILITY AND STERILITY 33(3): 267-271, March, 1980.

Serum levels of FSH, LH, estradiol-17 beta and progesterone following the administration of a combined oral contraceptive containing 20 micrograms ethinylestradiol, by K. Carlström, et al. GYNECOLOGIC AND OBSTETRIC INVESTIGATION 9(6):304-311, 1978.

Sister-chromatid exchanges in oral contraceptive users, by P. B. Murthy, et al. MUTATION RESEARCH 68(2):149-152, October, 1979.

Some estrogenic effects of two oral contraceptives consisting of norgestrel and two different doses of ethynylestradiol, by J. F. Miller, et al. CONTRACEPTION 20(1):5-10, July, 1979.

The vitamin B6 requirement in oral contraceptive users. NUTRITION REVIEWS 37(11):344-345, November, 1979.

CONTRACEPTIVE AGENTS: FEMALE: ORAL: COMPLICATIONS
Plasma levels of active ingredients after single and repeated administration of a new oral contraceptive containing 2 mg of cyproterone acetate and 50 micrograms of ethinyl estradiol (DIANE) to five young women, by B. Düsterberg, et al. ACTA OBSTETRICIA ET GYNECOLOGICA SCANDINAVICA 88(Suppl):27-31, 1979.

The role of hormones in the etiology of breast and endometrial cancer, by R. D. Gambrell. ACTA OBSTETRICIA ET GYNECOLOGICA SCANDINAVICA 88(Suppl): 73-81, 1979.

CONTRACEPTIVE AGENTS: FEMALE: POST-COITAL
Mode of action of DL-norgestrel and ethinylestradiol combination in postcoital contraception, by W. Y. Ling, et al. FERTILITY AND STERILITY 32(3):297-302, September, 1979.

Postcoital estrogens win backing of FDA advisors. MEDICAL WORLD NEWS 21:26+, May 26, 1980.

Steroid and nonsteroid postcoital contraceptives, by V. V. Korkhov, et al. FARMAKOLOGIYA I TOKSIKOLOGI-YA 43(1):94-96, January-February, 1980.

CONTRACEPTIVE AGENTS: FEMALE: SUPPOSITORY
Treatment of rhesus monkeys (Macaca mulatta) with intra-vaginal rings loaded with levonorgestrel, by P. F. Wads-worth, et al. CONTRACEPTION 20(6):559-567, De-cember, 1979.

CONTRACEPTIVE AGENTS: FEMALE: TECHNIQUE
Postovulatory and post-implantation inhibition of fertility—general account, by M. Oettel, et al. ZENTRALBLATT FUR GYNAEKOLOGIE 101(21):1381-1392, 1979.

CONTRACEPTIVE AGENTS: FEMALE: THERAPEUTIC
Estrogen therapy for the climateric and thromboembolic risk, by C. Campagnoli, et al. MINERVA GINECOLO-GIA 32(5):429-435, May, 1980.

Hemostatic changes associated with hormonal contraceptive treatment, by A. G. Dettori. THROMBOSIS AND HAE-MOSTASIS 42(1):24, 1979.

Maternal hormone therapy and congenital heart disease, by C. Ferenca, et al. TERATOLOGY 21(2):225-239, April, 1980.

Serum vitamin A and retinol-binding protein in malnourished women treated with oral contraceptives: effects of estro-gen dose and duration of treatment, by M. Mohan Ram, et al. AMERICAN JOURNAL OF OBSTETRICS AND GYNECOLOGY 135(4):470-472, October 15, 1979.

Silymarin in pregnancy and during hormonal contraceptive treatment. Blood chemistry and ultrastructural findings in the experimental model, by G. Martines, et al. AR-CHIVIO PER LE SCIENZE MEDICHE 136(3):443-454, July-September, 1979.

Successful control of refractory ventricular premature beat with an estrogen-progesterone compound, by K. Ishikawa, et al. JAPANESE CIRCULATION JOURNAL 44 (2):146-150, February, 1980.

Supportive hormone therapy and birth defects [letter], by D. T. Janerich. TERATOLOGY 20(3):483-486, December, 1979.

The use of oral prostaglandin E2 in the management of intrauterine fetal death, by F. H. Kho, et al. PROSTAGLANDINS 18(4):663-672, October, 1979.

Value of thyroid function tests after long term hormone therapy, by A. Vucic, et al. JUGOSLAVENSKA GINEKOLOGIJA I OPSTETRICIJA 18(5-6):405-409, 1978.

CONTRACEPTIVE AGENTS: MALE
Artificial regulation of the generative functions of men by means of contraceptive agents, by D. Vasilev. AKUSHERSTVOI GINEKOLOGIIA 19(3):259-260, 1980.

Epididymal and testicular enzymes as minitors for assessment of male antifertility drugs, by S. Nag, et al. JOURNAL OF STEROID BIOCHEMISTRY 11(1B):681-688, July, 1979.

Male contraception; synergism of gonadotropin-releasing hormone analog and testosterone in suppressing gonadotropin, by D. Heber, et al. SCIENCE 109(4459):936-938, August 22, 1980.

The metabolism of 3-amino-1-chloropropan-2-ol in relation to its antifertility activity in male rats, by A. R. Jones, et al. XENOBIOTICA 9(4):253-261, April, 1979.

The potential for an androgen male contraceptive, by G. R. Cunningham, et al. JOURNAL OF CLINICAL ENDOCRINOLOGY AND METABOLISM 49(4):520-526,

October, 1979.

Pregnancies associated with sperm concentrations below 10 million/ml in clinical studies of a potential male contraceptive method, monthly depot medroxyprogesterone acetate and testosterone esters, by A. Barfield, et al. CONTRACEPTION 20(2):121-127, August, 1979.

Studies with cyproterone acetate for male contraception, by S. Roy, et al. JOURNAL OF STEROID BIOCHEMISTRY 11(1 Part B):675-680, 1979.

Suppression of human spermatogenesis by depot androgen: potential for male contraception, by R. S. Swerdloff, et al. JOURNAL OF STEROID BIOCHEMISTRY 11(1 Part B):663-670, 1979.

Use of low-dosage oral cyproterone acetate as a male contraceptive, by C. Wang, et al. CONTRACEPTION 21(3): 245-272, March, 1980.

CONTRACEPTIVE AGENTS: MALE OR FEMALE
Unisex birth control chemical [luteinizing hormone-releasing hormone], by J. A. Miller. SCIENCE NEWS 117:331+, May 24, 1980.

CONTRACEPTIVE AGENTS: PARENTERAL
Further study on the effect of norethisterone enanthate, an injectable contraceptive on body functions, by M. N. Ali, et al. BANGLADESH MEDICAL RESEARCH COUNCIL BULLETIN 4(2):63-70, December, 1978.

Microanalysis of lipids in discrete brain areas of the rabbit following intramuscular administration of steroid contraceptive, by F. Islam, et al. CONTRACEPTION 21(4): 434-442, April, 1980.

CONTRACEPTIVE AGENTS: THERAPEUTIC USE
Strokes and contraceptive medication, by J. N. Currie, et al.

MEDICAL JOURNAL OF AUSTRALIA 1(2):58, January 26, 1980.

CONTRACEPTIVES
Contraception in 1980, by G. Grillet. INFIRMIERE FRANCAISE (213):23-26, March, 1980.

Contraception: which way for you?, by E. Blume. VOGUE 170:254+, April, 1980.

Contraceptives, by C. Channing. THE SCIENCES 19:14+, December, 1979.

—, by C. Lacoste. REVUE DE L'INFIRMIERE ET DE L'ASSISTANTE SOCIALE 30(6):51-56, June, 1980.

Modern contraception, by E. Paterok, et al. ZFA. ZEITSCHRIFT FUR ALLGEMEINMEDIZIN 55(29):1603-1604, October 20, 1979.

Post-coital contraception. DRUG AND THERAPEUTICS BULLETIN 18(2):5-7, January 18, 1980.

AUSTRALIA
Contraceptive use in Australia, by C. M. Young, et al. AUSTRALIAN AND NEW ZEALAND JOURNAL OF OBSTETRICS AND GYNAECOLOGY 19(1):1-6, February, 1979.

Use of contraception among married women in New South Wales, Australia, by F. Yusuf. JOURNAL OF BIOSOCIAL SCIENCE 12(1):41-49, January, 1980.

BANGLADESH
Use-pattern of oral contraceptive in rural Bangladesh: a case study of Sulla, by F. I. Chowdhury, et al. BANGLADESH DEVELOPMENT STUDIES 6(3): 271-300, 1978.

CONTRACEPTIVES

BRAZIL
Contraceptive use and fertility levels in Sao Paulo state, Brazil, by M. S. Nakamura, et al. STUDIES IN FAMILY PLANNING 11:236-246, July-August, 1980.

Service availability and the unmet need for contraceptive and sterilization services in Sao Paulo State, Brazil. INTERNATIONAL FAMILY PLANNING PERSPECTIVES 6:10-19, March, 1980.

CHINA
China invents male birth control pill, by W. Wen. AMERICAN JOURNAL OF CHINESE MEDICINE 8(1-2): 195-197, Spring-Summer, 1980.

Effects of changed contraception patterns on fertility in Taiwan: applications of a non-Markovian stochastic model, by G. Pickens, et al. INTERNATIONAL JOURNAL OF BIOMEDICAL COMPUTING 11(1): 1-19, January, 1980.

Plasma pogesterone levels in normal and pregnant Chinese women and effects of contraceptives on them, by Z. P. Gu, et al. CHINESE MEDICAL JOURNAL 93 (8):523-527, August, 1980.

CUBA
Recent trends in fertility, abortion and contraception in Cuba, by P. E. Hollerbach. INTERNATIONAL FAMILY PLANNING PERSPECTIVES 6:97-106, September, 1980.

DENMARK
The interaction between legalization of abortion and contraception in Denmark, by P. C. Matthiessen. WORLD HEALTH STATISTICS QUARTERLY 32 (4):246-256, 1979.

EGYPT

EGYPT
Household distribution of contraceptives in rural Egypt, by S. Gadalla, et al. STUDIES IN FAMILY PLANNING 11(3):105-113, March, 1980.

Statistico epidemiological study of changes in the vaginal flora of contraceptive pill users in Alexandria, by E. Fares, et al. JOURNAL OF THE EGYPTIAN PUBLIC HEALTH ASSOCIATION 54(1-2):49-63, 1979.

FRANCE
Avortement volontaire, incitations et resistances a la contraception, by M. Bourgeois. L'EVOLUTION PSYCHIATRIQUE 42(2):397-417, April-June, 1977.

La diffusion des methodes contraceptives modernes en France de 1971 a 1978 [results of recent French legislation permitting the distribution of various types of contraceptives], by P. Collomb. POPULATION 34(6):1045-1065, 1979.

Spread of the use of modern contraceptive methods in France: 1971-1978, by P. Collomb. POPULATION 34:1045-1066, November-December, 1979.

GREAT BRITAIN
British women sue pill manufacturer [Syntex], by J. Miller. BUSINESS INSURANCE 13:84, October 29, 1979.

Widespread contraceptive use found in Britain: condom popular, two-child families preferred. FAMILY PLANNING PERSPECTIVES 12:108-110, March-April, 1980.

GUATEMALA
Characteristics of successful distributors in the community based distribution of contraceptives in Guatemala, by J. T. Bertrand, et al. STUDIES IN FAMILY

GUATEMALA
PLANNING 11:274-285, September-October, 1980.

INDIA
Inter-spousal communication and practice of contraception in India, by J. C. Bhatia, et al. JOURNAL OF FAMILY WELFARE 26:18-30, June, 1980.

User preferences for contraceptive methods in India, Korea, the Philippines, and Turkey [based on a study conducted by two task forces of the World Health Organization, 1977-1979]. STUDIES IN FAMILY PLANNING 11:267-273, September/October, 1980.

IRAN
Variations in serum copper and ceruloplasmin activity following a long term intake of combined oral contraceptives in Iranian women, by S. Kamyab, et al. JOURNAL OF ENDOCRINOLOGICAL INVESTIGATION 3(2):173-175, April-June, 1980.

JAVA-BALI
Continuation of contraception on Java-Bali: preliminary results from the quarterly acceptor survey, by J. D. Teachman, et al. STUDIES ON FAMILY PLANNING 11(4):134-144, April, 1980.

KOREA
User preferences for contraceptive methods in India, Korea, the Philippines, and Turkey [based on a study conducted by two task forces of the World Health Organization, 1977-1979]. STUDIES IN FAMILY PLANNING 11:267-273, September/October, 1980.

MALAYSIA
Use-effectivness of the copper-7 intrauterine device in a Malaysian family planning clinic, by G. T. Heng. MEDICAL JOURNAL OF MALAYSIA 33(4):352, June, 1979.

THE NETHERLANDS
Contraceptive use rises in Netherlands: fertility falls among all groups. FAMILY PLANNING PERSPEC-TIVES 12:165-166, May-June, 1980.

NEW ZEALAND
Contraceptive practice among New Zealand women, by B. J. Kirkwood, et al. NEW ZEALAND MEDICAL JOURNAL 90(641):108-111, August 8, 1979.

THE PHILIPPINES
User preferences for contraceptive methods in India, Korea, the Philippines, and Turkey [based on a study conducted by two task forces of the World Health Organization, 1977-1979]. STUDIES IN FAMILY PLANNING 11:267-273, September/October, 1980.

SCANDINAVIA
Use of contraceptives and abortions in Scandinavia. NORDISK MEDICIN 95(5):157-159, May, 1980.

SWEDEN
Demographic techniques in describing contraceptive use applied on the situation in Sweden, by O. Meirik, et al. ACTA OBSTETRICIA ET GYNECOLOGICA SCANDINAVICA 88(Suppl):61-64, 1979.

SWITZERLAND
Recommendations of the swiss family planning associa-tion regarding the indications for oral contraceptives. PRAXIS 68(41):1330-1332, October 9, 1979.

THAILAND
A field study of the choice and continuity of use of three contraceptive methods in a rural area of Thailand, by A. Somboonsuk, et al. JOURNAL OF BIOSOCIAL SCIENCE 10(2):209-216, April, 1978.

The paper 'pill': an acceptability study in Thai women,

THAILAND
by S. Koetsawang, et al. JOURNAL OF THE MEDI-
CAL ASSOCIATION OF THAILAND 62(11):605-
610, November, 1979.

Return of ovulation after the cessation of depot-medroxy
progesterone acetate treatment in Thai women, by B.
N. Saxena, et al. JOURNAL OF THE MEDICAL
ASSOCIATION OF THAILAND 63(2):66-69, February, 1980.

TURKEY
User preferences for contraceptive methods in India,
Korea, the Philippines and Turkey. STUDIES IN
FAMILY PLANNING 11:267-273, September-
October, 1980.

YEMEN
Population processes in rural Yemen: temporary emigra-
tion, breastfeeding, and contraception, by C. Myntti.
STUDIES IN FAMILY PLANNING 10(10):282-289,
October, 1979.

CONTRACEPTIVES: ADVERTISING
Contraceptive ads could be coming to radio and tv. OUR
SUNDAY VISITOR 68:6, March 2, 1980.

CONTRACEPTIVES: ATTITUDES
Adolescent perspectives on sexuality, contraception, and
pregnancy, by V. McNamara, et al. JOURNAL OF THE
MEDICAL ASSOCIATION OF GEORGIA 68(9):811-
814, September, 1979.

Attitudes and choice of contraceptive, by A. E. Reading, et
al. PSYCHOLOGICAL REPORTER 44(3 Part 2):1243-
1246, June, 1979.

Attitudinal and nonattitudinal determinants of contraception: a cross-cultural study, by S. B. Kar, et al. STUDIES

IN FAMILY PLANNING 11(2):51-64, February, 1980.

Contraceptive attitude behavior consistency in adolescence, by S. Jorgensen. POPULATION AND ENVIRONMENT: BEHAVIORAL AND SOCIAL ISSUES 3(2):174-194, Summer, 1980.

Contraceptive efficacy: the significance of method and motivation [based on data from the 1970 and 1975 National fertility studies], by E. F. Jones, et al. STUDIES IN FAMILY PLANNING 11:39-50, February, 1980.

Differences in contraceptive knowledge, attitudes, and practice by rural-urban residence history: currently married women aged 15-44, Philippines, 1973. PHILIPPINE SOCIOLOGICAL REVIEW 23(1-4):101-118, January-October, 1975.

Locus of control and contraceptive knowledge, attitudes and practice, by I. Blignault, et al. BRITISH JOURNAL OF MEDICAL PSYCHOLOGY 52(4):339-345, December, 1979.

The patient's choice in contraception, by R. A. Kinch. INTERNATIONAL JOURNAL OF GYNAECOLOGY AND OBSTETRICS 16(6):561-563, 1978-1979.

Patterns of family building and contraceptive use of middle-class couples, by D. Woodward, et al. JOURNAL OF BIOSOCIAL SCIENCE 10(1):39-58, January, 1978.

Reason for nonuse of contraception by sexually active women aged 15-19, by M. Zelnik, et al. FAMILY PLANNING PERSPECTIVES 11:289-296, September-October, 1979.

Situational, attitudinal and normative determinants of coital, contraceptive and conceptive behavioral intentions: an integration of social exchange theory and the fishbein

model, by R. Venjohn. DISSERTATION ABSTRACTS
INTERNATIONAL 40(09):4574-B, 1979.

CONTRACEPTIVES: COMPLICATIONS
Contraceptive-induced unilateral retinopathy, by A. Giovannini, et al. OPHTHALMOLOGICA 179(5):302-305,
1979.

Contraceptives and acute salpingitis, by L. Weström. LA-
KARTIDNINGEN 77(14):1290-1291, April 2, 1980.

Diseases affecting contraceptive practice in middle age, by
R. J. Beard. JOURNAL OF BIOSOCIAL SCIENCE
Suppl(6):143-156, 1979.

CONTRACEPTIVES: FAILURES
The claim for wrongful conception. Forcing physicians to
raise their patients' children, by D. Savage. JOURNAL
OF REPRODUCTIVE MEDICINE 24(2):51-60, February, 1980.

Contraceptive failure: a blessed event? FLORIDA BAR
JOURNAL 54:587-592, October, 1980.

Contraceptive failures and psychosocial aspects of abortion.
Three regional inquiries, by M. Fresel-Losey, et al. POP-
ULATION 35:545-580, May-June, 1980.

Contraceptive practice and repeat induced abortion: an
epidemiological investigation, by M. J. Shepard, et al.
JOURNAL OF BIOSOCIAL SCIENCE 11(3):289-302,
July, 1979.

The contraceptive practice of abortion patients, by M. J.
Sparrow. NEW ZEALAND MEDICAL JOURNAL 91
(653):104-106, February 13, 1980.

Court takes unique position in wrongful birth case, by F.
Speaker. PENNSYLVANIA MEDICINE 82(12):15-16,

December, 1979.

Torts, wrongful conception, measuring the damages incurred by the parents of an unplanned child. DEPAUL LAW REVIEW 28:249-258, Fall, 1978.

Torts—wrongful pregnancy—when defendant's negligence or breach of contract in a sterilization procedure allows the conception and birth of a healthy child, damages may be recovered in an action for wrongful pregnancy without reduction for the value of the benefits derived from the child. UNIVERSITY OF DETROIT JOURNAL OF URBAN LAW 57:184-201, Fall, 1979.

CONTRACEPTIVES: FEMALE
American Academy of Pediatrics: Committee on Drugs. Medroxyprogesterone acetate (Depo-Probera). PEDI-ATRICS 65(1):A74, January, 1980.

Contraception in androgenised women with a low-dose cyproterone-acetate containing one-phase preparation, by L. Moltz, et al. DEUTSCHE MEDIZINISCHE WOCHEN-SCHRIFT 104(39):1376-1382, September 28, 1979.

Use of contraceptives prior to and after conception and exposure to other fetal hazards, by P. H. Shino, et al. CONTRACEPTION 20(2):105-120, August, 1979.

CONTRACEPTIVES: FEMALE: BARRIER
Barrier methods, by L. B. Tyrer, et al. CLINICAL OBSTE-TRICS AND GYNAECOLOGY 6(1):39-55, April, 1979.

Barrier methods of contraception: a reappraisal, by E. B. Connell. INTERNATIONAL JOURNAL OF GYNAE-COLOGY AND OBSTETRICS 16(6):479-481, 1978-1979.

Cervical cap, by J. M. Kintzing. MADEMOISELLE 86:108+, August, 1980.

Contraception: the cervical cap, by K. J. Littman. MS MAG-AZINE 9:91-92, October, 1980.

The diaphragm: an appealing and effective contraceptive for many teenagers, by A. Marks, et al. PEDIATRIC RE-SEARCH 13(4 Part 2):328, 1979.

The diaphragm: its effective use among college women, by I. M. Hagen, et al. JOURNAL OF THE AMERICAN COLLEGATE HEALTH ASSOCIATION 28(5):263-266, April, 1980.

Increase in diaphragm use in a university population, by L. E. Berlin, et al. JOGN NURSING 8(5):280-282, September-October, 1979.

Oral contraception, mechanical contraception, and carbohydrate and lipid metabolism: a two-year study, by V. Pribicevic, et al. INTERNATIONAL JOURNAL OF FERTILITY 24(2):114-119, 1979.

Profile of family planning service personnel for barrier method acceptability study [Egypt], by M. T. Hassouna, et al. POPULATION STUDIES p24-39, January/March, 1980.

Putting a better cap on the cerviix [news], by G. McBride. JAMA 243(16):1617-1618, April 25, 1980.

Social characteristics of diaphragm users in a family planning clinic, by J. McEwan. JOURNAL OF BIOSOCIAL SCIENCE 10(2):159-167, April, 1978.

Where did you get a cervical cap: a guide to area clinics, by K. J. Littman. BOSTON 72(1):179, June, 1980.

CONTRACEPTIVES: FEMALE: BARRIER: COMPLICATIONS
Barrier contraceptive practice and male infertility as related to factors to female breast cancer, by A. N. Gjorgov.

GODISEN ZBORNIK NA MEDICINSKIOT FAKULTET VO SKOPJE 24:101-121, 1978.

Barrier contraceptive practice and male infertility as related factors to breast cancer in married women. Preliminary results, by A. N. Gjorgov. GODISEN ZBORNIK NA MEDICINSKIOT FAKULTET VO SKOPJE 24:133-137, 1978.

CONTRACEPTIVES: FEMALE: COMPLICATIONS

Accumulation of ethinylestradiol in blood and endometrium of women taking oral contraceptives: the sequential therapy, by V. Cortes-Gallegos, et al. FERTILITY AND STERILITY 32(5):524-527, November, 1979.

Acrosin inhibitors as vaginal contraceptives in the primate and their acute toxicity, by L. J. Zaneveld, et al. BIO-LOGICAL REPRODUCTION 20(5):1045-1054, June, 1979.

Contraception in female risk patients, by A. S. Wolf. MEDI-ZINISCHE WELT 31(18):654-656, May 2, 1980.

Do contraceptives influence the incidence of acute pelvic inflammatory disease in women with gonorrhoea?, by G. Ryden, et al. CONTRACEPTION 20(2):149-157, August, 1979.

Effect of different contraception on microbial vaginal flora and immunoglobulin levels, by E. El Ghazzawi, et al. JOURNAL OF THE EGYPTIAN MEDICAL ASSOCIA-TION 54(3):138-153, 1979.

Increased occurrence of ectopic pregnancy. A relation to the contraceptive practice?, by M. Onsrud. TIDSSKRIFT FOR DEN NORSKE LAEGEFORENING 100(14):944-947, May 20, 1980.

Measuring contraceptive efficacy and side effects, by I. Sivin.

INTERNATIONAL JOURNAL OF GYNAECOLOGY
AND OBSTETRICS 16(6):460-465, 1978-1979.

Prevalence of premalignant lesions of the cervix uteri. Comparative study between a female population using contraceptives, by J. M. Arizaga Cruz, et al. GINECOLOGIA Y OBSTETRICIA DE MEXICO 46(273):37-44, July, 1979.

CONTRACEPTIVES: FEMALE: IUD
Bleeding and ovulation control with use of a small contraceptive vaginal ring releasing levonorgestrel and estradiol, by J. Toivonen, et al. CONTRACEPTION 20(1):11-18, July, 1979.

Comparison of metabolic and clinical effects of four oral contraceptive formulations and a contraceptive vaginal ring, by S. Roy, et al. AMERICAN JOURNAL OF OBSTETRICS AND GYNECOLOGY 136(7):920-931, April 1, 1980.

Contraception for teenage girls. Combination pill or IUD?, by E. Weiner, et al. ACTA OBSTETRICIA ET GYNECOLOGICA SCANDINAVICA 88(Suppl):65-69, 1979.

Experience with the copper 7 intrauterine device in an adolescent population, by J. W. Kulig, et al. JOURNAL OF PEDIATRICS 96(4):746-750, April, 1980.

IUD compared with oral contraception in nulliparae, by A. Bergqvist, et al. CONTRACEPTION 20(4):407-415, October, 1979.

I.U.D. debate [risk of pelvic infections]. TIME 115:60, May 26, 1980.

Insertion of a coil (Gravigard) in induced abortion, by S. Olsen, et al. UGESKRIFT FOR LAEGER 142(13):820-822, March 24, 1980.

Intracellular relationships of the rat uterine estrogen receptor: alteration by intra-uterine devices, by L. Myatt, et al. CANCER TREATMENT REPORTS 63(7):1164, 1979.

Intrauterine contraception: a combined histologic and cytologic study, by M. L. Carneiro De Moura, et al. PATHOLOGY, RESEARCH AND PRACTICE 165(1-2):73, 1979.

Intrauterine devices, by D. R. Mishell. CLINICAL OBSTETRICS AND GYNAECOLOGY 6(1):27-38, 1979.

Intrauterine devices: a story of pain—and risk, by C. Dreifus. REDBOOK 154:67+, March, 1980.

Intravaginal and intracervical devices for the delivery of fertility regulating agents. JOURNAL OF STEROID BIOCHEMISTRY 11(1B):461-467, July, 1979.

Intravaginal contraception with the synthetic progestin, R2010, by J. Toivonen. CONTRACEPTION 20(5):511-518, November, 1979.

Long-acting, more effective copper T IUDs [intrauterine devices]: a summary of U.S. experience, 1970-1975, by I. Sivin, et al. STUDIES IN FAMILY PLANNING 10: 263-281, October, 1979.

Many ways of looking at an IUD, by A. Kessler, et al. WORLD HEALTH p18-19, April, 1980.

Mechanism of action of intrauterine devices, by S. Correau, et al. GINECOLOGIA Y OBSTETRICIA DE MEXICO 45(271):419-428, May, 1979.

Oral contraception, mechanical contraception, and carbohydrate and lipid metabolism: a two-year study, by V. Pribicevic, et al. INTERNATIONAL JOURNAL OF

FERTILITY 24(2):114-119, 1979.

Our experience with intrauterine devices (IUD) for birth control, by J. J. Vidal, et al. ACTA OBSTETRICA Y GINECOLOGICA HISPANA-LUSITANA 28(2):87-94, February, 1980.

Psychological factors in IUD use: a review, by A. E. Reading, et al. JOURNAL OF BIOSOCIAL SCIENCE 9(3):317-323, July, 1977.

Restoration of ovarian function by progesterone administration following copper intrauterine device insertion in rats, by S. K. Nayyar. IRCS MEDICAL SCIENCE LIBRARY 7(4):175, 1979.

Restoration of ovarian function following prostaglandin F-2L administration in copper intrauterine device-bearing rats, by S. K. Nayyar, et al. IRCS MEDICAL SCIENCE LIBRARY 7(6):305, 1979.

The role of psycho-social factors in intrauterine device continuation, by A. Reading. SOCIAL SCIENCE AND MEDICINE 13(6):631-640, 1979.

Use-effectiveness of the copper-7 intrauterine device in a Malaysian family planning clinic, by G. T. Heng. MEDICAL JOURNAL OF MALAYSIA 33(4):352, June, 1979.

CONTRACEPTIVES: FEMALE: IUD: COMPLICATIONS
Actinomyces-like organisms in cervical smears from women using intrauterine contraceptive devices, by H. L. Duguid, et al. BRITISH MEDICAL JOURNAL 6239:534-537, August 23, 1980.

The case against IUD: the story continues [letters]. NEW WEST 5(2):86-87, June 2, 1980.

The case against IUD's, by J. Kasindorf. NEW WEST 5(10): 21, May 5, 1980.

Cerebral absess associated with an intrauterine contraceptive device, by N. Kum, et al. OBSTETRICS AND GYNE-COLOGY 54(3):375-378, 1979.

Cutaneous eruptions and intrauterine copper device, by G. Frentz, et al. ACTA DERMATO-VENEREOLOGICA 60(1):71, 1980.

Dalkon, or the case of the suspect shield, by N. Sheppard, Jr. NEW YORK TIMES pE-22, March 28, 1980.

Drugs: the CU-7—a new IUD risk, by J. Zackey. TRIAL 16 (5):68-70, May, 1980.

The effect of the intrauterine contraceptive device on the prevalence of morphologic abnormalities in human spontaneous abortions, by L. H. Honore. CONTRACEPTION 21(1):47-52, January, 1980.

Four case histories of severe genital infections following insertion of intrauterine contraceptive devices, by F. Ebert, et al. ZENTRALBLATT FUR GYNAEKOLOGIE 107 (6):362-267, 1980.

Frontlines: victory over Dalkon. (C. Palmer awarded $6.8 million for injuries suffered by using Dalkon IUD), by C. O'Connor. MOTHER JONES 5:12, January, 1980.

Heat induction in copper-bearing intrauterine devices during shortwave diathermy, by N. C. Nielson, et al. ACTA OBSTETRICIA ET GYNECOLOGICA SCANDINAVICA 58(5):495, 1979.

IUD users may have higher risk of contracting PID, studies find: pill may have protective effect. FAMILY PLANNING PERSPECTIVES 12:206-207, July-August, 1980.

Ovarian pregnancy and the intrauterine device: report of a case and review of the literature, by S. J. Wilson, et al. MT. SINAI JOURNAL OF MEDICINE 46(1):15-20, 1979.

Pathologist links IUDs worn for years with infetility risk. MEDICAL WORLD NEWS 21:50-51, April 14, 1980.

Pill, IUD users run no increased risk of ectopics, malformation, miscarriage in planned pregnancies [news]. FAMILY PLANNING PERSPECTIVES 12(3):156-157, May-June, 1980.

Possible relationship between lupus inhibitor and recurrent abortion in young women [letter], by B. G. Firkin, et al. LANCET 2(8190):366, August 16, 1980.

Primary abdominal pregnancy associated with the intrauterine device (2 cases), by D. Muzsnai, et al. EUROPEAN JOURNAL OF OBSTETRICS, GYNECOLOGY AND REPRODUCTIVE BIOLOGY 10(4):275-278, 1980.

A progressive rise in serum copper levels in women taking oral contraceptives: a potential hazard?, by Y. Rubinfeld, et al. FERTILITY AND STERILITY 32(5):599-601, November, 1979.

Rare position of transcervically penetrated IUP DANA-Super in intact gravidity, by H. H. Fröhlich. ZENTRALBLATT FUR GYNAEKOLOGIE 101(18):1200-1202, 1979.

Significance of T mycoplasma and actinomycetales in intrauterine device and nonintrauterine device wearing women, by C. D. Graben, et al. ANNALS OF CLINICAL AND LABORATORY SCIENCE 9(5):434, 1979.

CONTRACEPTIVES: FEMALE: IUD: FAILURE
Early human pregnancy with the intrauterine contraceptive

device in situ: incidence of heteroploidy, by L. H. Honore. TERATOLOGY 20(1):3-6, August, 1979.

Failure of gonadotropins in reversing the copper intrauterine device induced acyclicity in rats, by S. K. Nayyar. IRCS MEDICAL SCIENCE LIBRARY COMPENDIUM 7(4): 174, 1979.

Heteroploidy in IUD-associated pregnancy [editorial] , by D. Warburton. TERATOLOGY 20(1):2, August, 1979.

Hysterographic and hysterectomy findings after pregnancies in spite of a remaining intrauterine device, by T. Katzorke, et al. MEDIZINISCHE WELT 30(38):1393-1395, September 21, 1979.

Intact pregnancy of 7 weeks' duration with an intrauterine pessary in place, by A. Feige. MEDIZINISCHE KLINIK 75(2):54+, January 18, 1980.

Ovarian ectopic pregnancy in association with a copper 7 intrauterine device in situ, by A. Chidiac, et al. FERTIL-ITY AND STERILITY 32(1):127-129, 1979.

Pregnancy in IUD in situ—abortion from clinical-bacterio-logical viewpoint?, by G. E. Feichter, et al. ARCHIVES OF GYNECOLOGY 228(1-4):396, July 20, 1979.

CONTRACEPTIVES: FEMALE: IMPLANTED
Antifertility activities of newly synthesized steroids in rats administered postcoitally before and after implantation and their interceptive effects in the baboon, by J. Strecke, et al. PHARMAZIE 35(1):45-47, January, 1980.

Chronic occlusion of the rabbit Fallopian tube with silicone polymer, by R. H. Davis, et al. GYNECOLOGIC AND OBSTETRIC INVESTIGATION 10(6):281-288, 1979.

Contraception with implanted gestagens, by N. C. Nielsen, et al. UGESKRIFT FOR LAEGER 141(45):3100-3103, November 5, 1979.

Eighteen months contraception following subdermal insertion of silastic capsules containing norgestrienone, by A. R. Da Silva, et al. INTERNATIONAL JOURNAL OF FERTILITY 23(3):185-192, 1978.

Norplant: reversible implant contraception, by I. Sivin, et al. STUDIES IN FAMILY PLANNING 11(7-8):227-235, July-August, 1980.

CONTRACEPTIVES: FEMALE: ORAL
Advantages and disadvantages of low-dose oral contraceptives, by B. Law. JOURNAL OF GYNAECOLOGY AND OBSTETRICS 16(6):556-560, 1978-1979.

Advantages and limitations of steroid contraception: considerations on 14 cases of post-pill amenorrhea observed by the author, by M. Faggiano, et al. ARCHIVES OF OBSTETRICS AND GYNECOLOGY 83(5-6):143-155, May-December, 1978.

Biochemical basis for evaluating oral contraceptives, by M. H. Briggs. AUSTRALIAN FAMILY PHYSICIAN Suppl: 25-29, February, 1980.

Biochemical basis for the selection of oral contraceptives, by M. H. Briggs. INTERNATIONAL JOURNAL OF GYNAECOLOGY AND OBSTETRICS 16(6):509-517, 1978-1979.

Biological profile of 3-(2-benzofuranyl)-2,2-dimethyl-3-ethyl-propionic acid—a new oral antifertility agent, by K. V. Rao, et al. INDIAN JOURNAL OF EXPERIMENTAL BIOLOGY 17(7):678-679, July, 1979.

Cigarette smoking, alcohol intake, and oral contraceptives:

relationships to lipids and lipoproteins in adolescent school-children, by J. A. Morrison, et al. METABOLISM 28(11):1166-1170, November, 1979.

Clinical evaluation of two biphasic and one triphasic norgestrel/ethinyl estradiol regimens, by A. Larranaga, et al. INTERNATIONAL JOURNAL OF FERTILITY 23 (3):193-199, 1978.

Clinical pharmacology of contraceptive steroids. Report on a workshop conference held in Igls, Austria May 4-7, 1978, by J. Hammerstein, et al. CONTRACEPTION 20 (3):187-200, September, 1979.

Clinical trial of a new oral contraceptive pill containing the natural oestrogen 17 beta-oestradiol, by B. Astedt, et al. BRITISH JOURNAL OF OBSTETRICS AND GYNAE-COLOGY 86(9):732-736, September, 1979.

Comparative study of the effect of oral contraceptives containing 50 microgram of estrogen and those containing 20 microgram of estrogen on adrenal cortical function, by E. S. Amin, et al. AMERICAN JOURNAL OF OB-STETRICS AND GYNECOLOGY 137(7):831-833, August 1, 1980.

A comparison of birth control pill user data from two national surveys, by W. D. Mosher, et al. REVIEW OF PUBLIC DATA USE 8:1-12, June, 1980.

Comparison of metabolic and clinical effects of four oral contraceptive formulations and a contraceptive vaginal ring, by S. Roy, et al. AMERICAN JOURNAL OF OB-STETRICS AND GYNECOLOGY 136(7):920-931, April 1, 1980.

Comparison of a paper pill with a conventional oral contraceptive tablet, by H. K. Basu, et al. JOURNAL OF IN-TERNATIONAL MEDICAL RESEARCH 8(2):148-152,

1980.

Competition for the pill shapes up in lab. CHEMICAL WEEKLY 125:51-52, October 17, 1979.

Contraception for teenage girls. Combination pill or IUD? by E. Weiner, et al. ACTA OBSTETRICIA ET GYNE- COLOGICA SCANDINAVICA 88(Suppl):65-69, 1979.

Contraception in preclimacteric women with special regard to oral contraceptives, by H. Salzer, et al. WIENER MEDIZINISCHE WOCHENSCHRIFT 130(6):218-221, March 31, 1980.

Experiences with the new oral contraceptive Ovysmen, by A. James, et al. JOURNAL OF INTERNATIONAL MEDICAL RESEARCH 8(1):86-89, 1980.

Factors in the use of oral contraceptives by young women, by P. D. Werner, et al. JOURNAL OF APPLIED SO- CIAL PSYCHOLOGY 9:537-547, November-December, 1979.

Folate for oral contraceptive users may reduce cervical can- cer risk [news], by W. A. Check. JAMA 244(7):633- 634, August 15, 1980.

Folate-induced regression of cervical intraepithelial neo- plasia (CIN) in users of oral contraceptive agents (OCA) [from abstract of paper presented at the 20th annual meeting of the American Society for Clinical Nutrition, Washington, D. C., May 9-11, 1980], by C. E. Butter- worth, Jr., et al. AMERICAN JOURNAL OF CLINICAL NUTRITION 33:926, April, 1980.

Follow-up during oral contraception [letter], by P. G. Crosignani. JOURNAL OF ENDOCRINOLOGICAL IN- VESTIGATION 1(1):97-98, January, 1978.

Gas-liquid chromatographic analysis of lynestrenol in contraceptive tablets, by M. Rizk, et al. PHARMAZIE 33(8):
521-522, 1978.

IUD compared with oral contraception in nulliparae, by A.
Bergqvist, et al. CONTRACEPTION 20(4):407-415,
October, 1979.

IUD users may have higher risk of contracting PID, studies
find: pill may have protective effect. FAMILY PLAN-
NING PERSPECTIVES 12:206-207, July-August, 1980.

Immune studies in oral contraceptive users, by B. A. Rama-
lakshmi, et al. CONTRACEPTION 20(4):417-425,
October, 1979.

The incidence of gynecologic examination in pill monitoring,
by F. P. Wibaut. NEDERLANDS TIJDSCHRIFT VOOR
GENEESKUNDE 123(52):2230-2231, December 29,
1979.

Individual needs in oral contraception, by E. Weisberg. AUS-
TRALIAN FAMILY PHYSICIAN Suppl:20-24, Febru-
ary, 1980.

Influence of HLA types on carbohydrate effects of a low-
estrogen oral contraceptive, by W. N. Spellacy, et al.
FERTILITY AND STERILITY 33(5):506-509, May,
1980.

Initial pill selection and managing the contraceptive pill patient, by R. P. Dickey. INTERNATIONAL JOURNAL
OF GYNAECOLOGY AND OBSTETRICS 16(6):547-
555, 1978-1979.

Is the pill natural?, by M. Potts. POPULI 7(1):12-17, 1980.

Managing oral contraception, by M. D. Read. PRACTI-
TIONER 224(1340):179-181, February, 1980.

The mechanism of action of a new low-dosed combined oral contraceptive, by J. S. Dericks-Tan, et al. ARCHIVES OF GYNECOLOGY 229(2):107-114, 1980.

No association between oral contraceptives and malignant melanomas [letter], by R. G. Stevens, et al. NEW ENGLAND JOURNAL OF MEDICINE 302(17):966, April 24, 1980.

Oral contraception, by W. C. Andrews. CLINICAL OBSTE-TRICS AND GYNAECOLOGY 6(1):3-26, April, 1979.

—, by J. C. Guillat. SOINS 25(8):9-12, April 20, 1980.

—, by N. B. Loudon. PRACTITIONER 223(1337):641-645, November, 1979.

Oral contraception in a regional centre. Variation in age profile and profession, from 21,000 case notes in 5 years (1973-1977), by J. H. Soutoul, et al. JOURNAL DE GYNECOLOGIE, OBSTETRIQUE ET BIOLOGIE DE LA REPRODUCTION 8(3):193-199, April-May, 1979.

Oral contraception, mechanical contraception, and carbohy-drate and lipid metabolism: a two-year study, by V. Pribicevic, et al. INTERNATIONAL JOURNAL OF FERTILITY 24(2):114-119, 1979.

Oral contraceptive use and vitamin nutrition status of mal-nourished women—effects of continuous and inter-mittent vitamin supplements, by M. S. Bamji, et al. JOURNAL OF STEROID BIOCHEMISTRY 11(1B):487-491, July, 1979.

Oral contraceptives, by I. Lejins. AUSTRALIAN NURSES JOURNAL 9(2):23-25, August, 1979.

Oral contraceptives according to the normophasic principle, by N. E. Borglin, et al. ARZNEIMITTEL FORSCHUNG

28(12):2354-2357, 1978.

Oral contraceptives and physiological variables, by L. D. Ostrander, Jr., et al. JAMA 244(7):677-679, August 15, 1980.

Oral contraceptives and plasma protein metabolism, by M. H. Briggs, et al. JOURNAL OF STEROID BIOCHEMISTRY 11(aB):425-428, July, 1979.

Oral contraceptives and sex hormone binding globulin capacity, by K. G. Masurkar, et al. INDIAN JOURNAL OF MEDICAL RESEARCH 71:221-224, February, 1980.

Oral contraceptives in women over 40, by J. A. Desrosiers. UNION MEDICALE DU CANADA 108(8):909-918, August, 1979.

Oral contraceptives, norethindrone and mestranol: effect on serum vitamin A, retinol-binding protein and prealbumin in women, by V. K. Nonavinakere, et al. FEDERATION PROCEEDINGS 39(3):Abstract 908, 1980.

The pill, by H. P. Zahradnik. ZFA. ZEITSCHRIFT FUR ALLGEMEINMEDIZIN 55(26):1410-1412, September 20, 1979.

CONTRACEPTIVES: FEMALE: ORAL: COMPLICATIONS
Abortion, deformed fetus, and the Omega pill, by L. M. Fleck. PHILOSOPHICAL STUDIES 36:271-283, October, 1979.

Action of oral contraceptives on the gingival mucosa and some components of mixed saliva, by P. D. Laforgia, et al. RIVISTA ITALIANA DI STOMATOLOGIA 48(5): 13-18, May, 1979.

Active and inactive renin in pregnancy and in women on estrogen-containing oral contraceptives, by M. Hayashi,

et al. GYNECOLOGIC AND OBSTETRIC INVESTIGA-
TION 10(5):246-253, 1979.

Acute intermittent porphyria versus porphyria variegata: a
diagnostic uncertainty, by L. P. Betancor, et al. MED-
ICINA CLINICA 74(2):61-64, January 25, 1980.

Acute intermittent porphyria with pancreatitis and myo-
cardial damage due to oral contraceptives, by O. H.
Brinkmann, et al. ZFA. ZEITSCHRIFT FUR ALLGE-
MEINMEDIZIN 55(22):1227-1233, August 10, 1979.

Adenoma of the liver and focal nodular hyperplasia. Rela-
thionship with oral contraceptives, by G. Goldfarb, et
al. GASTROENTEROLOGIE CLINIQUE ET BIO-
LOGIQUE 3(5):465-472, May, 1979.

Adjustments of circulation including blood pressure to
orthostatic reaction and physical exercise during application of a low estrogen dose steroid oral contraceptive,
by B. Sandström, et al. ACTA OBSTETRICIA ET
GYNECOLOGICA SCANDINAVICA 88(Suppl):49-
55, 1979.

Adverse effects after use of oral contraceptives. A comparison of 1966-1970 and 1974-1978, by G. Boman, et al.
LAKARTIDNINGEN 77(24):2249-2252, June 11, 1980.

Altered haemorpheology in oral contraceptive users, by P.
C. Buchan, et al. BRITISH MEDICAL JOURNAL 6219:
978-979, April 5, 1980.

Anamnestic criteria for evaluation of the 'risk' in hormonal
contraception, by S. Gneo, et al. MINERVA GINECOL-
OGIA 31(9):625-628, September, 1979.

Anatomical lesions of the liver and oral contraceptives, by P.
Delavierre, et al. SEMAINES DES HOPITAUX DE
PARIS 55(23-26):1172-1176, June 18-25, 1979.

Androgens and sexual behaviour in women using oral contraceptives, by J. Bancroft, et al. CLINICAL ENDOCRINOLOGY 12(4):327-340, April, 1980.

Antiepileptic drugs and oral contraceptives. Preliminary note, by M. Meduri, et al. BOLLETTINO DELLA SOCIETA ITALIANA DI BIOLOGIA SPERIMENTALE 54(23):2462-2467, December 15, 1978.

Antiethinyloestradiol antibody activities in oral contraceptive users, by J. L. Beaumont, et al. CLINICAL AND EXPERIMENTAL IMMUNOLOGY 38(3):445-452, December, 1979.

Antithrombin and heparin-neutralizing activity in sera of women using and not using hormonal contraceptives, by M. Stepanauskas, et al. ZEITSCHRIFT FUR MEDIZINISCHE LABORATORIUMSDIAGNOSTIK 20(5): 295-301, 1979.

Assay of estradiol receptors in a liver adenoma observed after taking an estrogen-progestogen combination [letter] , by J. Gastard, et al. NOUVELLE PRESSE MEDICALE 9 (1):43, January 5, 1980.

Benign hepatomata while taking oral contraceptives, by W. Düsel, et al. MMW: MUENCHENER MEDIZINISCHE WOCHENSCHRIFT 122(19):693-696, May 9, 1980.

Benign tumours of the liver and oral contraceptives, by F. Lesbros, et al. ARCHIVES D'ANATOMIE ET DE CYTOLOGIE PATHOLOGIQUE 28(1):24-31, 1980.

Benign tumors of the liver and oral contraceptives. Apropos of 2 cases, by M. Peffault de Latour, et al. ANNALES D'ANATOMIE PATHOLOGIQUE 24(1):73-78, 1979.

Birth control pill: good news for some women, by E. R. Dobell. REDBOOK 155:27+, September, 1980.

Bleeding hepatic adenoma and its relation to oral contraceptives, by E. J. Eichelbaum, et al. GEN 32(4):355-361, April-June, 1978.

Blood pressure and oral progestational agents. A prospective study of 119 black women, by W. D. Hall, et al. AMERICAN JOURNAL OF OBSTETRICS AND GYNECOLOGY 136(3):344-348, February 1, 1980.

British women sue pill manufacturer [Syntex], by J. Miller. BUSINESS INSURANCE 13:84, October 29, 1979.

Carbohydrate metabolism prospectively studied in women using a low-estrogen oral contraceptive for six months, by W. N. Spellacy, et al. CONTRACEPTION 20(2):137-148, August, 1979.

Cardiovascular side effects resulting from oral contraceptives, by H. J. Engel, et al. THERAPEUTISCHE UMSCHAU 37(2):96-104, February, 1980.

Cerebral pseudotumor and oral contraceptives (cerebral case), by B. Jandolo, et al. RIVISTA DI NEUROBIOLOGIA 24(1-2):106-108, January-June, 1978.

Cerebral vascular occlusion and nodular hyperplasia of the liver caused by contraceptives, by I. Babaryka, et al. MEDIZINISCHE KLINIK 75(2):76-79, January 18, 1980.

Cerebrovascular accidents among users of oral contraceptives. An analysis of Japanese cases, by Y. Umeda, et al. GYNECOLOGIC AND OBSTETRIC INVESTIGATION 10 (2-3):88-94, 1979.

The change of urinary steroid excretions in liver disease with special reference to an implication of heaptic dysfunction in pill users, by M. Kodama, et al. JOURNAL OF CLINICAL ENDOCRINOLOGY AND METABOLISM 49(5):

748-752, November, 1979.

Chest pain among oral contraceptive users, by K. Williams. JOURNAL OF THE ROYAL COLLEGE OF GENERAL PRACTITIONERS 30(210):33-34, January, 1980.

Cholangiocarcinoma and oral contraceptives [letter], by E. R. Littlewood, et al. LANCET 1(8163):310-311, February 9, 1980.

Cholesterol cholelithiasis in adolescent females: its connection with obesity, parity, and oral contraceptive use—a retrospective study of 31 cases, by L. H. Honore. ARCHIVES OF SURGERY 115(1):62-64, January, 1980.

Chorea induced by oral contraceptives, by P. A. Nausieda, et al. NEUROLOGY 29(12):1605-1609, December, 1979.

Chromogenic and immunological determination of antithrombin III and of antiplasmin in subjects under treatment with oral hormonal contraceptives, by R. Savoldi, et al. QUADERNI SCLAVO DI DIAGNOSTICA CLINICA E DI LABORATORIO 15(1):152-163, March, 1979.

Cicloxilic acid and the bile lipids in oral contraceptive users, by M. Zuin, et al. ARZNEIMITTEL-FORSCHUNG 29 (5):837-838, 1979.

Circulatory disease in association with oral contraceptive use [letter], by C. Kay. LANCET 2(8141):521, September 8, 1979.

Clearance of bacteriuria on discontinuing oral contraception, by D. A. Evans, et al. BRITISH MEDICAL JOURNAL 280(6208):152, January 19, 1980.

Colonie Crohn's disease and oral contraceptive, by C. Conri, et al. SEMAINES DES HOPITAUX DE PARIS 55(37-38):1733-1735, November 8-15, 1979.

Combined epithelial and sarcomatous elements in a liver cancer associated with oral contraceptive use, by L. Ladaga, et al. AMERICAN JOURNAL OF SURGICAL PATHOLOGY 3(2):185-190, April, 1979.

Combined pills may decrease endometrial cancer risk; sequentials may increase it [news]. FAMILY PLANNING PERSPECTIVES 12(3):162, May-June, 1980.

Comparable effects of 30 and 50 microgram estrogen-progestogen oral contraceptives on blood clotting and fibrinolysis, by A. M. A. Sabra, et al. THROMBOSIS AND HAEMOSTASIS 42(1):25, 1979.

A contribution about serious ophthalmic complications with oral contraceptives, by H. Mayer. KLINISCHE MONATSBLAETTER FUR AUGENHEILKUNDE 175(5): 677-680, November, 1979.

Co-occurring liver cell adenoma and focal nodular hyperplasia due to contraceptives. Case report, by B. Reichlin, et al. SCHWEIZERISCHE MEDIZINISCHE WOCHENSCHRIFT 110(22):873-874, May 31, 1980.

The correlation of blood pressure, cholesterol and triglyceride concentration with the administration of hormonal contraceptives in women from 2 Erfurt large-scale plants, by J. Heinrich, et al. ZEITSCHRIFT FUR DIE GESAMTE INNERE MEDIZIN UND IHRE GRENZGEBIETE 34(18):540-544, September 15, 1979.

Cyclical variations in mood in normal women taking oral contraceptives, by A. R. Forrest. BRITISH MEDICAL JOURNAL 2(6202):1403, December 1, 1979.

DES daughters: new studies, same results. SCIENCE NEWS 117:182, March 22, 1980.

Decreased risk of endometrial cancer among oral contraceptive users, by D. W. Kaufman, et al. NEW ENGLAND JOURNAL OF MEDICINE 303:1045-1047, October 30, 1980.

Detection and composition of circulating immune complexes in oral contraceptive users, by V. Beaumont, et al. BIO-MEDICINE 30(5):256-260, November, 1979.

Dietary influence on the serum lipid profile of oral contraceptive users, by A. K. Kant, et al. FEDERAL PROCEEDINGS 39(3):Abstract 2028, 1980.

Do anticonvulsants reduce the efficacy of oral contraceptives?, by C. B. Coulam, et al. EPILEPSIA 20(5):519-525, October, 1979.

Does use of oral contraceptives enhance the toxicity of carbon disulfide through interactions with pyridoxine and tryptophan metabolism?, by E. J. Calabrese. MEDICAL HYPOTHESES 6(1):21-33, January, 1980.

Drug interaction with oral contraceptive steroids. BRITISH MEDICAL JOURNAL 6233:93-94, July 12, 1980.

Early fetal deaths due to the oral contraceptive lyndiol given to the male mouse, by B. N. Hemsowrth. IRCS: MEDICAL SCIENCE: LIBRARY COMPENDIUM 7(3):140, 1979.

The effect of ampicillin on oral contraceptive effectiveness, by C. I. Friedman, et al. OBSTETRICS AND GYNECOLOGY 55(1):33-37, January, 1980.

The effect of contraceptive steroids on sister chromatid exchange and nuclear morphology, by R. T. Dutkowski, et al. HUMAN GENETICS 31(6):46A, 1979.

Effect of dietary carbohydrate and use of oral contraceptives by women on serum glucose lipid and hormone levels, by

K. M. Behall, et al. FEDERAL PROCEEDINGS 39(3): Abstract 3763, 1980.

The effect of environment on tryptophan metabolism 'via kynurenine' in oral contraceptives users, by E. Zoghby, et al. ACTA VITAMINOLOGICA ET ENZYMOLOGICA 32(5-6):167-175, 1978.

The effect of hormonal contraceptives on the EEG, by K. Dvorak, et al. CESKOSLOVENSKA NEUROLOGIE A NEUROCHIRURGIO 43(1):71-77, January, 1980.

Effect of kind of carbohydrate in the diet and use or oral contraceptives on metabolism of young women; serum glucose, insulin, and glucagon, by K. M. Behall, et al. AMERICAN JOURNAL OF CLINICAL NUTRITION 33:1041-1048, May, 1980.

—. II. Serum lipid levels, by K. M. Behall, et al. AMERICAN JOURNAL OF CLINICAL NUTRITION 33(4):825-831, April, 1980.

—. III. Serum glucose, insulin, and glucagon, by K. M. Behall, et al. AMERICAN JOURNAL OF CLINICAL NUTRITION 33(5):1041-1048, May, 1980.

Effect of oral contraceptive agents on thiamin, riboflavin and pantothenic acid status in young women, by C. M. Lewis, et al. JOURNAL OF CLINICAL NUTRITION 33:832-838, April, 1980.

Effect of oral contraceptive agents on thiamin status, by S. C. Vir, et al. INTERNATIONAL JOURNAL FOR VITAMIN AND NUTRITION RESEARCH 49(3):291-295, 1979.

Effect of oral contraceptive agents on vitamin and mineral requirements, by V. J. Thorp. JOURNAL OF THE AMERICAN DIETETIC ASSOCIATION 76(6):581-584,

AMERICAN NEUROLOGICAL ASSOCIATION 103:53-55, 1978.

Effect of oral contraceptives on platelet noradrenaline and 5-hydroxytryptamine receptors and aggregation, by J. R. Peters, et al. LANCET 2(8149):933-936, November 3, 1979.

Effect of oral contraceptives on sex chromatin count during menstrual cycle, by F. Roohi, et al. JOURNAL OF THE ASSOCIATION OF PHYSICIANS OF INDIA 27(12): 1071-1074, December, 1979.

The effect of oral contraceptives on sister chromatid exchange and micronuclei formation, by R. Dutkowski. GENETICS 91(4 Part 2 Suppl):s28-s29, 1979.

The effect of oral contraceptives on venous thrombosis and coagulation parameters after gynecological operation in Chinese, by S. C. Tso, et al. THROMBOSIS AND HAEMOSTASIS 42(1):26, 1979.

Effect of oral contraceptives on vitamin B6 nutriture of young women, by S. C. Vir, et al. INTERNATIONAL JOURNAL FOR VITAMIN AND NUTRITION RESEARCH 50(1):29-34, 1980.

Effect of prior pregnancy and combined oral contraceptives on baseline menstrual blood loss and bleeding response to intrauterine devices, by A. T. Andrade, et al. CONTRACEPTION 20(1):19-26, July, 1979.

Effect of prostaglandins on the steroidogenic function of the feto-placental system in second trimester pregnancy, by V. G. Kolod'ko. AKUSHERSTVO I GINEKOLOGIIA (8):11-14, August, 1979.

The effect of sequential oral contraceptive pill (Fysioquens) administration on carbohydrate and lipid metabolism, by

June, 1980.

Effect of oral contraceptive on hematocrit level, by A. Fuertes-de la Haba, et al. BOLETIN-ASOCIACION MEDICA DE PUERTO RICO 71(11):425-433, November, 1979.

The effect of oral contraceptive steroids and enzyme inducing drugs on sex hormone binding globulin capacity in women [proceedings], by D. J. Back, et al. BRITISH JOURNAL OF CLINICAL PHARMACOLOGY 9(1): 115P, January, 1980.

Effect of oral contraceptive use on platelet prothrombin converting (platelet factor 3) activity, by B. Leff, et al. THROMBOSIS RESEARCH 15(5-6):631-638, 1979.

Effect of oral contraceptive usage on zinc and copper in serum and hair, by S. C. Vir, et al. INTERNATIONAL JOURNAL FOR VITAMIN AND NUTRITION RESEARCH 49(3):330-335, 1979.

The effect of oral contraceptives on blood vitamin A levels and the role of sex hormones. NUTRITION REVIEWS 37(11):346-348, November, 1979.

Effect of oral contraceptives on composition and volume of breast milk, by B. Lönnerdal, et al. AMERICAN JOURNAL OF CLINICAL NUTRITION 33(4):816-824, April, 1980.

The effect of oral contraceptives on mononuclear cell cholesteryl ester hydrolase activity, by F. C. Hagemenas, et al. LIPIDS 15(1):39-44, January, 1980.

The effect of oral contraceptives on mononuclear cell cholesterol ester hydrolase activity in premenopausal women taking oral contraceptives: relevance to atherosclerosis, by F. M. Yatsu, et al. TRANSACTIONS OF THE

J. Vähäpassi, et al. ANNALES CHIRURGIAE ET GY-
NAECOLOGIAE 68(2):75-81, 1979.

The effect of smoking and oral contraceptives on the urinary
excretion of epinephrine and norepinephrine, by F. P.
Zuspan. AMERICAN JOURNAL OF OBSTETRICS
AND GYNECOLOGY 135(8):1012-1015, December 15,
1979.

Effect of 3 long-acting steroid contraceptives on urinary
pregnanediol excretions in rats, by E. E. Galal, et al.
JOURNAL OF DRUG RESEARCH 10(1-2):59-72, 1978.

Effect of varying amounts of ethinyl oestradiol in the combined oral contraceptive on plasma sex hormone binding
globulin capacity in normal women, by J. R. Pogmore,
et al. BRITISH JOURNAL OF OBSTETRICS AND GY-
NAECOLOGY 86(7):563-567, July, 1979.

Effects if an angiotensin II antagonist; [sarcosine 1, isoleucine 8] angiotensin II, on blood pressure, plasma renin
activity and plasma aldosterone concentration in hypertensive and normotensive subjects taking oral contraceptives, by T. Ogihara, et al. ENDOCRINOLOGIA
JAPONICA 26(5):591-597, October, 1979.

Effects of contraceptive steroids on serum lipoproteins and
cardiovascular disease scrutinized at workshop in Bethesda, by B. Baggett, et al. CONTRACEPTION 21(2):115-
120, February, 1980.

Effects of hormonal contraception on hemostatic and lipidic
profiles, by R. Masure, et al. THROMBOSIS AND HAE-
MOSTASIS 42(1):483, 1979.

The effects of oral contraceptive manufacture on blood clotting, by L. Poller, et al. THROMBOSIS AND HAEMO-
STOSIS 42(1):25, 1979.

The effects of oral contraceptives on carbohydrate, lipid, and protein metabolism in subjects with altered nutritional status and in association with lactation, by U. M. Joshi. JOURNAL OF STEROID BIOCHEMISTRY 11(1B):483-485, July, 1979.

The effects of oral contraceptives on the cytology of the inferior segment of the female urethra, by D. Rondelaud, et al. JOURNAL DE GYNECOLOGIE OBSTETRIQUE ET BIOLOGIE DE LA REPRODUCTION 8(2):107-110, March, 1979.

Effects of oral contraceptives on the vascular wall, by A. Basdevant, et al. NOUVELLE PRESSE MEDICALE 9 (8):519-522, February 16, 1980.

Effects of pregnancy and contraceptive steroids on gallbladder function, by D. Z. Braverman, et al. NEW ENGLAND JOURNAL OF MEDICINE 302(7):362-364, February 14, 1980.

Endocrine effects of oral contraception, by S. C. MacLeod. INTERNATIONAL JOURNAL OF GYNAECOLOGY AND OBSTETRICS 16(6):518-524, 1978-1979.

Enhanced prostacyclin formation in veins of women under chronical treatment with oral contraceptive drugs, by H. Sinzinger, et al. PHARMACOLOGICAL RESEARCH COMMUNICATIONS 12(6):515-521, June, 1980.

Epithelial melanosis of the gingiva possible resulting from the use of oral contraceptives, by R. S. Hertz, et al. JOURNAL OF THE AMERICAN DENTAL ASSOCIATION 100(5):713-714, May, 1980.

Ethynyl-estradiol content in blood and endometrium caused by oral contraceptives, by V. Cortes-Gallegos, et al. JOURNAL OF STEROID BIOCHEMISTRY 12(0):487-490, 1980.

Evaluation of some blood clotting parameters in relation to the administration of estroprogestins, by F. Orlandi, et al. ARCHIVIO PER LE SCIENCE MEDICHE 135(4): 609-617, October-December, 1978.

Evolution of plasma levels of apolipoprotein B, cholesterol and triglycerides in women during long-term oral contraception, by A. Verine, et al. CLINICA CHIMICA ACTA 100(2):143-148, January 15, 1980.

Focal nodular hyperplasia and hepatocytic adenoma in the liver of women taking contraceptive tablets, by I. Bartok, et al. ORVOSI HETILAP 120(42):2541-2544, October 21, 1979.

Four cases of benign heaptic tumors associated with oral contraception, by J. M. Jankowski, et al. SEMAINES DES HOPITAUX DE PARIS 55(21-22):1085-1090, June 8-15, 1979.

Factors associated with oral contraceptive use, by S. C. Hartz, et al. AMERICAN JOURNAL OF PUBLIC HEALTH 70:1105-1107, October, 1980.

Fatal myocardial infarction and the role of oral contraceptives, by D. E. Krueger, et al. AMERICAN JOURNAL OF EPIDEMIOLOGY 111(6):655-674, June, 1980.

Female breast cancer: distribution, risk factors, and effect of steroid contraception, by K. C. Lyle. OBSTETRICAL AND GYNECOLOGICAL SURVEY 35(7):413-427, July, 1980.

Fetal damage caused by contraceptive tablets, by E. Czeizel. ORVOSI HETILAP 121(1):3-9, January 6, 1980.

Fewer adverse effects of oral contraceptives, by E. Johansson. LAKARTIDNINGEN 77(24):2241, June 11, 1980.

Fibrinolysis, renin activity, and prorenin in normal women: effects of exercise and oral contraceptive medication, by A. M. Hedlin, et al. JOURNAL OF CLINICAL ENDO-CRINOLOGY AND METABOLISM 49(5):663-671, November, 1979.

Fibroadenoma in oral contraceptive users: a histopathologic evaluation of epithelial atypia, by V. A. LiVolsi, et al. CANCER 44(5):1778-1781, November, 1979.

Field tests with an oral contraceptive. Results with an estrogen-reduced contraceptive for the symptom of 'tight breast', by R. Heithecker, et al. ZFA. ZEITSCHRIFT FUR ALLEGEMEINMEDIZIN 55(29):1665-1666, October 20, 1979.

Gall-bladder troubles and oral contraceptives, by J. P. Bourdais, et al. SEMAINES DES HOPITAUX DE PARIS 55 (27-30):1297-1304, September 8-15, 1979.

Haemoglobin levels in contraceptive users, by K. Prema. INDIAN JOURNAL OF MEDICAL RESEARCH 69:756-760, May, 1979.

Hageman factor deficiency and oral contraceptives [letter], by A. K. Mangal, et al. LANCET 1(8171):774, April 5, 1980.

Hepatic adenomas and oral contraceptives. Report of two cases and review of the literature, by M. Sabria Leal, et al. MEDICINA CLINICA 73(6):234-238, October 10, 1979.

Hepatic sinusoidal dilatation related to oral contraceptives. A study of two patients showing ultrastructural changes, by M. A. Spellberg, et al. AMERICAN JOURNAL OF GASTROENTEROLOGY 72(3):248-252, September, 1979.

The histology of liver tumors in oral contraceptive users observed during a national survey by the American College of Surgeons Commission on Cancer, by F. Nime, et al. CANCER 44(4):1481-1489, October, 1979.

Histomorphology of the breast under the influence of hormonal contraceptives, by K. Prechtel, et al. ARCHIVES OF GYNECOLOGY 228(1-4):459-460, July 20, 1979.

Hormonal contraception and lipid metabolism. Prospective and retrospective studies of lipid metabolic parameters during the use of contraceptives, by P. Brockerhoff, et al. FORTSCHRITTE DER MEDIZIN 97(41):1858-1861, November 1, 1979.

Hormone cytologic examination of the oral mucosa in women taking contraceptives pills, by M. Korondy, et al. FORGORVOSI SZEMLE 73(4):103-105, April, 1980.

Hormone therapy: three perspectives. Fibrocystic breast disease: contraindication for oral contraceptive therapy, by D. Cook. JOURNAL OF NURSE-MIDWIFERY 25 (2):15-16, March-April, 1980.

Hypertension, not pill use, found major factor in increased risk of subarachnoid hemorrhage [news]. FAMILY PLANNING PERSPECTIVES 12(1):53, January-February, 1980.

Icterus induced by oral contraceptives, by F. Darnis, et al. MEDECINE ET CHIRURGIE DIGESTIVES 8(5):423-425, 1979.

Impaired elimination of caffeine by oral contraceptive steroids, by R. V. Patwardhan, et al. JOURNAL OF LABORATORY AND CLINICAL MEDICINE 95(4):603-608, April, 1980.

Incidence of endometrial cancer in relation to the use of oral contraceptives, by N. S. Weiss, et al. NEW ENGLAND JOURNAL OF MEDICINE 302(10):551-554, March 6, 1980.

Increased blood viscosity in young women using oral contraceptives, by G. D. Lowe, et al. AMERICAN JOURNAL OF OBSTETRICS AND GYNECOLOGY 137(7):840-842, August 1, 1980.

Induction of aryl hydrocarbon hydroxylase by lumphocytes from women taking oral contraceptives, by D. R. Nash, et al. CONTRACEPTION 20(3):297-302, September, 1979.

Influence of age, cigarette smoking and the oral contraceptive on plasma concentrations of clomipramine, by D. K. Luscombe, et al. POSTGRADUATE MEDICAL JOURNAL 56(Suppl 1):99-102, 1980.

Interaction between oral contraceptives and other drugs [letter], by H. M. Burt. BRITISH MEDICAL JOURNAL 280(6225):1230, May 17, 1980.

Intermenstrual hemorrhage from the taking of oral contraceptives, by T. P. Barkhatova. FEL'DSHER I AKU-SHERKA 44(9):52-55, September, 1979.

Intrahepatic cholestasis and thromboembolism disease due to oral contraceptives, by M. Del Pilar Pla, et al. GEN 33(2):213-219, April-June, 1979.

An investigation of the association between cervical cancer and oral contraceptive use, by R. A. Willis. FEDERATION PROCEEDINGS 39(3):3250, 1980.

Jaundice from troleandomycin and oral contraceptives [letter], by J. P. Miguet, et al. ANNALS OF INTERNAL MEDICINE 92(3):434, March, 1980.

Jaundice in women taking both troleandomycin and oral contraceptives, an outbreak in France, by J. P. Miguet, et al. GASTROENTEROLOGIE CLINIQUE ET BIOLO-GIQUE 4(6-7):420-424, June-July, 1980.

Left ventricular size and function in women receiving oral contraceptives, by K. M. Kessler, et al. OBSTETRICS AND GYNECOLOGY 55(2):211-214, February, 1980.

Liver and the contraceptive pill, by S. P. Dixit. CANADIAN JOURNAL OF SURGERY 23(3):222-227+, May, 1980.

Liver and ovulation inhibitors. Effects on liver function of estrogen-progestagen containing steroid oral contraceptives, by J. Eisenburg, et al. NATURWISSENSCHAF-TEN 66(10):489-497, October, 1979.

Liver cancer and oral contraceptives [letter], by R. L. Goldman. AMERICAN JOURNAL OF SURGICAL PATHOLOGY 4(2):208, April, 1980.

Liver cell tumor induction by oral contraceptives, by K. J. Gräf, et al. DEUTSCHE MEDIZINISCHE WOCHEN-SCHRIFT 105(2):61-65, January 11, 1980.

Liver tumours and the contraceptive pill: controversies in aetiology, diagnosis and management, by J. Terblanche, et al. SOUTH AFRICAN MEDICAL JOURNAL 56(22): 932-940, November 24, 1979.

Liver tumors and contraceptive steroids, by E. D. Nissen. CANCER TREATMENT REPORTS 63(7):1204, 1979.

Liver tumours and oral contraceptives [letter], by J. Borst. LANCET 1(8167):549, March 8, 1980.

A long-lasting effect of oral contraceptives on the excretion of urinary steroids: an implication of hepatic dysfunction in pill-users, by T. Kodama, et al. CANCER

TREATMENT REPORTS 63(7):1205, 1979.

Major British study finds no association between use of the pill and development of breast cancer [news]. FAMILY PLANNING PERSPECTIVES 11(5):311+, October, 1979.

Massive arterial thrombosis and oral contraception [letter], by S. Adam, et al. BRITISH MEDICAL JOURNAL 280 (6210):332, February 2, 1980.

Mean cell volume in a working population: the effects of age, smoking, alcohol and oral contraception, by D. M. Chalmers, et al. BRITISH JOURNAL OF HAEMATOL-OGY 43(4):631-636, December, 1979.

Multiple births in former oral contraceptive users, by S. Harlap. BRITISH JOURNAL OF OBSTETRICS AND GYNAECOLOGY 86(7):557-562, July, 1979.

Obstruction of the axillary artery: cervical rib or adverse effects of oral contraceptives in the young woman? [letter], by M. Salzmann, et al. NOUVELLE PRESSE MEDICALE 8(24):2023, June 2, 1979.

Oral contraception and depression, by J. L. Garrison. SO-CIAL WORK 24(2):162-163, March, 1979.

Oral contraception and neoplasia, by G. Huggins, et al. FERTILITY AND STERILITY 32(1):1-23, 1979.

Oral contraception and oral mucosa, by P. Delaunay, et al. ACTUAL ODONTOSTOMATOL 34(129):149-156, 1980.

Oral contraception: candidates for the pill, by D. Hamilton. NURSING MIRROR 150(9):43-45, February 28, 1980.

Oral-contraceptive-associated liver tumours [letter], by Q. B.

Emerson, et al. LANCET 1(8180):1251, June 7, 1980.

Oral-contraceptive-associated liver tumours: occurrence of malignancy and difficulties in diagnosis, by J. Neuberger, et al. LANCET 1(8163):273-276, February 9, 1980.

Oral contraceptive hypertension and thromboembolism, by W. B. Kannel. INTERNATIONAL JOURNAL OF GYNAECOLOGY AND OBSTETRICS 16(6):466-472, 1978-1979.

Oral contraceptive-induced ischemic bowel disease, by W. A. Parker, et al. AMERICAN JOURNAL OF HOSPITAL PHARMACY 36(8):1103-1107, August, 1979.

Oral contraceptive pills and endometrial cancer [letter], by L. S. Acheson. ANNALS OF INTERNAL MEDICINE 91 (5):793, November, 1979.

Oral-contraceptive use and bacteriuria in a community-based study, by D. Evans, et al. NEW ENGLAND JOURNAL OF MEDICINE 299:536-537, September 7, 1978.

Oral contraceptive use, cigarette smoking and myocardial infarction, by C. H. Hennekens. CLINICAL RESEARCH 28(2):226A, 1980.

Oral contraceptive usein relation to nonfatal myocardial infarction, by L. Rosenberg, et al. AMERICAN JOURNAL OF EPIDEMIOLOGY 111(1):59-66, January, 1980.

Oral contraceptives and birth defects, by K. Rothman. NEW ENGLAND JOURNAL OF MEDICINE 299:522-524, September 7, 1978.

Oral contraceptives and endometrial cancer [editorial], by P. Cole. NEW ENGLAND JOURNAL OF MEDICINE 302 (10):575-576, March 6, 1980.

Oral contraceptives and fatal subarachnoid haemorrhage, by W. H. Inman. BRITISH MEDICAL JOURNAL 6203: 1468-1470, December 8, 1979.

Oral contraceptives and hepatic vein thrombosis, by D. R. Kent. CANCER TREATMENT REPORTS 63(7):1205, 1979.

Oral contraceptives and pituitary adenomas, by S. J. Wingrave, et al. BRITISH MEDICAL JOURNAL 280(6215): 685-686, March 8, 1980.

Oral contraceptives and prolactin-producing hypophyseal tumors, by S. W. Lamberts. NEDERLANDS TIJD-SCHRIFT VOOR GENEESKUNDE 124(4):111-113, January 26, 1980.

Oral contraceptives and the prothrombin time [letter], by J. Pangrazzi, et al. BRITISH MEDICAL JOURNAL 280 (6210):332-333, February 2, 1980.

Oral contraceptives and the risk of thrombosis [letter], by J. Dommisse. SOUTH AFRICAN MEDICAL JOURNAL 56(20):786, November 10, 1979.

Oral contraceptives and thromboembolic disease: effects of lowering oestrogen content, by L. E. Böttiger, et al. LANCET 1(8178):1097-1101, May 24, 1980.

Oral contraceptives and trisomy 21. A retrospective study of 730 cases, by J. Lejeune, et al. ANNALES DE GENE-TIQUE 22(2):61-66, June, 1979.

Oral contraceptives, antithrombin III and deep vein thrombo-sis, by S. Kakkar, et al. THROMBOSIS AND HAEMO-STASIS 42(1):26, 1979.

Oral contraceptives: cardiovascular complications and addi-tional risk factors, by C. Herzog. PRAXIS 68(41):1321-

1329, October 9, 1979.

Oral contraceptives in otosclerosis? [letter], by D. Plester. DEUTSCHE MEDIZINISCHE WOCHENSCHRIFT 104 (39):1368, September 28, 1979.

Oral contraceptives: mechanisms in thromboembolism [editorial]. LANCET 1(8178):1118-1119, May 24, 1980.

Oral contraceptives raise the cholesterol saturation of bile by increasing biliary cholesterol secretion, by L. J. Bennion, et al. METABOLISM 29(1):18-22, January, 1980.

Otolaryngologic effects of 'the pill', by S. W. Coulthard. OTOLARYNGOLOGY AND HEAD AND NECK SURGERY 87(5):555-556, September-October, 1979.

Paradoxical embolism associated with oral contraceptives: an underdiagnosed lesion?, by J. de Swiet. POSTGRADUATE MEDICAL JOURNAL 55(644):419-420, June, 1979.

The pill and cardiovascular disease [letter], by V. Beral, et al. FAMILY PLANNING PERSPECTIVES 11(3):205-206, May-June, 1979.

The pill and thromboembolism. 1. Thrombogenesis and additional risk factors. A review of the literature, by C. Herzog, et al. THERAPIE DER GEGENWART 118(10): 1550-1574, October, 1979.

—. 2. Pathogenesis and additional risk factors. Review of the literature, by C. Herzog, et al. THERAPIE DER GEGENWART 118(11):1722-1744, November, 1979.

Pill, IUD users run no increased risk of ectopics, malformation, miscarriage in planned pregnancies [news]. FAMILY PLANNING PERSPECTIVES 12(3):156-157, May-

June, 1980.

The pill, mesenteric vein thrombosis and the short, short bowel syndrome, by A. A. Barros D'Sa. BRITISH JOURNAL OF CLINICAL PRACTICE 34(2):47-52, February, 1980.

Pill use in pregnancy not strongly linked to infants' heart defects. FAMILY PLANNING PERSPECTIVES 11(4): 260, July-August, 1979.

Pituitary adenoma and contraceptives [letter] , by M. Batrinos. FERTILITY AND STERILITY 32(6):711, December. 1979.

Pituitary and ovarian function in women receiving hormonal contraception, by B. L. Cohen, et al. CONTRACEPTION 20(5):475-487, November, 1979.

Pituitary and ovarian responsiveness to a graded gonadotropin releasing factor stimulation test in women using a low-estrogen or a regular type of oral contraceptive, by W. N. Spellacy, et al. AMERICAN JOURNAL OF OBSTETRICS AND GYNECOLOGY 137(1):109-115, May 1, 1980.

Plasma alpha-feto protein levels and its relation to duration of oral contraceptive use, by S. Babu, et al. CONTRACEPTION 21(1):53-60, January, 1980.

Plasma lipids and high density lipoproteins during oral contraception with different combinations of ethinyl estradiol and levonorgestrel, by U. Larsson-Cohn, et al. HORMONE AND METABOLIC RESEARCH 11(7):437-440, July, 1979.

Plasma lipids, lipoproteins, and blood pressure in female adolescents using oral contraceptives, by R. B. Wallace, et al. JOURNAL OF PEDIATRICS 95(6):1055-1059,

December, 1979.

Plasma lipoprotein changes during oral contraception, by M. H. Briggs, et al. CURRENT MEDICAL RESEARCH AND OPINION 6(4):249-254, 1979.

Plasma renin activity, reactivity, concentration and substrate following hypertension during pregnancy. Effect of oral contraceptive agents, by T. A. Kotchen, et al. HYPER-TENSION 1(4):355-361, July-August, 1979.

A position paper on the relation between oral contraceptives and blood coagulation, by H. Ludwig. CONTRACEP-TION 20(3):257-261, September, 1979.

Post-pill amenorrhea. Analysis of the literature and a clinical contribution, by E. Zanardi, et al. RIVISTA ITALI-ANA DI GINECOLOGIA 58(4):223-241, July-August, 1977.

Post-pill amenorrhea and drugs, by P. Grella. RIVISTA ITALIANA DI GINECOLOGIA 58(4):243-246, July-August, 1977.

Post-pill amenorrhea and prolactin, bv A. Volpe, et al. RI-VISTA ITALIANA DI GINECOLOGIA 58(4):247-252, July-August, 1977.

The prevalence of actinomycete-like organisms found in cervicovaginal smears of 300 intrauterine device wearers, by M. Jones, et al. ACTA CYTOLOGICA 23(4):282-286, 1979.

Primary liver cancer in a woman taking oral contraceptives [letter], by H. Slaoui, et al. NOUVELLE PRESSE MED-ICALE 9(7):456, February 9, 1980.

Prolongation of normotest clotting times in rats on the pill, by M. C. Roncaglioni, et al. THROMBOSIS AND HAE-

MOSTASIS 43(1):73, February 29, 1980.

Prolonged amenorrhea and oral contraceptives, by G. Tolis, et al. FERTILITY AND STERILITY 32(3):265-268, September, 1979.

A prospective, randomized study of oral contraceptives: the effect of study design on reported rates of symptoms, by P. P. Talwar, et al. CONTRACEPTION 20(4):329-337, October, 1979.

Regressive ischemia of the small intestine and contraceptives, by C. L'Hermine, et al. LILLE MEDICAL 24(9):693-696, November, 1979.

Relation between hepatic lesions and use of oral contraceptives, by M. J. Wexler. CANADIAN JOURNAL OF SURGERY 23(3):216-217, May, 1980.

Relationship of estrogens and oral contraceptives to endometrial cancer in animals and women, by V. A. Drill. JOURNAL OF REPRODUCTIVE MEDICINE 24(1): 5-13, January, 1980.

Relative sensitivity of postpartum gestational diabetic women to oral contraceptive agents and other metabolic stress, by R. K. Kalkhoff. DIABETES CARE 3(3):421-424, May-June, 1980.

Renal artery thrombosis: systemic contraceptive-induced or spontaneous? [letter], by J. Montoliu. ANNALS OF INTERNAL MEDICINE 91(4):657, October, 1979.

Reply to paper by Dr. Edgren on 'progestational potency of oral contraceptives: a polemic', by R. P. Dickey. INTERNATIONAL JOURNAL OF FERTILITY 23(3):170-174, 1978.

Retinal migraine and the pill, by E. Byrne. MEDICAL

JOURNAL OF AUSTRALIA 2(12):659-660, December 15, 1979.

A review: adverse effects of oral contraceptives, by S. H. Tsung, et al. JOURNAL OF THE INDIANA STATE MEDICAL ASSOCIATION 72(8):578-580, August, 1979.

Riboflavin nutritional status and absorption in oral contraceptive users and nonusers, by P. J. Carrigan, et al. AMERICAN JOURNAL OF CLINICAL NUTRITION 32 (10):2047-2051, October, 1979.

Riboflavin nutriture of oral contraceptive users, by S. C. Vir, et al. INTERNATIONAL JOURNAL FOR VITAMIN AND NUTRITION RESEARCH 49(3):286-290, 1979.

The role of age, smoking habits, and oral contraceptives in the frequency of myocardial infarction in young women, by J. W. Goldzieher. REPRODUCCION 4(1):21-27, January-March, 1980.

The role of oral contraceptives in cervical infection with sexually transmitted diseases, by J. Gardner. DISSERTATION ABSTRACTS INTERNATIONAL 10(12):5619-B, 1980.

Rubella and oral contraceptives [letter], by H. P. Dunn. NEW ZEALAND MEDICAL JOURNAL 91(654):154, February 27, 1980.

Secondary effects of oral contraceptives, by E. Yeun, et al. SOUTH AFRICAN JOURNAL OF SCIENCE 75(7):319, 1979.

Serum bile acids in women taking combination contraceptives, by U. M. Donde, et al. CONTRACEPTION 20(6): 579-583, December, 1979.

Side effects of oral contraceptives, by K. Dawson. NURSE PRACTITIONER 4(6):53-55+, November-December, 1979.

Side effects of oral contraceptives from a dermatological viewpoint, by S. Marghescu. THERAPIE DER GEGEN-WART 118(8):1230-1243, August 17, 1979.

Smoking, age and the pill, by J. McEwan. INTERNATION-AL JOURNAL OF GYNAECOLOGY AND OB-STETRICS 16(6):529-534, 1978-1979.

Some thoughts on the epidemiology of cardiovascular disease, (with special reference to women 'on the pill'). Role of ascorbic acid, by C. A. Clemetson. MEDICAL HYPOTHESES 5(8):825-834, August, 1979.

Spontaneous mesenteric venous thrombosis, a rare complication of oral contraceptives, by F. Hofbauer, et al. WIENER KLINISCHE WOCHENSCHRIFT 92(6):191-194, March 14, 1980.

Statistico epidemiological study of changes in the vaginal flora of contraceptive users in Alexandria, by E. Fares, et al. JOURNAL OF THE EGYPTIAN PUBLIC HEALTH ASSOCIATION 54(1-2):49-63, 1979.

Therapeutic management of post-pill amenorrhea, by F. Bottiglioni, et al. RIVISTA ITALIANA DI GINECOLOGIA 58(4):253-273, July-August, 1977.

Thrombotic thrombocytopenic purpura, cholangiocarcinoma, and oral contraceptives [letter], by V. Caggiano, et al. LANCET 2(8190):365, August 16, 1980.

Thyroid function in women taking oral contraceptives, by N. Juras, et al. LIJECNICKI VJESNIK 102(1):19-21, January, 1980.

Twinning rates and the 'pill' [letter] , by W. H. James. AMERICAN JOURNAL OF OBSTETRICS AND GYNE-COLOGY 135(5):699-700, November 1, 1979.

Vitamin B6 nutriture during pregnancy and lactation. II. The effect of long-term use of oral contraceptives, by J. L. Roepke, et al. AMERICAN JOURNAL OF CLINI-CAL NUTRITION 32(11):2257-2264, November, 1979.

CONTRACEPTIVES: FEMALE: ORAL: FAILURE
Births following oral contraceptive failures, by S. Harlap, et al. OBSTETRICS AND GYNECOLOGY 55(4):447-452, April, 1980.

Pregnancy after oral contraception [news] , by C. Colas. PRESSE MEDICALE 8(48):3986, December 10, 1979.

Unplanned pregnancies and the pill [letter] , by D. C. Boden. MEDICAL JOURNAL OF AUSTRALIA 1(8):391, April 19, 1980.

CONTRACEPTIVES: FEMALE: ORAL: HISTORY
James Mackenzie Lecture 1979. The happiness pill?, by C. R. Kay. JOURNAL OF THE ROYAL COLLEGE OF GENERAL PRACTITIONERS 30(210):8-19, January, 1980.

The juridical status of the fetus: a proposal for legal protec-tion of the unborn, by P. A. King. MICHIGAN LAW RE-VIEW 77(7):1647-1687, 1979.

CONTRACEPTIVES: FEMALE: ORAL: TECHNIQUES
Prescribing an oral contraceptive for the individual woman, by P. Chick. AUSTRALIAN FAMILY PHYSICIAN Suppl:8-12, February, 1980.

CONTRACEPTIVES: FEMALE: ORAL: THERAPEUTIC USE
Are combined oral contraceptives appropriate therapy for primary dysmenorrhea?, by J. H. Goodwin. JOURNAL

OF NURSE-MIDWIFERY 25(2):17-19, March-April, 1980.

Breast cancer and oral contraceptive therapy in premenopausal women, by R. D. Gambrell, Jr., et al. JOURNAL OF REPRODUCTIVE MEDICINE 23(6):265-271, December, 1979.

Chorea associated with oral contraceptive therapy, by D. J. Dove. AMERICAN JOURNAL OF OBSTETRICS AND GYNECOLOGY 137(6):740-742, July 15, 1980.

Do oral contraceptives inhibit Trichomonas vaginalis?, by M. Bramley, et al. SEXUALLY TRANSMITTED DISEASES 6(4):261-263, October-December, 1979.

Hormone therapy: three perspectives. Fibrocystic breast disease: contraindication for oral contraceptive therapy, by D. Cook. JOURNAL OF NURSE-MIDWIFERY 25 (2):15-16, March-April, 1980.

Incidence of hyperprolactinemia during oral contraceptive therapy, by J. V. Reyniak, et al. OBSTETRICS AND GYNECOLOGY 55(1):8-11, January, 1980.

Oral contraception with an associated therapeutic action using a progestational method at two levels, by J. H. Soutoul, et al. JOURNAL DE GYNECOLOGIE, OBSTETRIQUE ET BIOLOGIE DE LA REPRODUCTION 8(6): 561-565, 1979.

Prevalence of acne [letter], by P. V. Harrison, et al. BRITISH MEDICAL JOURNAL 2(6188):495, August 25, 1979.

Prevention of recurrent menstrual psychosis by an oral contraceptive, by A. R. Felthous, et al. AMERICAN JOURNAL OF PSYCHIATRY 137(2):245-246, February, 1980.

Agonist (ovulation induction) and post-coital contraceptive properties of [D-Ala6] and [D-Trp6] -LHRH series, by A. Corbin, et al. ENDOCRINE RESEARCH COMMUNI-CATIONS 6(1):1-14, 1979.

Antifertility activities of newly synthesized steroids in rats administered postcoitally before and after implantation and their interceptive effects in the baboon, by J. Strecke, et al. PHARMAZIE 35(1):45-47, January, 1980.

A morning-after double, by C. Doyle. OBSERVER p48, April 27, 1980.

Postcoital contraception, by A. A. Yuzpe. INTERNATION-AL JOURNAL OF GYNAECOLOGY AND OBSTE-TRICS 16(6):497-501, 1978-1979.

CONTRACEPTIVES: FEMALE: PSYCHOLOGY
Factors influencing the time of introduction of steroidal contraception in the breast-feeding mother, by J. W. Cox. AUSTRALIAN AND NEW ZEALAND JOURNAL OF OBSTETRICS AND GYNAECOLOGY 19(1):7-9, February, 1979.

CONTRACEPTIVES: FEMALE: SUPPOSITORY
Clinical study results with the vaginal contraceptive preparation, traceptin, by K. V. Chachava, et al. AKUSHERST-VO I GINEKOLOGIIA (3):46-47, March, 1980.

Depo-provera: contraceptive risk? [letter], by A. Rosen-field. HASTINGS CENTER REPORT 10(2):4, April, 1980.

Depot gestagens as contraceptives, by S. Holbek, et al. UGESKRIFT FOR LAEGER 142(15):973-974, April 7, 1980.

A retrospective clinical study of a vaginal contraceptive sup-

pository, by J. Squire, et al. JOURNAL OF REPRO-
DUCTIVE MEDICINE 22(6):319-323, 1979.

Return of ovulation after the cessation of depot-medroxy
progesterone acetate treatment in Thai women, by B. N.
Saxena, et al. JOURNAL OF THE MEDICAL ASSOCIA-
TION OF THAILAND 63(2):66-69, February, 1980.

The role of a long-acting vaginal suppository of 15-ME-PGF2
alpha in first and second trimester abortion, by N. H.
Lauersen, et al. ADVANCES IN PROSTAGLANDIN
AND THROMBOXANE RESEARCH 8:1435-1441,
1980.

CONTRACEPTIVES: FEMALE: TECHNIQUES
An analysis of the influences of maternal age, gestational age,
contraceptive method, and the mode of primary treatment of patients with hydatidiform moles on the incidence of subsequent chemotherapy, by M. STone, et al.
BRITISH JOURNAL OF OBSTETRICE AND GYNE-
COLOGY 86(10):782-792, October, 1979.

Appropriate contraception for middle-aged women, by R.
B. Greenblatt, et al. JOURNAL OF BIOSOCIAL SCI-
ENCE (6):119-141, 1979.

Biodegradable systems for the sustained release of fertility-
regulating agents, by G. Benagiano, et al. JOURNAL OF
STEROID BIOCHEMISTRY 11(1B):449-455, July,
1979.

Factors influencing the time of introduction of steroidal
contraception in the breast-feeding mother, by J. W. Cox.
AUSTRALIAN AND NEW ZEALAND JOURNAL OF
OBSTETRICS AND GYNAECOLOGY 19(1):7-9, February, 1979.

Hysteroscopic oviductal blocking with formed-in-place silicone rubber plugs. I. Method and apparatus, by R. A.

Erb, et al. JOURNAL OF REPRODUCTIVE MEDI-
CINE 23(2):65-68, August, 1979.

—. II. Clinical studies, by T. P. Reed, et al. JOURNAL OF
REPRODUCTIVE MEDICINE 23(2):69-72, August,
1979.

Locus-of-control, perceived susceptibility to pregnancy and
choice of contraceptive among college students, by M.
B. Dignan. PERCEPTUAL AND MOTOR SKILLS 48
(3 Part 1):782, June, 1979.

Outcome of pregnancy in women using different methods of
contraception, by M. Vessey, et al. BRITISH JOURNAL
OF OBSTETRICS AND GYNAECOLOGY 86(7):548-
556, July, 1979.

CONTRACEPTIVES: FEMALE: TOPICAL
Contraception via topical application? A review, by H.
Schaefer, et al. CONTRACEPTION 20(3):225-236,
September, 1979.

Contraceptive properties of Lithospermum officinale L.
grown under different agrotechnical conditions, by S.
Stanosz. POLSKI TYGODNIK LEKARSKI 34(50):
1971-1972, December 10, 1979.

Taking the real worry out of being close [spermicides], by V.
Ross. MACLEAN'S 93:48, March 3, 1980.

Vaginal contraceptives: available but—[vaginal spermicides],
by A. Hecht. CONSUMER REPORTS 14:29-30, February, 1980.

CONTRACEPTIVES: HERBAL (see . . . CONTRACEPTIVE
AGENTS: FEMALE)

CONTRACEPTIVES: MALE
Acceptability of drugs for male fertility regulation: a pro-

spectus and some preliminary date. World Health Organization Task Force on Psychosocial Research in Family Planning. CONTRACEPTION 21(2):121-134, February, 1980.

Antifertility effects of 6-chloro-6-deoxy-glucose in the male rat, by F. Heitfeld, et al. CONTRACEPTION 19(6):543-555, June, 1979.

Antifertility efficacy of twice daily oral administration of 6-chloro-6-deoxy-D-glucose (6 CDG) in male rats, by L. A. Warren, et al. CONTRACEPTION 20(3):275-289, September, 1979.

Condom effectiveness [letter], by E. C. Corderoy. FAMILY PLANNING PERSPECTIVES 11(5):271, October, 1979.

Condoms for sexually active adolescents, by A. B. Bergman. AMERICAN JOURNAL OF DISEASES OF CHILDREN 134(3):247-249, March, 1980.

Contraception for the male: problems with progress, by H. Jackson, et al. CLINICAL OBSTETRICS AND GYNAECOLOGY 6(1):129-155, April, 1979.

Widespread contraceptive use found in Britain: condom popular, two-child families preferred. FAMILY PLANNING PERSPECTIVES 12:108-110, March-April, 1980.

CONTRACEPTIVES: MALE: COMPLICATIONS
Experimental findings with spermantibodies: condom therapy (a case report), by D. R. Franken, et al. ANDROLOGIA 11(6):413-416, 1979.

CONTRACEPTIVES: MALE: FAILURE
Is today's condom better than its reputation? by G. K. Döring. FORTSCHRITTE DER MEDIZIN 98(4):113-117, January 31, 1980.

China invents male birth control pill, by W. Wen. AMERI-
CAN JOURNAL OF CHINESE MEDICINE 8(1-2):195-
197, Spring-Summer, 1980.

The combined use of oral medroxyprogesterone acetate and
methyltestosterone in a male contraceptive trial programme, by J. Bain, et al. CONTRACEPTION 21(4):
365-379, April, 1980.

Cottoning on to a pill for men, by D. Baird. MACLEAN'S
93:44-45, August 11, 1980.

Gossypol as an oral contraceptive for men. JOURNAL OF
THE MEDICAL SOCIETY OF NEW JERSEY 77(1):50,
January, 1980.

Gossypol—a new antifertility agent for males. GYNECOLO-
GIC AND OBSTETRIC INVESTIGATION 10(4):163-
176, 1979.

Gossypol, a new contraceptive agent for men, by F. Havranek. CESKOSLOVENSKA GYNEKOLOGIE 44(9):
701, November, 1979.

Gossypol related hypokalemia. Clinicopharmacologic
studies, by S. Z. Qian, et al. CHINESE MEDICAL JOUR-
NAL 93(7):477-482, July, 1980.

CONTRACEPTIVES: MALE: PARENTERAL
Injectable non-occlusive chemical contraception in the male-
I, by M. Misro, et al. CONTRACEPTION 20(5):467-473,
November, 1979.

CONTRACEPTIVES: PARENTERAL
Birth-control shots: FDA moves slowly [Depo-Provera].
MEDICAL WORLD NEWS 21:40, December 8, 1980.

Body weight and cycle control of injectable contraceptives,
by S. el-Mahgoub. JOURNAL OF REPRODUCTIVE

MEDICINE 24(3):119-126, March, 1980.

Injectable contraceptive synthesis: an example of international cooperation, by P. Crabbe, et al. SCIENCE 209 (4460):992-994, August 29, 1980.

CONTRACEPTIVES: TECHNIQUES
Contraceptive choice of limiters ages 35-44 in the United States: an examination of selection of method from among a number of possible choices, by R. T. Gillaspy. SOCIAL BIOLOGY 26(1):72-79, Spring, 1979.

Contraceptives—what you need to know to choose the best one for you, by A. Comer. MADEMOISELLE 7210:11, August, 1980.

Selecting the optimum method of contraception for each patient, by J. Gavin. INTERNATIONAL JOURNAL OF GYNAECOLOGY AND OBSTETRICS 16(6):542-546, 1978-1979.

CONTRACEPTIVES AND COLLEGE STUDENTS
Contraceptive a responsibility among male university students, by J. B. Cole. JOURNAL OF THE AMERICAN COLLEGE HEALTH ASSOCIATION 8(3):168-172, December, 1979.

The diaphragm: its effective use among college women, by I. M. Hagen, et al. JOURNAL OF THE AMERICAN COLLEGATE HEALTH ASSOCIATION 28(5):263-266, April, 1980.

Increase in diaphragm use in a university population, by L. E. Berlin, et al. JOGN NURSING 8(5):280-282, September-October, 1979.

Influence of parents, peers, and partners on the contraceptive use of college men and women, by L. Thompson, et al. JOURNAL OF MARRIAGE AND THE FAMILY 40(3):

481-492, August, 1978.

Locus-of-control, perceived susceptability to pregnancy and choice of contraceptive among college students, by M. Dignan. PERCEPTUAL AND MOTOR SKILLS 48:782, June, 1979.

The purchase of contraceptives by college students, by D. Kallen, et al. FAMILY RELATIONS 29(3):358-363, July, 1980.

Sexual behaviour and contraceptive practice of undergraduates at Oxford University. JOURNAL OF BIOSOCIAL SCIENCE 10(3):277-286, July, 1978.

CONTRACEPTIVES AND HERBS
Antifertility activity of a medicinal plant of the genus Andrografis wall (family Acanthaceae). Part II, by M. Shamsuzzoha, et al. BANGLADESH MEDICAL RESEARCH COUNCIL BULLETIN 5(1):14-18, June, 1979.

CONTRACEPTIVES AND NURSES
The nurse and contraception for adolescents, by R. Gagne. INFIRMIERE CANADIENNE 22(1):18-22, January, 1980.

Nurse's role in voluntary pregnancy interruption and contraception, by A. Vagogne. SOINS 25(8):25-29, April 20, 1980.

Pill power for nurses? by A. Shevas. NURSING MIRROR 150(9):9, February 28, 1980.

CONTRACEPTIVES AND PHARMACISTS
Contraceptive market on a seesaw; OTC's fare better than oral Rx's, by A. W. Weil. PRODUCT MARKETING 9: 1+, February, 1980.

CONTRACEPTIVES AND PHYSICIANS

The claim for wrongful conception. Forcing physicians to raise their patients' children, by D. Savage. JOURNAL OF REPRODUCTIVE MEDICINE 24(2):51-60, February, 1980.

Contraception and psychiatry, by M. Bourgeois. CONFRONTATION PSYCHIATRIQUES (16):237-284, 1978.

Contraception in adolescence: an overview for the pediatrician, by D. E. Greydanus. PEDIATRIC ANNALS 9 (3):111-118, March, 1980.

Contraception in the adolescent: current concepts for the pediatrician, by D. E. Greydanus, et al. PEDIATRICS 65(1):1-12, 1980.

How do you manage the teenage patient who comes to you for contraception? INTERNATIONAL JOURNAL OF FERTILITY 24(2):78-85, 1979.

Psychiatric aspects of oral contraceptive use, by D. Sheehan, et al. PSYCHIATRIC ANNALS 6(10):500-508, October, 1976.

CONTRACEPTIVES AND RELIGION
Catholics agree with Protestants that abortion and contraception should be widely available [news]. FAMILY PLANNING PERSPECTIVES 12(1):51, January-February, 1980.

Conscience, infallibility and contraception, by J. Finnis. MONTH 11:410-417, December, 1978.

Contraception and responsibility, by E. Vacek. CATHOLIC CHARISMATIC 5:14-17, June-July, 1980.

Contraception and the synod, by B. Cooke. COMMUNITIES 107:648-650, November 21, 1980.

New context for contraception teaching, by J. Quinn. ORI-
GINS 10:263-267, October 9, 1980.

The pill, by C. Anthony. OUR SUNDAY VISITOR 68:6-7,
April 6, 1980.

Sexual misunderstanding: the true cause of the Magisterium's ban on contraception, by F. Price. CLERGY
REVIEW 65:157-163, May, 1980.

U. S. bishops cite dissent: ask contraception review, by P.
Hebblethwaite. NATIONAL CATHOLIC REPORTER
16:1+, October 10, 1980.

CONTRACEPTIVES AND SEXUAL BEHAVIOR
Contraception and sexual behavior, by C. Thonet. REVISTA
CHILENA DE OBSTETRICIA Y GINECOLOGIA 43
(2):104-108, 1978.

Contraceptive practice and trends in coital frequency, by J.
Trussell, et al. FAMILY PLANNING PERSPECTIVES
12:246-149, September-October, 1980.

Does contraception discourage sex? [L. Tiger's study of
stumptail macaque monkeys], by S. Begley. NEWS-
WEEK 96:77, July 21, 1980.

Dyadic and social network influences on adolescent exposure
to pregnancy risk, by S. R. Jorgensen, et al. JOURNAL
OF MARRIAGE AND FAMILY 42:141-155, February,
1980.

Sexual behavior and contraceptive practice of undergraduates
at Oxford University, by P. Anderson. JOURNAL OF
BIOSOCIAL SCIENCE 10(3):277-286, July, 1978.

CONTRACEPTIVES AND YOUTH
Acceptability and use-effectiveness of contraception for
teenagers, by R. Coles. JOURNAL OF BIOSOCIAL

SCIENCE Suppl(5):159-170, 1978.

Adolescent contraceptive use: comparisons of male and female attitudes and information, by E. W. Freeman, et al. AMERICAN JOURNAL OF PUBLIC HEALTH 70: 790-797, August, 1980.

Adolescent contraceptive use: experience in 1,762 teenagers, by L. E. Edwards, et al. AMERICAN JOURNAL OF OBSTETRICS AND GYNECOLOGY 137(5):583-587, July 1, 1980.

Cigarette smoking, alcohol intake, and oral contraceptives: relationships to lipids and lipoproteins in adolescent school-children, by J. A. Morrison, et al. METABOLISM 28(11):1166-1170, November, 1979.

Compliance with contraception among adolescent females, by I. F. Litt, et al. PEDIATRIC RESEARCH 13(4 Part 2):327, 1979.

Condoms for sexually active adolescents, by A. B. Bergman. AMERICAN JOURNAL OF DISEASES OF CHILDREN 134(3):247-249, March, 1980.

Contraception for teenage girls. Combination pill or IUD? by E. Weiner, et al. ACTA OBSTETRICIA ET GYNECOLOGICA SCANDINAVICA 88:65-69, 1979.

Contraception in adolescence: an overview for the pediatrician, by D. E. Greydanus. PEDIATRIC ANNALS 9(3): 111-118, March, 1980.

Contraception in adolescence—a review of the literature, by E. Ryde-Blomqvist. JOURNAL OF BIOSOCIAL SCIENCE [Suppl] (5):129-158, 1978.

Contraception in the adolescent: current concepts for the pediatrician, by D. E. Greydanus, et al. PEDIATRICS

65(1):1-12, 1980.

Contraception in the teenager. A comparison of four methods of contraception in adolescent girls, by J. A. Goldman, et al. ISRAEL JOURNAL OF MEDICAL SCIENCES 16(7):510-513, July, 1980.

Contraceptive education favored by teenagers [news]. FAMILY PLANNING PERSPECTIVES 11(4):255, July-August, 1979.

Contraceptive patterns and premarital pregnancy among women aged 15-19 in 1976, by M. Zelnik, et al. FAMILY PLANNING PERSPECTIVES 10(3):135-142, May-June, 1978.

The diaphragm: an appealing and effective contraceptive for many teenagers, by A. Marks, et al. PEDIATRIC RESEARCH 13(4 Part 2):328, 1979.

The effects of group counseling on locus of control with pregnant teenagers, by M. C. Golant. DISSERTATION ABSTRACTS INTERNATIONAL 40(10):5321-A, 1979.

Experience with the copper 7 intrauterine device in an adolescent population, by J. W. Kulig, et al. JOURNAL OF PEDIATRICS 96(4):746-750, April, 1980.

Factors affecting adolescent contraception practices: implications for sex education, by M. H. Dembo, et al. ADOLESCENCE 14(56):657-664, Winter, 1979.

How do you manage the teenage patient who comes to you for contraception? INTERNATIONAL JOURNAL OF FERTILITY 24(2):78-85, 1979.

Identifying adolescents at risk for noncompliance with contraceptive therapy, by I. F. Litt, et al. JOURNAL OF PEDIATRICS 96(4):742-745, April, 1980.

Minor's right to abortion and contraception: prospects for invalidating less than absolute restrictions, by D. Klassel, et al. WOMEN'S RIGHTS LAW REPORTER 4(3):165-183, Spring, 1978.

The nurse and contraception for adolescents, by R. Gagne. INFIRMIERE CANADIENNE 22(1):18-22, January, 1980.

Plasma lipids, lipoproteins, and blood pressure in female adolescents using oral contraceptives, by R. B. Wallace, et al. JOURNAL OF PEDIATRICS 95(6):1055-1059, December, 1979.

Premarital contraceptive usage among male and female adolescents, by J. P. Hornick. FAMILY COORDINA-TOR 28:181-190, April, 1979.

Reason for nonuse of contraception by sexually active women aged 15-19, by M. Zelnik, et al. FAMILY PLAN-NING PERSPECTIVES 11:289-296, September-October, 1979.

Sexual activity, contraceptive use and pregnancy among metropolitan area teenagers—1971-1979, by M. Zelnik, et al. FAMILY PLANNING PERSPECTIVES 12:230-237, September-October, 1980.

Sexual knowledge and attitudes of adolescents: relationship to contraceptive use, by C. C. Nadelson, et al. OB-STETRICS AND GYNECOLOGY 55(3):340-345, March, 1980.

Symposium on adolescent gynecology and endocrinology. Part III: venereal diseases in adolescents and contraception in teenagers, by P. A. Oill, et al. WESTERN JOUR-NAL OF MEDICINE 132(1):39-48, January, 1980.

Teenagers and contraception, by H. Rozenbaum. INTERNA-

TIONAL JOURNAL OF GYNAECOLOGY AND OB-
STETRICS 16(6):564-567, 1978-1979.

Twenty-seven strategies for teaching contraception to adolescents, by J. Chesler. JOURNAL OF SCHOOL HEALTH
50(1):18-21, January, 1980.

When should contraceptive agents be given to minors? [edi-
torial], by G. Schewe. MMW 122(25):923-924, June 20,
1980.

FAMILY PLANNING
Choosing to be child free, by W. H. Harris, et al. JOURNAL
OF SCHOOL HEALTH 49(7):379-382, September,
1979.

Community-based integrated family planning programs, by
E. S. Trainer. STUDIES ON FAMILY PLANNING 10
(5):177-182, May, 1979.

Declines in the age and family size of family planning pro-
gram acceptors: international trends, by J. A. Ross.
STUDIES IN FAMILY PLANNING 10(10):290-299,
October, 1979.

Development without family planning will not speed, and
may hinder, fertility decline [news]. FAMILY PLAN-
NING PERSPECTIVES 12(1):60-61, January-February,
1980.

Does you mother know . . . ? by A. Torres. FAMILY PLAN-
NING PERSPECTIVES 10(5):280-282, September-
October, 1978.

The future of family planning [editorial]. MIDWIFE,
HEALTH VISITOR AND COMMUNITY NURSE 16(2):
43, February, 1980.

Family planning, by J. Peel. PRACTITIONER 223(1337):

611-612, November, 1979.

Family planning: implications for marital stability, by F. Johnson. JOURNAL OF DIVORCE 3(3):273-281, Spring, 1980.

Family planning/MCH training of foreign nurse-midwives and related personnel in the United States: a comparative assessment of curricula in use by the six leading training institutions, by G. Vansintejan. DISSERTATION AB-STRACTS INTERNATIONAL 40(09):4910-A, 1979.

Family planning: a new challenge. PEOPLE 7(2):18, 1980.

Fertility control, by I. M. Gardner. PUBLIC HEALTH 94 (2):103-104, March, 1980.

Fertility in adolescence: proceedings of the 7th International Planned Parenthood Federation Biomedical Workshop, London, November 17-18, 1977. JOURNAL OF BIOSOCIAL SCIENCE [Suppl] (5):1-259, 1978.

Government efforts to influence fertility: the ethical issues, by B. Berelson, et al. POPULATION AND DEVELOPMENT REVIEW 5:581-613, December, 1979.

High infant mortality may signal readiness for family planning [news]. FAMILY PLANNING PERSPECTIVES 12(1):58-59, January-February, 1980.

Implementing the user perspective, by J. Bruce. STUDIES IN FAMILY PLANNING 11(1):29-34, January, 1980.

Integration of nutrition and family planning into primary health care [news]. WHO CHRONICLES 34(2):77, February, 1980.

An interdisciplinary approach to population dynamics and family planning, by C. Adick. DIE DRITTE WELT 6

(3-4):345-356, 1978.

Malnutrition, fertility and family planning, by P. N. Gupta. JOURNAL OF THE INDIAN MEDICAL ASSOCIATION 72(8):194-199, April 16, 1979.

Menstrual regulation clients in a village-based family planning programme, by S. Bhatia, et al. JOURNAL OF BIOSOCIAL SCIENCE 12(1):31-39, January, 1980.

NAF sets sights on quality care, by D. Maine. FAMILY PLANNING PERSPECTIVES 11(5):303-307, October, 1979.

Natural family planning, by C. Anthony. OUR SUNDAY VISITOR 69:6-7, November 30, 1980.

—, by C. A. Lanctot. CLINICAL OBSTETRICS AND GY-NAECOLOGY 6(1):109-128, 1979.

— [editorial], by J. J. Billings. PAPAU NEW GUINEA MEDICAL JOURNAL 21(4):286-287, December, 1978.

—. II. Basal body temperature and estimated time of ovulation, by T. W. Hilgers, et al. OBSTETRICS AND GYNE-COLOGY 55(3):333-339, March, 1980.

—: a case history, by J. Margeot. ORIGINS 10:282-283, October 16, 1980.

—: the couple to couple appraoch, by E. Barkley. COLUM-BIA 60:8-17, September, 1980.

—: unlocking the mystery of woman, by T. Flynn. LI-GUORIAN 68:16-19, March, 1980.

On the efficient allocation of resources for fertility reduction, by B. Berelson, et al. INTERNATIONAL FAMILY PLANNING PERSPECTIVES 5:133-142, December,

1979.

One is best, two is most, by B. Beedham, et al. ECONOMIST 273:24-25, December 29, 1979.

One is fine, two is more than adequate, by S. E. Fraser. FAR EASTERN ECONOMIC REVIEW 106:61-62, October 5, 1979.

Parents' social status found to play key role in daughters' sexual activity, contraceptive use. FAMILY PLANNING PERSPECTIVES 12:208-209, July-August, 1980.

Participation of community members in family planning programs, by E. S. Cruz Zapata. REVISTA DEL COLEGIO NACIONAL DE ENFERMERAS 24-25(101):7, September-February, 1978.

Planned Parenthood charges its opponents with acts of violence. SECURITY SYSTEMS DIGEST 11(15):10, July 16, 1980.

Population and family planning, by H. Romero. REVISTA MEDICA DE CHILE 105(12):946-950, December, 1977.

Population and family planning programs: a compendium of data through 1978, by D. L. Nortman, et al. POPULATION COUNCIL 1980.

The prediction of adoption and continued practice of contraception among enrolees in family planning clinics: 1972, by Z. Zablan. PHILIPPINE SOCIOLOGICAL REVIEW 23(1-4):29-54, January-October, 1975.

Profile of family planning service personnel for barrier method acceptability study [Egypt], by M. T. Hassouna, et al. POPULATION STUDIES (CAIRO)p24-39, January-March, 1980.

Reclaiming reproductive control: a feminist approach to
fertility consciousness, by S. Bell, et al. SCIENCE FOR
THE PEOPLE 12:6-9+, January-February, 1980.

The second national family planning and population survey
in Singapore 1977, by A. J. Chen, et al. NURSING
JOURNAL OF SINGAPORE 19(2):67-71, December,
1979.

Service statistics: aid to more effective FP program management, by H. Elkins, et al. POPULATION REPORTS
(17):321-337+, November, 1977.

Social marketing: does it work? by D. L. Altman, et al.
POPULATION REPORTS (21):393-434, January, 1980.

Survey on family planning, by J. Berzosa, et al. ACTA OB-
STETRICIA Y GINECOLOGICA HISPANA-LUSITANA
28(2):97-26, February, 1980.

Toward a predictive model of family planning, by S. Pick-
Deweiss. REVISTA LATINOAMERICANA DE PSI-
COLOGIA 12(1):119-126, 1980.

Traditional midwives and family planning. POPULATION
REPORTS 8(3):52, May, 1980.

Use of automated record linkage to measure patient fertility
after family planning service, by C. A. Burnett, 3d, et al.
AMERICAN JOURNAL OF PUBLIC HEALTH 70(3):
246-250, March, 1980.

ASIA
Fertility control programs in Asia: another look at the
data, by K. A. Laidlow, et al. ASIAN SURVEY 20:
803-811, August, 1980.

The role of traditional birth attendants in family planning
programs in Southeast Asia, by J. Y. Peng. INTER-

ASIA
>NATIONAL JOURNAL OF GYNAECOLOGY OBSTETRICS 17(2):108-113, September-October, 1979-1980.

AUSTRALIA
>Family planning in urban Aboriginal and Islander communities. Part II, by M. T. Samisoni, et al. AUSTRALIAN NURSES JOURNAL 9(9):45-47+, April, 1980.

>Natural family planning in Australia: accidental pregnancies, discontinuation frequent. FAMILY PLANNING PERSPECTIVES 12:214-218, July-August, 1980.

BANGLADESH
>The Matlab family planning-health services project [project to distribute oral contraceptives and condoms in 150 villages in rural Bangladesh], by S. Bhatia, et al. STUDIES IN FAMILY PLANNING 11:202-212, June, 1980.

>Risk, fertility, and family planning in a Bangladesh village, by M. Cain. STUDIES IN FAMILY PLANNING 11:219, June, 1980.

BELGIUM
>Family planning of Portuguese immigrants and integration in Belgium, by J. S. Ferro Bucher. PSYCHOLOGICA BELGICA 18(1):12-26, 1978.

CANADA
>Program of family planning in the United Kingdom, West Germany, Denmark and Sweden and its repercussions in Canada, by E. S. Smith. BOLETIN DE LA OFICINA SANITARIA PANAMERICAN 87(1):35-49, July, 1979.

CANADA
Resources from the community; planned parenthood of Toronto. ORBIT 11(2):27, August 1, 1980.

CHILE
Family planning in Chile, by H. Romero. REVISTA MEDICA DE CHILE 105(10):724-730, October, 1977.

CHINA
Age of discontinuity, by R. E. Miles, Jr. POPULATION BULLETIN 34:42-48, December, 1979.

Baby budgeting. ECONOMIST 274:38, March 1, 1980.

China sets ever more stringent targets for fertility reduction, by M. Chen. POPULATION AND DEVELOPMENT REVIEW 5:723-730, December, 1979.

China's all-out push to slash its birth rate, by H. Ellithorpe. BUSINESS WEEK p67, November 19, 1979.

China's birth planning: organization since the cultural revolution, by K. C. Lyle. HUMAN ORGANIZATION 39:197-201, Summer, 1980.

China's new birth policy: one baby is enough, by B. J. Culliton. SCIENCE 206:429, October 26, 1979.

Family intentions and behavior: some findings from Taiwan, by N. K. Nair, et al. STUDIES IN FAMILY PLANNING 11(7-8):255-263, July-August, 1980.

In China, three's a crowd. NEWSWEEK 94:97, November 26, 1979.

Let only two children bloom. SCIENTIFIC AMERICAN 242:64, April, 1980.

389

CHINA

Wan, xi, shao [later, longer, fewer] : how China meets
its population problem [based on address] , by H.
Tien. INTERNATIONAL FAMILY PLANNING
PERSPECTIVES 6:65-73, June, 1980.

DENMARK

Program of family planning in the United Kingdom, West
Germany, Denmark and Sweden and its repercussions
in Canada, by E. S. Smith. BOLETIN DE LA OFICI-
NA SANITARIA PANAMERICAN 87(1):35-49,
July, 1979.

DEVELOPING COUNTRIES

Social workers and family planning [developing coun-
tries] , by A. H. Reda. POPULATION STUDIES
p1-13, April-June, 1979.

Training developing-world personnel in family planning
and population: accomplishments and patterns, by
T. L. Hall, et al. STUDIES IN FAMILY PLANNING
11(5):167-177, May, 1980.

EGYPT

Assessment of family planning service delivery in Egypt,
by M. T. Hassouna. STUDIES IN FAMILY PLAN-
NING 11:159-166, May, 1980.

Egypt's population explosion, by O. Yinon. JERUSA-
LEM QUARTERLY (15):106-120, September, 1980.

EUROPE

Europe's fertility transition: new evidence and lessons
for today's developing world, by E. van de Walle, et
al. POPULATION BULLETIN 34:3-43, February,
1980.

FIJI

Fertility and family planning in Fiji, by T. U. Bavadra, et

FIJI

al. STUDIES IN FAMILY PLANNING 11(1):17-23, January, 1980.

FRANCE

France fears falling birth rate, by J. Jessel. NEW STATESMAN 98:836, November 30, 1979.

Role of the family planning counselor in French Switzerland, by V. Champod, et al. REVUE MEDICALE DE LA SUISSE ROMANDE 99(12):931-934, December, 1979.

GERMANY

From natural fertility to family limitation: the onset of fertility transition in a sample of German villages, by J. Knodel. DEMOGRAPHY 16:493-521, November, 1979.

Program of family planning in the United Kingdom, West Germany, Denmark and Sweden and its repercussions in Canada, by E. S. Smith. BOLETIN DE LA OFICINA SANITARIA PANAMERICAN 87(1):35-49, July, 1979.

GREAT BRITAIN

Program of family planning in the United Kingdom, West Germany, Denmark and Sweden and its repercussions in Canada, by E. S. Smith. BOLETIN DE LA OFICINA SANITARIA PANAMERICAN 87(1):35-49, July, 1979.

The scandle that grew up to respectability, by P. Chorlton. GUARDIAN 8:8, July, 1980.

GUATEMALA

Ethnic differences in family planning acceptance in rural Guatemala, by J. T. Bertrand, et al. STUDIES IN FAMILY PLANNING 10(8-9):238-245, August-

GUATEMALA
September, 1979.

HAITI
Fertility, mortality, migration and family planning in Haiti, by J. Allman, et al. POPULATION STUDIES 33:505-521, November, 1979.

HUNGARY
Birth control and family planning in Hungary in the last two decades, by A. Klinger. WORLD HEALTH STATISTICS QUARTERLY 32(4):257-268, 1979.

INDIA
Coital frequency of urban couples attending a family planning clinic at Bombay, by I. Kapoor, et al. JOURNAL OF FAMILY WELFARE 26:50-63, June, 1980.

Fertility control without modernization: evidence from a rural Indian community, by C. Vlassoff. JOURNAL OF BIOSOCIAL SCIENCE 11(3):325-339, July, 1979.

The no-birth bonus scheme: the use of savings accounts for family planning in South India [offers a deferred payment, in effect an old-age pension, to couples who limit their family size], by R. G. Ridker. POPULATION AND DEVELOPMENT REVIEW 6:31-46, March, 1980.

Paediatric aspects of family planning, by B. N. Walia, et al. JOURNAL OF THE INDIAN MEDICAL ASSOCIATION 73(1):21-22, July 1, 1979.

Role of physician for promoting the involvement of other health personnel and auxiliaries in implementing programmes of fertility regulation and family, by A. Chandy. NURSING JOURNAL OF INDIA 70(10):

INDIA
269-271, October, 1979.

The strategy of communication [how family planning information is relayed in rural India], by M. Chadda. POPULI 7(1):30-37; (2):24-31, 1980.

Testing the quantity-quality fertility model: the use of twins as a natural experiment, by M. R. Rosenzweig, et al. ECONOMETRICA 48:227-240, January, 1980.

IRAN
The experience of visitors of family planning clinics in Shiraz, Iran: contraceptive practice, side effects and rumers, by S. Tolnay. PAHLAVI MEDICAL JOURNAL 9(4):367-387, 1978.

The role of community health nurses in family health education at home in a southern province of Iran, by M. K. Jinadu. INTERNATIONAL JOURNAL OF NURSING STUDIES 17(1):47-53, 1980.

The use of paramedics in family planning services in Iran, by F. S. Ghorbani. INTERNATIONAL JOURNAL OF GYNAECOLOGY AND OBSTETRICS 17(2): 135-138, September-October, 1979-1980.

IRELAND
The Irish solution: an account of the novel legislation on family planning which has been introduced in the Republic of Ireland, by D. Nowlan. POPULI 7(2): 8-15, 1980.

JAPAN
Japan: 7 in 10 married women want no more children; fertility falls [news]. FAMILY PLANNING PERSPECTIVES 12(1):52-53, January-February, 1980.

KENYA

KENYA
Kenya's maternal, child health/family planning programme, by S. Kanani. EAST AFRICAN MEDICAL JOURNAL 57(2):80-86, February, 1980.

KOREA
The effect of reproductive intentions on subsequent fertility among low-parity Korean women, 1971-1976, by K. G. Foreit, et al. STUDIES IN FAMILY PLANNING 11(3):91-104, March, 1980.

Impact of the national family planning program on fertility in rural Korea: a multivariate areal analysis, by K. G. Foreit, et al. STUDIES IN FAMILY PLANNING 11(3):79-90, March, 1980.

MEXICO
Fertility and family planning in Mexico, by R. Rodriguez-Barocio, et al. INTERNATIONAL FAMILY PLANNING PERSPECTIVES 6:2-9, March, 1980.

National program of the Plan of Education for Family Planning, by M. Urbina Fuentes. GINECOLOGIA Y OBSTETRICIA ET MEXICO 46(278):475-481, December, 1979.

The teaching of family planning in the medical schools of Mexico, by S. C. Azcona, et al. GINECOLOGIA Y OBSTETRICIA DE MEXICO 46(278):465-474, December, 1979.

NEW GUINEA
Observations on family planning acceptors in Papua, New Guinea, by A. M. Saloheimo. PAPAU NEW GUINEA MEDICAL JOURNAL 21(4):299-305, December, 1978.

NEW ZEALAND
Women in New Zealand, by D. Black. NEW ZEALAND

NEW ZEALAND
NURSING JOURNAL 73(5):42, May, 1980.

PAKISTAN
Desired family size and contraceptive use in Pakistan, by
N. M. Shah, et al. INTERNATIONAL FAMILY
PLANNING PERSPECTIVES 5:143-149, December,
1979.

THE PHILIPPINES
Survey findings on family planning program effects in
the Philippines, 1968-1973, by J. Laing, et al.
PHILIPPINE SOCIOLOGICAL REVIEW 23(1-4):91-
99, January-October, 1975.

SWEDEN
Program of family planning in the United Kingdom, West
Germany, Denmark and Sweden and its repercussions
in Canada, by E. S. Smith. BOLETIN DE LA OFICI-
NA SANITARIA PANAMERICAN 87(1):35-49,
July, 1979.

SWITZERLAND
Genital infections in prenatal and family planning at-
tendants in Switzerland, by A. Meheus, et al. EAST
AFRICAN MEDICAL JOURNAL 57(3):212-217,
March, 1980.

Indications for ovulation inhibitors. Recommendations
of the Swiss Society for Family Planning. THERA-
PIE DER GEGENWART 119(3):297-299, March,
1980.

Recommendations of the Swiss Family Planning Association regarding the indications for oral contraceptives.
PRAXIS 68(41):1330-1332, October 9, 1979.

THAILAND
Family planning policy and community based innova-

THAILAND
tions in Thailand, by C. R. Krannich, et al. ASIAN
SURVEY 20:1023-1037, October, 1980.

Thailand's continuing reproductive revolution [declining
fertility and increasing contraceptive use], by J.
Knodel, et al. INTERNATIONAL FAMILY PLAN-
NING PERSPECTIVES 6:84-96, September, 1980.

UNITED STATES
Bioethical issues in family planning, by D. Brieland. SO-
CIAL WORK 24(6):478-484, 1979.

Fertility control in the United States before the contra-
ceptive revolution, by D. A. Dawson, et al. FAMILY
PLANNING PERSPECTIVES 12(2):76-86, March-
April, 1980.

Fertility planning status of Chicano couples in Los
Angeles, by G. Sabagh. AMERICAN JOURNAL OF
PUBLIC HEALTH 70(1):56-61, January, 1980.

Home teaching in the North-West: a pilot survey, by I.
Petrie, et al. CHILD: CARE, HEALTH AND DE-
VELOPMENT 6(1):57-64, January-February, 1980.

If young women have the family size they say they want,
U. S. population will not replace itself [news].
FAMILY PLANNING PERSPECTIVES 12(1):57-58,
January-February, 1980.

The National Reporting System for Family Planning
Services—a new look, by J. G. Dryfoos. FAMILY
PLANNING PERSPECTIVES 12:193-201, July-
August, 1980.

Organized family planning services in the United States,
1976-1977, by A. Torres. FAMILY PLANNING
PERSPECTIVES 11:342-347, November-December,

UNITED STATES
1979.

Quantitative aspects of marriage, fertility and family limitation in nineteenth century America: another application of the Coale specifications, by W. C. Sanderson. DEMOGRAPHY 16:339-358, August, 1979.

Racism and the availability of family planning services in the United States, by G. C. Wright, Jr. SOCIAL FORCES 56:1087-1098, June, 1978.

Six in 10 U. S. Catholic hospitals provide family planning: one in five offers medical sterilization [news]. FAMILY PLANNING PERSPECTIVES 11(5):308-309, October, 1979.

Unintended pregnancies in the United States, 1970-1972, by C. Tietze. FAMILY PLANNING PERSPECTIVES 11(3):186-188, May-June, 1979.

FAMILY PLANNING: HISTORY
China's birth planning: organization since the cultural revolution, by K. C. Lyle. HUMAN ORGANIZATION 39: 197-201, Summer, 1980.

Fifty years of natural family planning, by W. Fijalkowski. GINEKOLOGIA POLSKA 50(11):909-916, November, 1979.

Natural family planning in the past and present, by A. Löfström. LAKARTIDNINGEN 76(34):2779-2780, August 22, 1979.

Quantitative aspects of marriage, fertility and family limitation in nineteenth century America: another application of the Coale specifications, by W. C. Sanderson. DEMOGRAPHY 16(3):339-358, August, 1979.

Judge Dooling's decision: ' . . . allied to her right to be',
by J. I. Rosoff. FAMILY PLANNING PERSPECTIVES
12(1):4+, January-February, 1980.

Medico-legal aspects of family planning, by I. E. Black.
LEGAL MEDICAL QUARTERLY 2(3):198-203, 1978.

FAMILY PLANNING: RESEARCH
Family planning and questionnaire, by S. Pobric, et al. MED-
ICINSKI ARHIV 33(2):145-150, March-April, 1979.

FAMILY PLANNING: SOCIOLOGY OF
Socio-demographic characteristics of early and late adopters
of family planning, by P. Kumar. ASIAN JOURNAL OF
PSYCHOLOGY AND EDUCATION 3(3):12-15, November, 1978.

FAMILY PLANNING AND COLLEGE STUDENTS
Sexual experience and family planning among freshmen, by
K. Starke. AERZTLICHE JUGENDKUNDE 70(3):210-
217, June, 1979.

FAMILY PLANNING AND GENETICS
Genetic screening and genetic counseling: knowledge, attitudes, and practices in two groups of family planning
professionals, by E. W. Naylor. SOCIAL BIOLOGY 22
(4):304-314, Winter, 1975.

FAMILY PLANNING AND THE HANDICAPPED
Family life education for the handicapped, by S. Gordon, et
al. JOURNAL OF SCHOOL HEALTH 50(5):272-274,
May, 1980.

FAMILY PLANNING AND NURSES
Education in family planning in schools of nursing in various
European countries. SOINS 25(8):33-37, April 20, 1980.

School nurse helps develop new program, by R. Laidlaw.
ARIZONA NURSE 33(3):11, May-June, 1980.

The gynecologist's role in the natural family planning program, by A. Barba, Jr. LINACRE 47:274-278, August, 1980.

Involvement of the private physician to the family planning programs: pilot study, by J. Campos, et al. GINECOLOGIA Y OBSTETRICIA DE MEXICO 45(267):11-23, January, 1979.

Psychiatric aspects in rejection of family planning, by R. Taufa. PAPAU NEW GUINEA MEDICAL JOURNAL 21(3):264-266, September, 1978.

Role of physician for promoting the involvement of other health personnel and auxiliaries in implementing programmes of fertility regulation and family, by A. Chandy. NURSING JOURNAL OF INDIA 70(10):269-271, October, 1979.

The teaching of family planning in the medical schools of Mexico, by S. C. Azcona, et al. GINECOLOGIA Y OBSTETRICIA DE MEXICO 46(278):465-474, December, 1979.

Traditional midwives and family planning, by M. Simpson-Hebert, et al. POPULATION REPORTS 8(3):438-491, May, 1980.

FAMILY PLANNING AND RELIGION
Bioethical issues in family planning, by D. Brieland. SOCIAL WORK 24:478-484, November, 1979.

Choosing to adopt on your own, by M. Hellwig. OUR SUNDAY VISITOR 69:6, August 10, 1980.

Dilemma of getting involved or playing safe, by M. Murphy. NATIONAL CATHOLIC REPORTER 16:18, March 28, 1980.

Family planning imperative. NATIONAL CATHOLIC RE-
PORTER 16:14, August 15, 1980.

Proceedings of Natural Family Planning Meeting. LINACRE
45:327-422, November, 1978.

Six in 10 U. S. Catholic hospitals provide family planning:
one in five offers medical sterilization [news]. FAMILY
PLANNING PERSPECTIVES 11(5):308-309, October,
1979.

FAMILY PLANNING AND YOUTH
Adolescent sexual behavior. An indication of the need for
comprehensive family planning programs, by J. R.
Faulkenberry, et al. THE HEALTH OF THE PEOPLE
10(3):5-7, May-June, 1979.

Family-planning program effects and attitudes of adolescent
females toward authority, by V. D. Gill. DISSERTA-
TION ABSTRACTS INTERNATIONAL 40(08):4423-A,
1979.

Fertility in adolescence: proceedings of the 7th International
Planned Parenthood Federation Biomedical Workshop,
London, November 17-18, 1977. JOURNAL OF BIO-
SOCIAL SCIENCE Suppl(5):1-259, 1978.

School nurse helps develop new program, by R. Laidlaw.
ARIZONA NURSE 33(3):11, May-June, 1980.

Second pregnancies to premaritally pregnant teenagers, 1976
and 1971, by M. Zelnik. FAMILY PLANNING PER-
SPECTIVES 12(2):69-76, March-April, 1980.

Sexual experience and family planning among freshmen, by
K. Starke. AERZTLICHE JUGENDKUNDE 70(3):210-
217, June, 1979.

Teen clinics get good rating in NEW survey; teens want

confidentiality, treatment as adults [news]. FAMILY
PLANNING PERSPECTIVES 11(4):248-251, July-
August, 1979.

Teenagers and health care: a growing right to choose. IN-
TERNIST 20(8):13, October, 1979.

Unwed adolescent primigravidas indentify subject matter for
prenatal classes, by D. Z. Copeland. JOGN NURSING
8(4):248-253, July-August, 1979.

FAMILY PLANNING CLINICS
Abortion, by L. K. Crockett. CLINICAL OBSTETRICS
AND GYNAECOLOGY 6(1):57-76, 1979.

Characteristics of vasectomy patients at a family planning
clinic, by R. J. Gandy. JOURNAL OF BIOSOCIAL
SCIENCE 10(2):125-132, April, 1978.

The experience of visitors of family planning clinics in
Shiraz, Iran: contraceptive practice, side effects and
rumers, by S. Tolnay. PAHLAVI MEDICAL JOURNAL
9(4):367-387, 1978.

Genital infections in prenatal and family planning attendants
in Switzerland, by A. Meheus, et al. EAST AFRICAN
MEDICAL JOURNAL 57(3):212-217, March, 1980.

A twenty-year prospective follow-up study of 2164 cases at
the child guidance clinics in Stockholm, by I. Nylander.
ACTA PAEDIATRICA SCANDINAVICA 276:1-45,
1979.

FAMILY PLANNING COUNSELING
Family-planning—is it working in the NHS? by M. Jones.
MIDWIFE, HEALTH VISITOR AND COMMUNITY
NURSE 16(2):58+, February, 1980.

FAMILY PLANNING EDUCATION

Communicating the message: family planning campaigns can only be truly successful if the communicators avoid the "hard sell"—or avoid ignoring the issue altogether, by O. J. Sikes. POPULI 7(1):6-11, 1980.

Education in family planning in schools of nursing in various European countries. SOINS 25(8):33-37, April 20, 1980.

Education in family planning: what route to take? What difference does it make? by O. J. Sikes. INTERNA-TIONAL JOURNAL OF HEALTH EDUCATION 22(4): 206-210, 1979.

LOVE CANAL
Adverse pregnancy outcomes in the Love Canal area, by N. Fianna, et al. NEW YORK STATE DEPARTMENT OF HEALTH REPORT (34):April, 1980.

SANGER, MARGARET (see . . . BIRTH CONTROL: HISTORY)

STERILIZATION
Contraceptive sterilization: no panacea for human problems, by W. May. HOSPITAL PROGRESS 61:38-39+, September, 1980.

Long-term outcome of sterilization as a function of the indication, marital status, age, number of children and concurrently performed therapeutic abortions, by U. Bänninger, et al. GEBURTSHILFE UND FRAUEN-HEILKUNDE 39(6):492-496, June, 1979.

OSHA cites cyanamid on pigments operation. CHEMICAL MARKETING REPORTER 216:3+, October 15, 1979.

OSHA cites cyanamid on sterilization issue. CHEMICAL AND ENGINEERING NEWS (57):7-8, October 22, 1979.

Reversible sterilization; socio-ethical considerations, by G.

Largey. SOCIAL BIOLOGY 25:143-144, Summer, 1978.

Sterilization and the birth rate, by D. L. Nortman. STUDIES IN FAMILY PLANNING 11:286-300, September-October, 1980.

Sterilization: a comparative review, by J. D. Keeping, et al. AUSTRALIAN AND NEW ZEALAND JOURNAL OF OBSTETRICS AND GYNAECOLOGY 19(4):193-292, November, 1979.

Sterilization concurrent with abortion is as safe as interval sterilization. FAMILY PLANNING PERSPECTIVES 12: 213-214, July-August, 1980.

Sterilization in family planning. The psychology of voluntary sterilization, by P. Petersen. MMW 122(15):557-559, April 11, 1980.

Sterilization is becoming a leading method of birth control. Here's a look at the trend, by T. Moon. AIR FORCE TIMES 41:53-54, December 15, 1980.

Sterilization issues [letter], by L. Gostin. LANCET 2(8148): 909-910, October 27, 1979.

Voluntary sterilization, by M. S. Morain. HUMANIST 40: 51+, July-August, 1980.

Voluntary sterilization: suggestions for consultation practice, by W. Heidenreich, et al. MEDIZINISCHE KLINIK 74(48):1829-1831, November 30, 1979.

BANGLADESH
A survey of sterilization acceptors in a family planning program in rural Bangladesh, by S. Bhatia, et al. INTERNATIONAL JOURNAL OF GYNAECOLOGY AND OBSTETRICS 17(3):268-273, November-December, 1979.

BRAZIL
Service availability and the unmet need for contraceptive and sterilization services in Sao Paulo State, Brazil. INTERNATIONAL FAMILY PLANNING PERSPECTIVES 6:10-19, March, 1980.

CANADA
Comments on the sterilization of mental incompetents in Canadian civil and common law, by R. P. Kouri, et al. REVUE DE DROIT UNIVERSITE DE SHERBROOKE 10:599-628, 1980.

GREAT BRITAIN
Signing away their birth rights: women are often given little choice but to be sterilized, by M. Bailey, et al. NEW STATESMAN p5, August 29, 1980.

INDIA
Implementation of a successful outpatient laparoscopic sterilization program in Calcutta, by D. Lilaram, et al. INTERNATIONAL JOURNAL OF GYNAECOLOGY AND OBSTETRICS 17(1):15-18, July-August, 1978-1979.

The sterilization decision: a socio-demographic and fertility profile of the Indian woman, by S. A. Jamshedji, et al. JOURNAL OF FAMILY WELFARE 26:27-41, March, 1980.

LATIN AMERICA
Tubal occlusion via laparoscopy in Latin America: an evaluation of 8186 cases, by L. P. Cole, et al. INTERNATIONAL JOURNAL OF GYNAECOLOGY AND OBSTETRICS 17(3):253-259, November-December, 1979.

UNITED STATES
Puerto Rico: recent trends in fertility and sterilization, by H. B. Presser. FAMILY PLANNING PERSPEC-

UNITED STATES
TIVES 12(2):102-106, March-April, 1980.

Six in 10 U. S. Catholic hospitals provide family planning: one in five offers medical sterilization [news].
FAMILY PLANNING PERSPECTIVES 11(5):308-309, October, 1979.

Sterilization services at Planned Parenthood of Maryland, by F. H. Trimble. MARYLAND STATE MEDICAL JOURNAL 29(5):68-69, May, 1980.

U. S. A. Voluntary sterilization is legal [news], by E. Roseau. NOUVELLE PRESSE MEDICALE 9(18): 1271+, April 19, 1980.

Vermont's voluntary sterilization statutes and the rights of the mentally handicapped. VERMONT LAW REVIEW 4:331-352, Fall, 1979.

STERILIZATION: ATTITUDES
Comparative popularity of vasectomy and tubectomy, by S. D. R. Devi. JOURNAL OF FAMILY WELFARE 26: 79-93, June, 1980.

Marked preference for female sterilization in a semirural squatter settlement, by L. Gulati. STUDIES IN FAMILY PLANNING 10(11-12):332-336, November-December, 1979.

Quality of life and factors affecting the response to hysterectomy, by N. C. Roeske. JOURNAL OF FAMILY PRACTICE 7(3):483-488, September, 1978.

STERILIZATION: COMPLICATIONS
Discussion on sterilization and abortion in middle age.
JOURNAL OF BIOSOCIAL SCIENCE Suppl(6):157-162, 1979.

Life risks associated with reversible methods of fertility regulation, by C. Tietze, et al. INTERNATIONAL JOURNAL OF GYNAECOLOGY AND OBSTETRICS 16(6): 456-459, 1978-1979.

The sequelae of female sterilization in one general practice, by D. M. Curtis. JOURNAL OF THE ROYAL COLLEGE OF GENERAL PRACTITIONERS 29(203):366-369, June, 1979.

STERILIZATION: FEMALE

Activists fight sterilization of women in hazardous jobs, by M. E. MdKee. BUSINESS INSURANCE 13:2+, October 29, 1979.

Comparative popularity of vasectomy and tubectomy, by S. D. R. Devi. JOURNAL OF FAMILY WELFARE 26:79-93, June, 1980.

Contraception by female sterilization [editorial]. BRITISH MEDICAL JOURNAL 280(6224):1154-1155, May 10, 1980.

Counseling women for tubal sterilization, by E. Barron, et al. HEALTH AND SOCIAL WORK 3(1):48-58, February, 1978.

The effect of laparoscopic sterilization by diathermy or silastic bands on post-operative pain, menstrual symptoms and sexuality, by S. Lawson, et al. BRITISH JOURNAL OF OBSTETRICS AND GYNAECOLOCY 86 (8):659-663, August, 1979.

Empirical contraindications to the sterilization of women, by H. J. Rönnau, et al. BEITRAEGE ZUR GERICHTLICHEN MEDIZIN 37:245-247, 1979.

Female sterilization, by H. G. Hillemans, et al. ZFA. ZEITSCHRIFT FUR ALLGEMEINMEDIZIN 55(26):1419-

1427, September 20, 1979.

Female sterilization, by R. M. Soderstrom, et al. CLINICAL OBSTETRICS AND GYNAECOLOGY 6(1):77-95, April, 1979.

Female tubal sterilization [editorial], by G. P. Dutta. JOURNAL OF THE INDIAN MEDICAL ASSOCIATION 72 (8):193-194, April 16, 1979.

Heterosexual interactions in laboratory-housed stumptail macaques (*Macaca arctoides*): observations during the menstrual cycle and after ovariectomy, by A. K. Slob, et al. HORMONES AND BEHAVIOR 10(2):193-211, April, 1978.

Hysterectomy following sterilization, by C. O'Herlihy, et al. INTERNATIONAL JOURNAL OF GYNAECOLOGY AND OBSTETRICS 17(3):263-264, November-December, 1979.

Hysterectomy for sterilization? [letter], by J. Swinnen. NEW ZEALAND MEDICAL JOURNAL 90(649):477, December 12, 1979.

Hysterosalpingographic control of patients sterilized by laparoscopy, by S. Davidsen, et al. UGESKRIFT FOR LAEGER 142(7):434-435, February 11, 1980.

Internal sterilization using the Falope ring, by P. H. Roberts. TRANSACTIONS OF THE PACIFIC COAST OBSTETRICAL AND GYNECOLOGICAL SOCIETY 46:72-76, 1979.

The intra-operative proof of occlusion of the tubes in tubal sterilizations, by B. Henkel. GEBURTSHILFE UND FRAUENHEILKUNDE 39(8):682-686, August, 1979.

Laparoscopic sterilization, by M. Eskes. NEDERLANDS

TIJDSCHRIFT VOOR GENEESKUNDE 124(19):729-734, May 10, 1980.

Marked preference for female sterilization in a semirural squatter settlement, by L. Gulati. STUDIES IN FAMILY PLANNING 10(11-12):332-336, November-December, 1979.

Microsurgical tubal anastomosis in the rabbit following three types of sterilization procedure, by O. M. Petrucco. CONTRACEPTION 20(1):55-60, July, 1979.

Morphological alterations of rabbit oviducts following ligature of the tubal isthmus, by D. Bernhardt-Huth, et al. VIRCHOWS ARCHIV 384(2):195-211, 1979.

NCCB issues statement on tubal ligation. HOSPITAL PROGRESS 61:18-19, August, 1980.

NCCB statement on tubal ligation: issued July 9. ORIGINS 10:175, August 28, 1980.

A new technique for minilaparotomy, by B. Palaniappan. INTERNATIONAL JOURNAL OF GYNAECOLOGY AND OBSTETRICS 17(3):260-262, November-December, 1979.

An outpatient approach to female sterilization with methylcyanoacrylate, by R. S. Neuwirth, et al. AMERICAN JOURNAL OF OBSTETRICS AND GYNECOLOGY 136 (7):951-956, April 1, 1980.

Outpatient laparoscopy with local anesthesia, by H. Zevallos, et al. INTERNATIONAL JOURNAL OF GYNAECOLOGY AND OBSTETRICS 17(4):379-381, January-February, 1980.

Pain during laparoscopic sterilization least likely with clips, three-country study finds [news]. FAMILY PLANNING

PERSPECTIVES 12(1):56-57, January-February, 1980.

Postpartum sterilization, by L. R. Green, et al. CLINICAL OBSTETRICS AND GYNECOLOGY 23(2):647-659, June, 1980.

Puerperal laparoscopic sterilization, by C. F. McDonnell, Jr. AMERICAN JOURNAL OF OBSTETRICS AND GYNE-COLOGY 137(8):910-913, August 15, 1980.

Reproductive performance of women following end-to-end anastomosis of fallopian tubes after previous sterilization, by J. J. Marik. FERTILITY AND STERILITY 32(4): 497, 1979.

Restatement on tubal ligation confuses policy with normative ethics, by R. McCormick. HOSPITAL PROGRESS 61: 40, September, 1980.

Safety of post-abortion sterilization [letter], by G. Chamberlain. LANCET 2(8150):1020, November 10, 1979.

Safety of postabortion sterilization compared with interval sterilization. A controlled study, by M. C. Cheng, et al. LANCET 2(8144):682-685, September 29, 1979.

Signing away their birth rights: women are often given little choice but to be sterilized, by M. Bailey, et al. NEW STATESMAN p5, August 29, 1980.

Sterilization of women, by W. P. Black. PRACTITIONER 223(1337):627-632, November, 1979.

—, by P. E. Treffers. NEDERLANDS TIJDSCHRIFT VOOR GENEESKUNDE 124(19):748-749, May 10, 1980.

—: benefits vs risks, by J. E. Rioux. INTERNATIONAL JOURNAL OF GYNAECOLOGY AND OBSTETRICS 16(6):488-492, 1978-1979.

—. A five year material, by P. E. Bordahl, et al. UGE-SKRIFT FOR LAEGER 142(7):431-433, February 11, 1980.

Sterilization performed in connection with induced abortion, by F. Hald, et al. UGESKRIFT FOR LAEGER 142(5): 321, January 28, 1980.

Tubal anastomosis in the New Zealand White rabbit using a circular suturing instrument, by P. J. Taylor, et al. FERTILITY AND STERILITY 33(2):204-206, February, 1980.

Tubal ligation and medical indications, by M. Reidy. IRISH THEOLOGICAL QUARTERLY 46(2):88-98, 1979.

Tubal ligations: a review of three years' work by a medical axuiliary, by P. R. Crouch. TROPICAL DOCTOR 9(4): 189-191, October, 1979.

Vaginal tubal ligation concurrent with medical termination of pregnancy, by I. Gupta, et al. INDIAN JOURNAL OF MEDICAL RESEARCH 70:960-964, December, 1979.

BANGLADESH
A follow-up of tubectomy clients in Bangladesh, by I. Swenson, et al. INTERNATIONAL JOURNAL OF GYNAECOLOGY AND OBSTETRICS 17(1):47-50, July-August, 1978-1979.

INDIA
A follow-up study of tubectomy acceptors in Bikaner, by C. K. Joshi, et al. JOURNAL OF THE INDIAN MEDICAL ASSOCIATION 73(1):1-4, July 1, 1979.

The sterilization decision: a socio-demographic and fertility profile of the Indian woman, by S. A. Jamshedji, et al. JOURNAL OF FAMILY WELFARE 26:27-41, March, 1980.

NEW ZEALAND
Female sterilization: a five-year follow-up in Auckland,
by P. Jackson, et al. NEW ZEALAND MEDICAL
JOURNAL 91(654):140-143, February 27, 1980.

Laparoscopy in Southland, by G. T. Thomas, et al. NEW
ZEALAND MEDICAL JOURNAL 91(651):10-12,
January 9, 1980.

UNITED STATES
Demographic trends of tubal sterilization in the United
States, 1970-1975, by P. M. Layde, et al. AMERI-
CAN JOURNAL OF PUBLIC HEALTH 70:808-812,
August, 1980.

STERILIZATION: FEMALE: COMPLICATIONS
Blood coagulation and fibrinolysis in laparoscopic tubal
sterilization, by K. Schander, et al. ARCHIVES OF GY-
NECOLOGY 228(1-4):627-628, July 20, 1979.

Complications of laparoscopic tubal sterilization, by R. G.
Cunanan, Jr., et al. OBSTETRICS AND GYNECOLOGY
55(4):501-506, April, 1980.

Does laparoscopic tubal sterilization cause menstruation disorders? by A. Weil, et al. ARCHIVES OF GYNECOLO-
GY 228(1-4):278-279, July 20, 1979.

Early and late complications after tubal ligations with the
tupla-clip, by J. Babenerd, et al. GEBURTSHILFE UND
FRAUENHEILKUNDE 39(10):888-891, October, 1979.

Ectopic pregnancy after sterilization, by G. J. Hughes. MED-
ICAL JOURNAL OF AUSTRALIA 1(6):275, March 22,
1980.

Effects of tubal sterilization on morbidity rates analyzed
[news]. HOSPITAL PRACTICE 15(5):153+, May, 1980.

An epidemiologic study of risk factors associated with pregnancy following female sterilization, by I. C. Chi, et al. AMERICAN JOURNAL OF OBSTETRICS AND GYNECOLOGY 136(6):768-773, March 15, 1980.

Female sterilization and subsequent ectopic pregnancy, by G. C. Wolf, et al. OBSTETRICS AND GYNECOLOGY 55 (1):17-19, January, 1980.

Female sterilization—no more tubal coagulation [letter], by K. M. Huntington. BRITISH MEDICAL JOURNAL 280 (6228):1377, June 7, 1980.

Gynecologist used different suture material for tubal ligation; patient's complaint that she was not informed of this declared unfounded. NEDERLANDS TIJDSCHRIFT VOOR GENEESKUNDE 124(24):987-988, June 14, 1980.

Haemoperitoneum due to cornual endometriosis after laparoscopic sterilization, by F. I. Uri, et al. BRITISH JOURNAL OF OBSTETRICS AND GYNAECOLOGY 86(8): 664-665, August, 1979.

Hysterectomy-induced facilitation of lordosis behavior in the rat, by H. I. Siegel. HORMONES AND BEHAVIOR 11 (3):273-278, December, 1978.

Immediate and late complications of laparoscopic sterilization, by B. L. Hejl, et al. UGESKRIFT FOR LAEGER 142(7):436-438, February 11, 1980.

Incidence of pain among women undergoing laparoscopic sterilization by electrocoagulation, the spring-loaded clip, and the tubal ring, by I. C. Chi, et al. AMERICAN JOURNAL OF OBSTETRICS AND GYNECOLOGY 135(3):397-401, October 1, 1979.

Laparoscopic tubal sterilization: postoperative follow-up and late gynecological complaints, by P. Buytaert, et al. EUROPEAN JOURNAL OF OBSTETRICS, GYNECOLOGY AND REPRODUCTIVE BIOLOGY 10(2):119-124, February, 1980.

Later hospitalizations of tubal sterilization patients, by P. A. Poma. JOURNAL OF THE NATIONAL MEDICAL ASSOCIATION 71(11):1085-1089, NOvember, 1979.

Long-term effects of interval laparoscopic sterilization by bipolar electrocoagulation on menstruation, by A. Weil, et al. ARCHIVES OF GYNECOLOGY 227(2):141-146, August, 1979.

Macroscopic and microscopic studies of fallopian tube after laparoscopic sterilization, by J. Donnez, et al. CONTRA-CEPTION 20(5):497-509, November, 1979.

Morbidity following vaginal tubal ligation, by I. Gupta, et al. INDIAN JOURNAL OF MEDICAL RESEARCH 69:770-775, May, 1979.

Post-operative analgesia following laparoscopic sterilization, by I. T. Leggat, et al. SCOTTISH MEDICAL JOURNAL 24(3):220, July, 1979.

Poststerilization pain: a comparison of band versus clip, by M. A. Cognat, et al. JOURNAL OF REPRODUCTIVE MEDICINE 25(1):29-30, July, 1980.

Sterilization of women—not as effective or harmless as assumed, by J. F. Larsen. UGESKRIFT FOR LAEGER 142(7):467-468, February 11, 1980.

Tuboovarian abscess following laparoscopic sterilization with silicone rubber bands, by R. H. Glew, et al. OBSTE-TRICS AND GYNECOLOGY 55(6):760-762, June, 1980.

Use of relaxation training to reduce pain following vaginal hysterectomy, by K. Perri. PERCEPTUAL AND MOTOR SKILLS 48(2):478, April, 1979.

Vaginal tubal ligation—is infection a significant risk? by R. R. Miesfeld, et al. AMERICAN JOURNAL OF OBSTETRICS AND GYNECOLOGY 137(2):183-188, May 15, 1980.

STERILIZATION: FEMALE: FAILURE
Failed laparoscopic clip sterilization, by A. Kenney, et al. BRITISH MEDICAL JOURNAL 2(6189):526, September 1, 1979.

High rate of ectopic pregnancy following laparoscopic tubal coagulation failures. Incidence and etiology, by A. McCausland. AMERICAN JOURNAL OF OBSTETRICS AND GYNECOLOGY 136(1):97-101, January 1, 1980.

The history of pregnancies that occur following female sterilization, by I. C. Chi, et al. INTERNATIONAL JOURNAL OF GYNAECOLOGY AND OBSTETRICS 17(3): 265-267, November-December, 1979.

Pregnancy after laparoscopic sterilization, by F. D. Loffer, et al. OBSTETRICS AND GYNECOLOGY 55(5):643-648, May, 1980.

Pregnancy following laparoscopic sterilization, by W. Vlaanderen. NEDERLANDS TIJDSCHRIFT VOOR GENEESKUNDE 124(19):727-729, May 10, 1980.

STERILIZATION: FEMALE: TECHNIQUES
Abdominal hysterectomy for abortion-sterilization. A report of 500 consecutive cases, by P. G. Stumpf, et al. AMERICAN JOURNAL OF OBSTETRICS AND GYNECOLOGY 136(6):714-720, March 15, 1980.

Analysis of tubal sterilization in the Maternity Unit of the

Hospital Salvador over a 12-month period, by P. Gayan, et al. REVISTA CHILENA DE OBSTETRICIA Y GINECOLOGIA 43(2):124-125, 1978.

Celioscopic sterilizations with Yoon rings. 300 cases. Immediate complications, effectiveness and reversibility, by J. M. Lambercy, et al. JOURNAL DE GYNECOLOGIE OBSTETRIQUE ET BIOLOGIE DE LA REPRODUCTION 8(2):157-162, March, 1979.

Comparative study of abdominal tubal ligation at minilaparotomy by standard Pomeroy and Yoon ring technique, by S. Dhaniram, et al. JOURNAL OF THE INDIAN MEDICAL ASSOCIATION 72(4):75-77, February 16, 1979.

Diagnostic miniculdoscopy preceding laparoscopy when bowel adhesions are suspected, by D. A. van Lith, et al. JOURNAL OF REPRODUCTIVE MEDICINE 23(2):87-90, August, 1979.

Interval mini-laparotomy: an alternative to laparoscopic sterilization? by H. W. Foster, Jr. JOURNAL OF THE NATIONAL MEDICAL ASSOCIATION 72(6):567-570, June, 1980.

Laparoscopic sterilization with the aid of the Yoon ring, by F. Zabransky. CESKOSLOVENSKA GYNEKOLOGIE 45(4):231-233, May, 1980.

Laparoscopic sterilization with electrocautery, silastic bands and spring-loaded clips: report of our experience with 790 patients, by P. Buytaert, et al. EUROPEAN JOURNAL OF OBSTETRICS, GYNECOLOGY AND REPRODUCTIVE BIOLOGY 10(2):109-118, February, 1980.

Laparoscopic sterilization with the Falope ring, by B. L. Hejl, et al. UGESKRIFT FOR LAEGER 142(7):429-430, February 11, 1980.

Laparoscopic sterilization with Hulka-Clemens clips. A
technical modification with a preliminary assessment, by
P. Ladehoff, et al. UGESKRIFT FOR LAEGER 142
(31):1998-1999, July 28, 1980.

Laparoscopic sterilization with a silicone rubber ring
(Falope-ring), by P. Hansen, et al. UGESKRIFT FOR
LAEGER 142(7):438-440, February 11, 1980.

Laparoscopic sterilization with the spring clip: instrumentation development and current clinical experience, by J.
F. Hulka, et al. AMERICAN JOURNAL OF OBSTE-
TRICS AND GYNECOLOGY 135(8):1016-1020, December 15, 1979.

Laparoscopic tubal ligation. A follow-up report on the Yoon
falope ring methodology, by I. Yoon, et al. JOURNAL
OF REPRODUCTIVE MEDICINE 23(2):76-80, August,
1979.

Laparoscopic tubal sterilization by bipolar electrocoagulation, by K. Decker, et al. ARCHIVES OF GYNECOL-
OGY 228(1-4):278, July 20, 1979.

Laparoscopic tubal sterilization under local anesthesia, by H.
A. Hirsch, et al. ARCHIVES OF GYNECOLOGY 228(1-
4):282-283, July 20, 1979.

Laparoscopic tubal sterilization using thermal coagulstion, by
J. E. Gunning, et al. OBSTETRICS AND GYNECOLO-
GY 54(4):505-509, October, 1979.

Laparoscopy and minilaparotomy: two major advances in
female sterilization, by M. F. McCann, et al. STUDIES
IN FAMILY PLANNING 11(4):119, April, 1980.

Laparoscopy or minilaparotomy for sterilization of women,
by A. T. Letchworth, et al. OBSTETRICS AND GYNE-
COLOGY 56(1):119-121, July, 1980.

Mechanism of single-stich failure of tubal ligation: a morphologic appraisal, by P. V. Mehta, et al. OBSTETRICS AND GYNECOLOGY 54(4):509-512, October, 1979.

Mini-laparotomy for bilateral tubal ligation in lithotomy position, by W. E. Byrd. SOUTHERN MEDICAL JOURNAL 72(12):1554-1556, December, 1979.

Minilaporotomy provides safety and savings [interview], by E. Hakim-Elahi. SAME-DAY SURGERY 3(7):88+, July, 1979.

Minilaparotomy under local anesthesia for outpatient sterilization: a preliminary report, by R. B. Lee, et al. FERTILITY AND STERILITY 33(2):129-134, February, 1980.

Minilaparotomy and salpingoclasis. Modification of the instruments, by J. Casasola Garcia, et al. GINECOLOGIA Y OBSTETRICIA DE MEXICO 47(281):181-190, March, 1980.

Sterilization by cesarean hysterectomy, by J. J. Britton. AMERICAN JOURNAL OF OBSTETRICS AND GYNECOLOGY 137(8):887-892, August 15, 1980.

Sterilization of the female by tubal ligation and by inserting the Fallopian tube ring of Yoon, by H. Toumi. TUNISIE MEDICALE 56(4):359-365, July-August, 1978.

Sterilization of women by laparoscopic electrocoagulation of the ovarian duct, by E. Pitner, et al. JUGOSLAVENSKA GINEKOLOGIJA I OPSTETRICIJA 18(5-6):411-415, 1978.

Sterilization via the mini-laparotomy technique, by L. Weinstein. CLINICAL OBSTETRICS AND GYNECOLOGY 23(1):273-280, March, 1980.

Suprapubic endoscopy for internal female sterilization, by
L. E. Laufe. AMERICAN JOURNAL OF OBSTETRICS
AND GYNECOLOGY 136(2):257-259, 1980.

Timing of laparoscopic sterilization in abortion patients, by
H. M. Kwak, et al. OBSTETRICS AND GYNECOLOGY
56(1):85-89, July, 1980.

Tubal occlusion via laparoscopy in Latin America: an evalua-
tion of 8186 cases, by L. P. Cole, et al. INTERNA-
TIONAL JOURNAL OF GYNAECOLOGY AND OB-
STETRICS 17(3):253-259, November-December, 1979.

Tubal occlusion with silicone rubber: an update, by T. P.
Reed, et al. JOURNAL OF REPRODUCTIVE MEDI-
CINE 25(1):25-28, July, 1980.

Typical complications of tubal ligation by laparoscopy with
the tupla-clip and measures to avoid these complications,
by B. Henkel. GEBURTSHILFE UND FRAUENHEIL-
KUNDE 39(10):892-896, October, 1979.

STERILIZATION: HISTORY
Compulsory sterilization in the Opole district during 1934-
1938, by S. Kasperek. PRZEGLAD LEKARSKI 37(1):
33-39, 1980.

STERILIZATION: LAWS AND LEGISLATION
Comments on the sterilization of mental incompetents in
Canadian civil and common law, by R. P. Kouri, et al.
REVUE DE DROIT UNIVERSITE DE SHERBROOKE
10:599-628, 1980.

Sterilization abuse: current state of the law and remedies for
abuse. GOLDEN GATE UNIVERSITY LAW REVIEW
10:1147-1189, Summer, 1980.

Eugenic sterilization: medico-legal and sociological aspects,
by F. C. Robinson, et al. JOURNAL OF THE NA-

TIONAL MEDICAL ASSOCIATION 71(6):593-598, June, 1979.

Sterilization abuse: a proposed regulatory scheme. DEPAUL LAW REVIEW 28:731-768, Spring, 1979.

Sterilization of the mentally retarded—parents of mentally retarded children found to have no statutory right to consent to sterilization of child. State statute providing only for sterilization of inmates of certain state institutions held under-inclusive and violative of the equal protection clause of the fourteenth amendment. JOURNAL OF FAMILY LAW 17:834-841, August, 1979.

Voluntary sterilization: legal and ethical aspects, by D. I. Wilson. LEGAL MEDICAL QUARTERLY 3(1):13-23, 1979.

Worldwide laws and policies on contraception, abortion and sterilization affect service provision. FAMILY PLANNING PERSPECTIVES 12:210-211, July-August, 1980.

STERILIZATION: MALE
Behavioral response to vasectomy, by R. L. Vaughn. ARCHIVES OF GENERAL PSYCHIATRY 36(7):815-821, July, 1979.

Characteristics of vasectomy patients at a family planning clinic, by R. J. Gandy. JOURNAL OF BIOSOCIAL SCIENCE. 10(2):125-132, April, 1978.

Clinical application of vas deferens puncture, by S. Li. CHINESE MEDICAL JOURNAL 93(1):69-70, 1980.

Comparative popularity of vasectomy and tubectomy, by S. D. R. Devi. JOURNAL OF FAMILY WELFARE 26:79-93, June, 1980.

Consequences of vasectomy: an immunological and histological study related to subsequent fertility, by I. L. Jenkins, et al. BRITISH JOURNAL OF UROLOGY 51(5):406-410, 1979.

Demographic and socio-economic characteristics of men choosing vasectomy, by M. A. Parsons, et al. JOURNAL OF BIOSOCIAL SCIENCE 10(2):133-139, April, 1978.

The effects of vasectomy on viscosity, pH and volume of semen in man, by V. Nikkanen. NDROLOGIA 11(2): 123-125, 1979.

A follow-up study of 200 cases of vasectomy, by V. K. Gandotra, et al. ACTA PHYSIOLOGICA SCANDINAVICA 107:19-32, September, 1979.

Immunological observations following vasectomy, by Y. Choi. EXPERIENTIA 35(9):1243-1244, 1979.

Male sterilization, by J. E. Davis. CLINICAL OBSTETRICS AND GYNAECOLOGY 6(1):97-108, 1979.

Masculinity-femininity and the desire for sexual intercourse after vasectomy: a longitudinal study, by D. Williams, et al. SOCIAL PSYCHOLOGY QUARTERLY 43:347-352, September, 1980.

Prophylactic vasectomy, by A. Kambal. BRITISH JOURNAL OF UROLOGY 51(4):310-311, 1979.

Quick cut straight to the heart (vasectomy), by S. Zwarun. MACLEAN'S 93:58-60, October 20, 1980.

A study of determinants and impact of the vasectomy programme in a rural community block of Madhya-Pradesh, by D. P. Akhand, et al. JOURNAL OF FAMILY WELFARE 26:41-53, September, 1979.

Vasectomy and biochemical composition of human seminal

plasma, by R. Mendirattan, et al. INDIAN JOURNAL OF EXPERIMENTAL BIOLOGY 18(4):409-410, 1980.

Vasectomy: 1980. UROLOGIC CLINICS OF NORTH AMERICA 7(1):89-106, 1980.

Vasectomy with transurethral resection of prostate, by N. W. Whitlock, et al. UROLOGY 13(2):135-138, 1979.

Vasorasotomy, by S. S. Howards. UROLOGIC CLINICS OF NORTH AMERICA 7(1):165-169, 1980.

What vasectomy means to a man and his marriage, by J. R. Heilman. READERS DIGEST 116:33-36+, April, 1980.

STERILIZATION: MALE: COMPLICATIONS
The effect of vasectomy on serum uric acid levels, by G. Singh. IRCS MEDICAL SCIENCE LIBRARY COMPENDIUM 7(8):406, 1979.

Involvement of vasectomy in endocrine aspects of aging, by G. Kinson. FERTILITY AND STERILITY 32(2):247-248, 1979.

Vasectomy and its consequences, by G. Singh. IRCS MEDICAL SCIENCE LIBRARY COMPENDIUM 7(10):488-491, 1979.

Vasectomy may clog up your veins, by R. Hoult. NEW SCIENTIST 86:392, June 26, 1980.

STERILIZATION: MALE: TECHNIQUES
Chemical sterilization of male dogs (Canis familiaris) after single intratesticular administration of methallibure (ICI-33828), dexamethasone, metopiron (SU-4885, Ciba), niridazole (33644-Ba, Ciba), alpha-chlorohydrin (U-5897) and danazol, by V. P. Dixit. INDIAN JOURNAL OF EXPERIMENTAL BIOLOGY 17(9):937-940, September, 1979.

Double conjoining vas deferens, by R. G. Gravesen. UROL-OGY 15(3):283-284, 1980.

Modes of male contraception: vasectomy and non-hormonal drug sterilization, by J. L. Alloza y Gascon-Molins, et al. MEDICINA CLINICA 73(5):209-214, September 15, 1979.

Vasectomy in cryosurgery of the prostate, by W. Hiroto, et al. CRYOBIOLOGY 16(6):596, 1979.

STERILIZATION: PSYCHOLOGY OF
Sterilization in family planning. The psychology of voluntary sterilization, by P. Petersen. MMW 122(15):557-559, April 11, 1980.

STERILIZATION: SOCIOLOGY OF
Eugenic sterilization: medico-legal and sociological aspects, by F. C. Robinson, et al. JOURNAL OF THE NATIONAL MEDICAL ASSOCIATION 71(6):593-598, June, 1979.

STERILIZATION: TECHNIQUES
Influence of sterilization methods and medium composition on the growth of *Brucella abortus* strain 19 in shake-flasks, by O. Y. Yantorno, et al. REVISTA DE LA ASOCIACION ARGENTINA DE MICROBIOLOGIA 10(3):83-93, 1978.

Quinacrine hydrochloride. Review and mode of action of an antimalarial, used as an occlusive agent for transvaginal human sterilization, by E. Patek. ACTA OBSTETRICIA ET GYNECOLOGICA SCANDINAVICA 58(6):561-564, 1979.

STERILIZATION AND GENETICS
Genetic indications for sterilization [letter], by E. Czeizel. ORVOSI HETILAP 121(2):117, January 13, 1980.

Comments on the sterilization of mental incompetents in Canadian civil and common law, by R. P. Kouri, et al. REVUE DE DROIT UNIVERSITÉ DE SHERBROOKE 10:599-628, 1980.

Consent, sterilization and mental incompetence: the case of "Eve", by C. L. Sklar. CANADIAN NURSE 76:14-16+, March, 1980.

Involuntary sterilization of the mentally retarded: blessing or burden? SOUTH DAKOTA LAW REVIEW 25:55-68, Winter, 1980.

Legal aspects. Mental deficiency and sterilization: the case of Eve, by C. L. Sklar. INFIRMIERE CANADIENNE 22 (6):30-32, June, 1980.

Procreative rights and the sterilization of the retarded: with special reference to Roman Catholic theory of human rights, by R. Sherlock. HARVARD THEOLOGICAL RE-VIEW 71:324-325, July-October, 1978.

Ruby v. Massey (452 F Supp 361): sterilization of the mentally retarded. CAPITOL UNIVERSITY LAW REVIEW 9:191-206, 1979.

Sterilization of the mentally handicapped [letter], by J. Dunelm. LANCET 2(8151):1081, November 17, 1979.

Sterilization of the mentally handicapped. Working group in current medical/ethical problems. LANCET 2(8144): 685-686, September 29, 1979.

Sterilization of the mentally retarded—parents of mentally retarded children found to have no statutory right to consent to sterilization of child. State statute providing only for sterilization of inmates of certain state institutions held under-inclusive and violative of the equal protection clause of the fourteenth amendment. JOURNAL

OF FAMILY LAW 17:834-841, August, 1979.

Sterilization—where mentally retarded and presumable fertile daughter cannot understand or exercise her constitutional right to voluntary sterilization, equity court has jurisdiction to empower parents to exercise right on her behalf. JOURNAL OF FAMILY LAW 18:648-653, April, 1980.

Sterilizing the mentally-handicapped: who can give consent? CANADIAN MEDICAL ASSOCIATION JOURNAL 122 (2):234-236+, January 26, 1980.

Vermont's voluntary sterilization statutes and the rights of the mentally handicapped. VERMONT LAW REVIEW 4:331-352, Fall, 1979.

You and the law. Consent, sterilization and mental incompetence: the case of "Eve," by C. Sklar. CANADIAN NURSE 76(3):14-16+, March, 1980.

STERILIZATION AND PHYSICIANS
Psychiatric aspects of sterilization: a prospective survey, by A. H. Smith. BRITISH JOURNAL OF PSYCHIATRY 135:304-309, October, 1979.

STERILIZATION AND RELIGION
Bishops' Conference reaffirms Church's stand on contraceptive sterilization. L'OSSERVATORE ROMANO 31 (644):2+, August 4, 1980.

Bishops reassert sterilization position, by S. Russell. NATIONAL CATHOLIC REPORTER 16:4+, July 18, 1980.

Forced sterilization inhuman, Virginia bishop asserts. OUR SUNDAY VISITOR 68:3, March 16, 1980.

Procreative rights and the sterilization of the retarded: with special reference to Roman Catholic theory of human rights, by R. Sherlock. HARVARD THEOLOGICAL REVIEW 71:324-325, July-October, 1978.

Six in 10 U. S. Catholic hospitals provide family planning: one in five offers medical sterilization [news]. FAMILY PLANNING PERSPECTIVES 11(5):308-309, October, 1979.

Sterilization ban draws ire, by B. Kenkelen. NATIONAL CATHOLIC REPORTER 16:20, September 12, 1980.

Sterilization: the dilemma of Catholic hospitals, by C. Bayley, Sr., et al. AMERICA 143:222-225, October 18, 1980.

Sterilization: who says it's anti-life. NATIONAL CATHO-LIC REPORTER 16:2, August 1, 1980.

U. S. bishops contraceptive sterilization immoral. OUR SUNDAY VISITOR 69:6, July 20, 1980.

Voluntary sterilization: legal and ethical aspects, by D. I. Wilson. LEGAL MEDICAL QUARTERLY 3(1):13-23, 1979.

STERILIZATION AND SEXUAL BEHAVIOR
The effect of laparoscopic sterilization by diathermy or silastic bands on post-operative pain, menstrual symptoms and sexuality, by S. Lawson, et al. BRITISH JOURNAL OF OBSTETRICS AND GYNAECOLOGY 86(8):659-663, August, 1979.

Heterosexual interactions in laboratory-housed stumptail macaques (*Macaca arctoides*): observations during the menstrual cycle and after ovariectomy, by A. K. Slob, et al. HORMONES AND BEHAVIOR 10(2):193-211, April, 1978.

Masculinity-femininity and the desire for sexual intercourse after vasectomy: a longitudinal study, by W. Williams, et al. SOCIAL PSYCHOLOGY QUARTERLY 43:347-352, September, 1980.

UNWED MOTHERS

Follow-up study of school-age unwed pregnant girls in Escambia County, Florida, by J. Dewitt. DISSERTATION ABSTRACTS INTERNATIONAL 40(09):4809-A, 1979.

Precocious pregnancies: patterns of sexuality among white adolescent women in the rural south, by K. P. J. Fischer. DISSERTATION ABSTRACTS INTERNATIONAL 40(12):6346-A, 1979.

AUTHOR INDEX

427

430

Gandy, R. J. 40
Gardner, I. M. 80
Gardner, J. 154, 176
Gardner, R. F. 73
Garrison, J. L. 124
Garton, J. S. 2
Garvey, J. 2, 142
Gastard, J. 30
Gavin, J. 157
Gayan, P. 28
Geary, P. 177
Geekie, D. A. 19
Geijerstam, G. 77
Geisel, J. 71, 79
Geraedts, J. P. M. 42
Gerardo, H. R. 22
Gethmann, U. 82
Gever, L. N. 84
Ghazzaui, E. 65
Ghorbani, F. S. 180
Ghosh, A. K. 150
Ghosh, B. 178
Gilbert, C. 73
Gill, V. D. 78
Gillaspy, R. T. 52
Gillette, R. D. 150
Gillie, O. 121, 176
Giovannini, A. 52
Gjorgov, A. N. 32
Glenn, J. 22
Glew, R. H. 176
Gloor, P. A. 146
Gneo, S. 28
Goeretzlehner, G. 76
Golant, M. C. 70
Gold, J. A. 62
Gold, R. B. 25
Goldfarb, G. 24
Goldman, A. H. 12
Goldman, J. A. 51
Goldman, R. L. 109
Goldsmith, A. 18

Goldzieher, J. W. 154
Golomb, M. 98
Goodwin, J. H. 30
Gordon, S. 77
Göretzlehner, G. 76, 90
Gorosh, M. E. 36
Göser, R. 100
Gosling, P. H. 9
Gostin, L. 166
Gould, M. 9
Gould, N. B. 136
Graben, C. D. 160
Grady, T. 108
Graf, K. J. 109
Graham-Brown, R. 10
Granberg, D. 12
Grandjean, J. P. 84
Granitzka, S. 45
Gravesen, R. G. 63
Green, L. R. 137
Green, M. 118
Greenblatt, R. B. 29
Greenstein, J. S. 168
Grella, P. 137
Grescoe, A. 148
Greydanus, D. E. 50, 51
Griffin, M. 20
Grillet, G. 51
Grimes, D. A. 78, 109, 115, 116
Grindel, B. 98
Grisez, G. 2
Gryzhak, I. P. 84
Gu, Z. P. 134
Guidotti, R. J. 27
Guillat, J. C. 41, 50, 124
Gula, R. M. 153
Gulati, L. 112
Gulick, T. G. 74
Gunning, J. E. 106
Gupta, I. 117, 181
Gupta, M. L. 154

437

441